G.A. HENTY

December 8, 1832 — November 16, 1902

Won by the Sword
A Story of the Thirty Years' War

by
G. A. Henty

ILLUSTRATED BY CHARLES M. SCHELDON .

PrestonSpeed Publications

Historiae Dona Repertum
Pennsylvania

A note about our name: Preston/Speed Publications
In an age where it has become fashionable to denigrate fathers, we
have decided to honor ours.   Our name is in loving memory of
Preston Louis Schmitt and Speed - Lester Herbert Maynard ("Speed"
is a nickname that was earned for prowess in baseball).

This book is printed on acid-free paper, and its binding
materials have been chosen for strength and durability. The
paper is natural booktext for ease and comfort of viewing.

Published June 1, 1899 by
BLACKIE & SON, LONDON

Blackie & Son Title Page Date: 1900

Heirloom Hardcover Edition ISBN 1-887159-45-2
Popular Softcover Edition ISBN 1-887159-44-4
Printed in the U.S.A.

PRESTON/SPEED PUBLICATIONS
51 RIDGE ROAD
MILL HALL, PENNSYLVANIA 17751
(570) 726-7844
www.prestonspeed.com
2000

INTRODUCTION:

G. A. Henty's life was filled with exciting adventure. Completing Westminster School, he attended Cambridge University. Along with a rigorous course of study, Henty participated in boxing, wrestling and rowing. The strenuous study and healthy, competitive participation in sports prepared Henty to be with the British army in Crimea, as a war correspondent witnessing Garibaldi fight in Italy, visiting Abyssinia, being present in Paris during the Franco-Prussian war, in Spain with the Carlists, at the opening of the Suez Canal, touring India with the Prince of Wales (later Edward VII) and a trip to the California gold fields. These are only a few of his exciting adventures.

G. A. Henty lived during the reign of Queen Victoria (1837-1901) and began his story telling career with his own children. After dinner, he would spend an hour or two in telling them a story that would continue the next day. Some stories took weeks! A friend was present one day and watched the spell-bound reaction of his children suggesting that he write down his stories so others could enjoy them. He did, and was dubbed "The Prince of Story-Tellers" and "The Boy's Own Historian." One of Mr. Henty's secretaries reported that he would quickly pace back and forth in his study dictating stories as fast as the secretary could record them.

Henty's stories revolve around a fictional boy hero during fascinating periods of history. His heroes are diligent, courageous, intelligent and dedicated to their country and cause in the face, at times, of great peril. His histories, particularly battle accounts, have been recognized by historian scholars for their accuracy. There is nothing dry in Mr. Henty's stories and thus he removes the drudgery and laborious task often associated with the study of history.

Henty's heroes fight wars, sail the seas, discover land, conquer evil empires, prospect for gold, and a host of other exciting adventures. They meet famous personages like Josephus, Titus, Hannibal, Robert the Bruce, Sir William Wallace, General Marlborough, General Gordon, General Kitchner, Robert E. Lee, Frederick the Great, the Duke of Wellington, Huguenot leader Coligny, Cortez, King Alfred, Napoleon, and Sir Francis Drake just to mention a *few*. The heroes go through the fall of Jerusalem, the Roman invasion of Britain, the Crusades, the Viking invasion of Europe, the Reformation in various countries, the Reign of Terror, etc. In short, Henty's heroes live through tumultuous historic eras meeting the leaders of that time.

Preston/Speed Publications is delighted to offer again the works of G. A. Henty. Action-packed exciting adventure awaits adults and a whole new generation. The books have been reproduced with modern type-setting. However, the original grammar, spellings and punctuation remains the same as the original versions.

The Rencontre In The Streets Of Paris.

PREFACE.

MY DEAR LADS,

In my preface to the *Lion of the North* I expressed a hope that I might some day be able to continue the history of the Thirty Years' War. The deaths of Gustavus and his great rival Wallenstein and the crushing defeat of the Swedes and their allies at the battle of Nördlingen brought the first period of that war to a close. Hostilities, indeed, never ceased, but the Swedes no longer played the leading part on the Protestant side that they had hitherto occupied. Oxenstiern, the great chancellor of Sweden, saw that the only hope of eventual success lay in engaging France in the struggle, and he and the Duke of Weimar went to Paris and pointed out to Richelieu that unless France intervened, Austria must become the master of all Germany, and as the ally of Spain would have it in her power to completely dominate France. Richelieu perceived the opportunity, made a treaty with the Swedes and Weimar, and engaged to grant large subsidies to the former, and to send an army to co-operate with the latter.

Then began the second period of this long and terrible struggle, France now taking the place that Sweden had hitherto occupied, and bearing the brunt of the conflict. She emerged triumphant with her territories largely increased, while Austria was crushed and humiliated, and Spain was dethroned from her position as the dominating power of Europe. The success of France was greatly due to the fact that her armies were led by two of the greatest military geniuses of all times, viz., Condé and Turenne, men of very different types, but equally great as commanders, and equally at the time of which we are speaking devoted to the cause of France. Both were men of extraordinary personal courage, and although one was as prudent and careful of the lives of his troops as the other was impetuous and careless at what cost he won his victories, they worked together with a harmony that could have hardly been expected among men so differently constituted. Although, in the subsequent wars of the Fronde they took different sides, their friendship, except during a short period of alienation, was never shaken, and their admiration for each other's genius never abated.

Yours sincerely,

G.A. HENTY.

CONTENTS

ILLUSTRATIONS

WON BY THE SWORD

CHAPTER I
A STROKE OF GOOD FORTUNE

A MOUNTED officer, followed by two orderlies, was proceeding at a brisk trot from Paris to St. Denis, in October, 1639, when he came upon a large party of boys, who, armed with sticks, were advancing in something like military order against a wall on the top of a low hill.

"What are you doing?" he asked the lad who appeared to be the leader.

"We are playing at war, sir. We are advancing against the fortress of La Motte. This is the regiment of Turenne."

"And who are you at other times?" the officer asked with a smile.

"My name is Hector Campbell, sir."

"Then you are not French?"

"No, sir; my father was an officer in the Scotch regiment. He was killed at the siege of La Rochelle."

"And who is taking care of you?"

"I live with Angus MacIntosh. He was a sergeant in my father's company. He was badly wounded at La Rochelle, and not being fit for further service, he took a cabaret near the barracks. The officers are very kind. They allow him a

1

sum for taking care of me. Of course I am often in barracks, and have learned the drill, and I have heard and read about battles and sieges, so I am chosen to command."

"And so you know something of the battles in which Turenne was engaged?"

"I think I know about them all, sir, both in Holland and on the Rhine, and have seen plans of the battles. Of course this is not at all like La Motte, which was on the top of a high rock, so that when Turenne was ordered to attack with his regiment after the general's son had failed, he had to pass not only through a heavy fire, but through the huge stones that the enemy hurled down. It was grand; and he did well at all the other sieges. Then, again, there was Saverne. See how he fought there, and stormed the place when even the Swedes, who are good soldiers, had failed. I think he is going to be the greatest of our captains."

"Turenne is only a learner in the art of war," the other said gravely.

"I think he has learnt more than any of the rest," the boy said boldly; "and all the soldiers love him more than any of the other generals, for he takes such care of them, and does not treat them as if they were dirt under his feet, only meant to obey orders, and go and get killed when told."

"You have heard him very much over-praised," the officer said quietly. I think that he does his best; but he is a young man yet, not older than I am. His advance has been due to fortune rather than to his own merits."

"I don't think so," the boy said sturdily. "Do you think that he would be a lieutenant-general at twenty-eight, and that all the soldiers would speak of him as they do, if it were only fortune? Look how he captured Landrecies and Solre, and drove the Austrians back from Maubeuge, and aided the Duke of Weimar to thrash them at Weilenweir, and stormed the main fort of Breisach! He has been successful in all his enterprises, and now it is said he is to command in Italy, where things have been going on badly. The cardinal would not have chosen him had he not considered that no one could do better than he."

Hector meets Turenne.

The officer laughed.

"Well, young sir, I see that you are so well acquainted with the sieges and battles of our time that I cannot argue with you."

"I did not mean that, sir," the boy said in some confusion. "I was only saying what our soldiers think, and it is natural that I, being only a boy, should make him my hero, for he went to the wars when he was a year younger than I am, and at fourteen carried a musket as a volunteer under Maurice of Nassau, and for five years he was in all the battles in Holland, and raised the first battery that opened on Bois-le-duc."

"And do you receive no pension as the son of an officer killed in battle?"

"No, sir. When the living soldiers often have to go months without their pay, the sons of dead ones can hardly expect to be thought of. But I don't care; in two years I shall be old enough to enlist, and I shall go to the frontier and join Hepburn's Scottish brigade, who are now, they say, in the French service."

"They are fine soldiers—none better," the officer said. "But why does not the colonel of your father's regiment ask for a commission for you?"

"The regiment is not in favour with the cardinal," the boy replied with a smile. "They are too Protestant for his eminence, and the colonel is not a man to ask favours if he is likely to be refused."

"Well," the officer said, "it is clear to me that you are a lad of spirit, and that you have done your best to prepare yourself for your profession as a soldier by studying military history, and I think it hard that, as the son of an officer who died in battle for France, France should have done nothing for you. I have some little influence myself. What is the name of this cabaret that Sergeant MacIntosh keeps?"

"The Scottish Soldier, sir. It is near the gate of the barracks of St. Denis."

"Do not go out to-morrow afternoon. I will have a talk with him, and maybe I can be of some assistance to you."

So saying, he touched his horse's flank with his heel and rode on, while the boys continued their play. The next afternoon the lad remained at home, to the surprise of the sergeant.

"What keeps you in to-day, Hector? It is rare indeed that you are indoors in the afternoon."

"An officer came along while we were playing," the lad said, "and asked me some questions. I told him who I was. He said that he had some influence, and might be able to assist me."

"What sort of assistance?" the sergeant grumbled. "He must have influence indeed if he can get you a pension."

"I don't think it was that," the boy said. "I said that I should like to enlist as a volunteer."

The sergeant laughed.

"Well, they do take volunteers as young as you are, Hector, but they must be cadets of a noble family. You will have to wait another couple of years before they will enlist you, much less take you as a volunteer."

There were a good many Scottish soldiers sitting in the room, when an officer rode up to the door and dismounted.

"It is a general officer," one of the men said, looking out of the window, and as the door opened and the officer entered, all stood up and saluted.

"Sit down, men," he said. I am not here to disturb you, but to have a talk with Sergeant MacIntosh. Have you a room, sergeant, where we can speak privately?"

"Yes, general," the sergeant said, saluting again, and led the way into a little room generally devoted to the use of non-commissioned officers. The officer caught Hector's eye, and beckoned to him to follow.

"Do you know me, sergeant?"

"Yes, general, you are Viscount Turenne."

Hector gave an involuntary exclamation of horror at the thought of the freedom with which he had the day before discoursed with this famous commander. Military officers at that time did not wear any set uniforms, and indeed there was very considerable latitude among the soldiers, and it

5

was only because he was followed by two attendants that the
boy had taken him to be an officer, probably a young captain.
The quietness of his dress had not even led him to believe
that he belonged to a noble family.

"This lad tells me that he is the son of Captain Campbell
of the Scottish regiment?"

"That is so, general."

"And also that you were a sergeant in his father's
company, and have since taken care of him."

"I have done the best I could for him, general; but
indeed the officers of the regiment allow me quite as much
as the lad's food costs."

"He seems to be a careful student of military history,
sergeant?"

"That he is, sir. I don't think there has been a battle, or
even a skirmish, in the past ten years which he cannot tell
you the ins and outs of. He will sit here for hours as quiet as
a mouse when some soldiers from the wars come in, and
sometimes he gets books lent him with the plans of battles
and sieges, and when he is not doing that he is in the barrack-
yard watching the men drill. I believe he knows all the words
of command as well as any captain in the Scottish regiment.
As to handling his musket, I have taught him that myself,
and the use of a sword, too, since he was ten years old, and
the men of his father's company have taken pleasure in
teaching the lad all they knew in that way."

"He reminds me of my own boyhood," the general said.
"I like his looks, and it seems to me that he has the making
of a good officer. All the officers of the regiment are men of
good Scottish families, and as such can serve in any capacity.
I have often need of a young officer who can carry my
messages on a field of battle, and can be trusted to
understand their import and deliver them faithfully. Now,
Campbell," he said, turning to the lad, who was standing
with flushed face and eyes beaming with delight and
gratitude, "I will give you the choice. I will either appoint
you a volunteer for a year, in which time, if your conduct is
satisfactory, I will name you lieutenant, or I will take you

directly into my own household. My object in either case would be to produce an officer likely to be useful to his Majesty.

"I should certainly not have adopted that course had it not been that you appear already to have learned the duties of a soldier, and to be acquainted with the ordinary drill and with the necessities of a soldier's life. If you enter my household you will find it no child's play, certainly no life of ease and comfort. I do not spare myself, nor do I spare the officers immediately under me. In a regiment you would learn better, perhaps, the duties of a regimental officer, but with me you will have more opportunities of learning the art of war, and of some day becoming a distinguished officer, always supposing that you are not shot down in battle or die of fatigue and hardship. Which do you choose?"

"Oh, sir, how can I thank you for your goodness? There is nothing in the world that I should like so much as to be in your service."

"So be it," the general said. "I shall obtain an appointment for you as lieutenant attached to my household. At first, you will simply have to carry messages for me; but when I have learnt more of your character I shall employ you as one that I can trust. Sergeant, here is a purse, use the contents in furnishing the lad with clothes suitable for his position, and let him call on me in three days at the hotel of the Duc de Bouillon, where I am staying. Can you ride?" he asked suddenly.

"Yes, sir."

"I will see to the matter of a horse for you. I shall be leaving at the end of a week to join the army in Italy. And remember always, lad," he added with a smile, "that I am still but a learner in the art of war."

So saying he nodded kindly to him and the sergeant, went out, returned the salute of the soldiers, mounted his horse, which his orderly was holding for him, and rode off.

"Well, well," said the sergeant, who with Hector had followed him out, "the like of this I never saw before: to think that the Viscount of Turenne should visit the cabaret of a soldier, and should have deigned to offer you a position in his household! I can scarce believe that I am not dreaming. How did it all come about, and how have you thus gained his favour?"

"I am ashamed to say, sergeant, that I gained it by my presumption; now that I know who he was, I may say by my insolence. A party of us were having a mimic battle. We were acting as the regiment of Turenne at the storming of La Motte. I was in command, and so acting as Turenne, when a gentleman, whom, by his appearance and age, and by the fact that two troopers rode behind him, I took to be a captain in the army, came up and questioned me as to what we were doing. I told him, then he talked about Turenne. I said I thought he was our greatest general. He, that Turenne was only a learner in the art of war. I upheld him, and spoke of the battles and sieges in which he had taken part. Then he asked me about myself, and I told him my birth and bringing up, and he said he might be of assistance to me, and would call here and see you."

"Well, well, it almost passes belief, Hector, that a boy like you should have dared to enter into an argument with an officer, even if only, as you believed, a captain. And to think that this has come of it, instead of his having laid his whip across your back, as you deserved. Your fortune is made, lad, that is, if you behave yourself. Turenne is a great soldier; and more than that, from what I have heard he is loved by his men more than any other general, and they will do anything for him. His regiment here, though he was but nineteen when he obtained his command, was admitted to be one of the best drilled and the best disciplined of any in the service.

"He saw to everything himself, spent his whole time in drilling them as if he had been only a lieutenant with nothing but his sword for his fortune, instead of a great noble. When he was with de la Valette and Weimar, and the army had to fall back and were well-nigh starved, Turenne sold his plate and his carriages to buy food for the men. He had his own baggage thrown out of the wagons to make room for those who were too weak to march; and on one occasion gave up his own horse to a soldier who was sinking from fatigue and hunger, and himself marched on foot. He always leads his troops in battle, and wherever he goes they will follow. He was right in saying that he does not spare himself. The soldiers believe that he does without any sleep when on a campaign, for he is for ever going round seeing that everything is in order, that the outposts are properly placed and vigilant, and that the soldiers have food, and such comfort as can be obtained. Now let us go in and tell my comrades of your good fortune. There is not a man in the regiment who will not be glad to hear of it. I will go across with you myself to the colonel's lodging."

"But please, sergeant, do not say a word about my folly; only say that the general, coming across a party of us playing at war, questioned me, and finding that I was the son of a Scottish officer who had been killed at La Rochelle, and that I had worked hard at getting up the history of the wars, and longed much to go into the army, had promised to come round the next day, and said that he might be able to aid me."

"I understand, lad. Yes, it is better that your foolishness should not be known."

The colonel was greatly pleased when he heard of what had happened.

"I had intended myself to have asked for a commission for you when you were a couple of years older," he said to Hector, "but I was by no means sure of getting it, for the cardinal is not partial to the regiment. Turenne, however, stands high in his favour—in spite of the fact that his brother, the Duc de Bouillon, has left Richelieu's party, and is regarded by him as an enemy—so we may be sure that your commission will be at once signed. You must sup with me and the officers of the regiment to-night. There is not one who will not rejoice that your father's son has met with such good fortune, for assuredly you could not have entered the army under better auspices.

WON BY THE SWORD

It is just like Turenne to have thus come forward to assist the son of a brave soldier killed in action. As a rule, I am sorry to say that the officers of our army concern themselves but little with the affairs of the soldiers under their command. Of course in our regiment it is different, as we have many gentlemen of well-known Scottish families serving in the ranks, and most of the others are our own clansmen, or come from our dales. We all cling together as countrymen among strangers, though indeed we can hardly regard them as strangers, seeing that Scotland and France have ever been allies, and that our Queen Mary was a French princess. And now that Scotland has given kings to England, and English troops fought side by side with the French under Henry of Navarre against the Spaniards and Guises, and, although not in strict alliance, are alike enemies of the Spaniards, we can scarce feel ourselves as strangers here. Besides, is not a French princess wife of King Charles?

"I do not say that either England or France has altogether forgotten the long wars between them, but that is a very old story now, and as long as Spain threatens to extend her power over all Europe, so long are we likely to remain good friends. If the power of Spain is once broken, old quarrels may break out again, but I trust that that will not be in my time, for assuredly the regiment, although willing to fight against all other enemies of France, would refuse to march against our countrymen. Now, Sergeant MacIntosh, I know that you must be anxious to get back to your inn. You will have a busy time this afternoon unless I am greatly mistaken. Leave Campbell with me.

"In the first place, it will be as well that he should not be down there, for the fun is likely to get fast and furious. There is not a man in the regiment who knew his father but will be drinking the lad's health, and it were better that he should go to-morrow through the barracks and shake their hands, than that he should be among them there. You can tell them, that I have taken the boy off, so that they may not think that he stayed away on his own account. We will see

10

him fitted out. It is a matter that touches the honour of the regiment that the son of our old comrade should make a fair show in the household of the viscount."

"The general has left me a purse for that purpose, colonel."

"It was a kindly thought, but let the lad start with it in his pocket. It is our duty to see that he has everything befitting his father's son."

As soon as the sergeant left, the colonel said, "Now, Campbell, do you go into the ante-room. I shall be ready to go out with you in half an hour."

Orderlies were then despatched to the various officers' lodgings, and in a few minutes they assembled. The colonel told them what had happened, and said that in his opinion it concerned the honour of the regiment to see that their comrade's son was properly equipped.

All those who had known Captain Campbell were greatly pleased with the news, and there was not a dissenting voice when the colonel proposed that there should be a general subscription of two days' pay. He himself, however, and Captain Campbell's friends, gave a much larger amount, and the total was amply sufficient for the equipment of a young man of good family joining the army. Hector was then called in and informed of what had taken place, and heartily congratulated by the officers. He was greatly affected by their kindness and the proof of the estimation in which his father had been held.

"We had always intended to do this," the colonel said, "when the time came for your entering the army, for we felt that it would indeed be a discredit to the regiment were you to go into the world without the equipment that a Scottish gentleman should have. Now, Captain Mackenzie and Captain Home, I will ask you to act as furnishers. You know what is required for a young officer on the staff of a general like Viscount Turenne, who would be called upon to accompany him to court, and must do him no discredit; besides which, he must of course have clothes for a campaign. He will not need arms, for I have kept for him his father's sword and pistols. See that the tailors undertake to get his clothes ready quickly, for he is to accompany Turenne to Italy in four or five days. One suit at least must be finished in two days, for on the third he is to wait upon Turenne, who is staying at the hotel of the Duc de Bouillon, and he may possibly be presented to the cardinal."

The dress of a French gentleman in the reign of Louis XIII. differed but slightly from that worn at the same time by the cavaliers of Charles I. It consisted of a loose cloak of cloth, silk, satin, or velvet, according to the occasion and the wealth of the wearer. It generally hung loosely on the shoulders, but two or three of the top buttons were sometimes fastened; the sleeves were loose and open from the elbow. Sometimes the cloak was richly embroidered. Over it fell a collar of rich lace, with Vandyke border. Beneath it was worn a short tightly-fitted doublet embroidered in front, with puffed sleeves, and with a belt or sash round the waist. The breeches were very full, reaching to the knee. For walking or riding, loose high boots turned down at the top and trimmed with lace or frillings joined the breeches; while in court-dress, silk stockings and shoes with rosettes were worn. The swords hung from a richly-embroidered baldrick going over the right shoulder.

Officers of the different regiments were distinguished by the colour of their sashes, which was the only point of regimental uniformity. When on a campaign doublets were usually worn of thick buff leather; armour was still used, but was far less cumbrous than it had been, consisting for the most part solely of shoulder-pieces and cuirass, with plates covering the upper part of the arm, thick buff-leather gauntlets being considered sufficient protection below the elbow. Four suits were ordered for Hector: one for court, another for general use when in Paris or other large towns, the third for travelling and when in attendance with the general, the fourth for actual service in the field.

Almost as expensive as the suits were the shirts, with their deep lace collars and ruffle; while for service in the field half a dozen plain shirts were purchased. The head-dress on ordinary occasions was a broad beaver hat with plumes, and in the field a close-fitting helmet with cheek-pieces. Visors had been almost entirely given up.

On the third day Hector presented himself at the appointed hour at the hotel of the Duc de Bouillon. He was dressed in the second best of his costumes, and wore for the first time his father's sword. In the hall were numbers of soldiers and lackeys. One of the latter came up to him.

"I am here to see the Viscount Turenne by appointment," he said.

The lackey led the way to a large chamber, where several officers and gentlemen were waiting. Here Hector gave his name to a chamberlain, who took it into another apartment. He waited for half an hour, and observed that while the officers, one by one, were taken into the room where the lackey had carried his name, the nobles and gentlemen, who were much more numerous, were shown into another, which was evidently the principal reception-room. He guessed at once that it was here that the Duc de Bouillon was receiving visitors, while his brother was engaged in giving interviews to officers, who perhaps desired appointments in his army, or in arranging details of stores, arms, and ammunition required for its use. At last his turn came; and on his name being called, he followed the usher into a small apartment, where Turenne was sitting at a table covered with letters. The general looked at him critically.

"You make a very good figure," he said, "and better, I can tell you, than I did at your age, for I was but weakly, while you are well-grown and strong. Among your other exercises you have not neglected the use of your sword. I could tell that as soon as my eyes fell upon you."

"No, general, I have practised for two or three hours a day since I was ten years old, and I think that almost every soldier in the regiment has been my instructor in turn, and the maître-d'armes of the regiment himself gave me lessons twice a week."

"I have managed your business for you," the viscount said. "I saw the cardinal yesterday and asked for a commission for you. He simply asked for what regiment, and I said that at present I intended to keep you about my own person, as I thought you would make a good officer and would some day do me credit. He was busy at the time, so he simply signed an appointment as a lieutenant and gave it to me to fill in your name. I asked if I should bring you to his levee to-morrow, but he said, 'There is no occasion, viscount, we have both plenty on our hands; neither you nor I can waste time on young lieutenants. You can present him to me when you return from the war.' You know the cardinal by sight, I suppose?"

"Yes, general, I have seen him many times."

"He is a great man," Turenne said thoughtfully, rather as if speaking to himself than to Hector; "the greatest that France has ever known—he is the soul of France. It is well, indeed, that we have at present a king who recognizes how great a man he is, and is wise enough to know that although he himself is somewhat overshadowed, France is made greater and stronger and his own reign more glorious by his genius." Then he broke off with a smile. "I was talking to myself rather than to you. I shall ride to St. Denis at two o'clock to-day; be here at that time. I will order the horse, that I have purchased for you, to be brought round here."

Hector was about to express his gratitude, but the general at once stopped him. "I need no thanks," he said. "I perceived in the ardour with which you have studied military matters that you would make a good officer, and you remind me of my own boyhood. I always like to help forward officers whom I see ready, not only to do their actual business but to go beyond it, in order to acquire knowledge, and I doubt not that I shall find this in you. But you must remember, lad, that you are now no longer a civilian, but a soldier, that you must be not only obedient but respectful to those above you in rank, that discretion as well as courage is necessary for success, that you must be thoughtful for the comfort of the soldiers, ready to expose your life in battle to encourage them, and also to set them an example of endurance, cheerfulness, and good spirits in times of hardship and distress. Remember that, to the soldier, there is no such thing as party; he fights for France and for France only, and should hold himself aloof from even the smallest expression of opinion on political matters. Then, at two o'clock."

Hector bowed deeply and left the room. When he returned to the hotel at two o'clock, six grooms were standing with the horses before the entrance; he waited outside until the viscount, followed by four officers, came out.

"Oh, here you are, lieutenant!" he said, as his eye fell on Hector; "I was afraid that punctuality was not among your virtues. Gentlemen, this is Lieutenant Hector Campbell, son of a brave officer of the Scottish regiment who fell at La Rochelle; he is, for the present, attached to my household, and will ride with us for Italy the day after to-morrow. Campbell, this gentleman is Colonel d'Estampes, who is the head of my staff; this Major Mutton, who will have the control of all matters connected with the artillery; these are Messieurs de Lisle and Emile de Chavigny, who are my aides-de-camp. Now, gentlemen, let us mount."

As the Scottish regiment was a mounted one, Hector had had ample opportunities to learn to ride well, and he now fell in with the two aides-de-camp, who were both young men of eighteen or nineteen years of age, members of good families, and together they followed the Viscount Turenne, who rode on ahead with the two staff-officers. While they were making their way through the narrow streets of Paris they rode but slowly, but as soon as they passed through the gates they went on at a brisk pace.

"You are fortunate," de Lisle said, "in having obtained a commission so young, although I do not say that there are not many of similar age in the army."

"I am fortunate indeed," Hector replied, "fortunate beyond anything that I could have believed possible, thanks to the goodness of Viscount Turenne."

"You could not enter the army under better patronage," de Chavigny said. "We have both served under him for two years on the Rhine, and had we been his brothers he could not have been more kind; but the work, ma foi, was tremendous. The soldiers may well say that the general is sleepless. Happily he does not expect us to go altogether without rest. Frequently he is away all night by himself in the saddle, sometimes he takes one or other of us with him, but at any rate we get a nights sleep by turns. Much as he has to worry him—what with the ignorance of some and the carelessness of others—I have never seen him out of temper; but then a reproof, however mildly spoken, by him, is more dreaded than a volley of abuse from any other general. He was telling us before he came out that you are already well up in drill, and in the use of arms."

"Yes; I have been brought up, I may say, in the Scottish regiment, and after my father's death the officers and men were all very kind to me, and I learnt my drill both as a soldier and an officer, to fence, use my pistols, and ride. The officers lent me books on military history and tactics."

"The viscount said you were wonderfully well read in such matters," de Lisle said. "I own that beyond the campaigns that I have taken part in I have a very vague idea of such things. My time before I joined was taken up with learning the use of arms, equitation, and certain dry studies under an abbé. I wish now that instead of Latin I had learned something of military history; it seems to me that when one is intended for the army it is a good deal more important than Latin or theology."

"I fancy, de Lisle," his companion said laughing, "that from what I know of you your objection was not so much to the course of study as to study altogether. I know that that was my case."

"Well, perhaps so; still, I might as well have been whipped into learning something useful, instead of something that, so far as I can see, will never be of any value whatever. Were you born over here, lieutenant?"

A STROKE OF GOOD FORTUNE

"No, I was born in Scotland; but my father, who was a younger son, saw no chance of making his way by his sword at home. It was certain that James would never go to war, and as there was no regular army, there seemed no opening for a penniless cadet in England or Scotland, so he came over here and obtained a commission, and as soon as he did so sent for my mother and myself. She died two years later; he kept me with him. When he went on service I was left in the charge of a Huguenot family, and it was well that it was so, for otherwise I might have grown up unable to read or write. The last time that I saw him was before he rode to La Rochelle. After his death I was adopted by the regiment, for the good people I was with left Paris to join their friends in the south. Had it been otherwise I should have stayed with them. The good man would probably have brought me up to be, like himself, a minister, and I am afraid I should have made a very poor one."

The two young men laughed.

"Just at present," de Lisle said, the two religions get on quietly together. The cardinal, churchman as he is, knows that if France is to be great religious enmities must cease, and that the wars of the last reign cost tens of thousands of lives, and drove great numbers of men to take refuge in Holland or England, to the benefit of those countries and our loss. Still, his successor, whoever he may be, may think more of party and less of France, and in that case you might have found your vocation of a Huguenot minister as full of danger as that of a soldier."

"It would have been much worse," Hector said, "for it would not have been a question of fighting, but of being massacred. I know nothing of either religious disputes or of politics. In the regiment these things were never talked about, either among the men or the officers; all were for the king. But at the same time, as it seemed to them that it was the cardinal who had stopped the persecution of the Huguenots, and who had now gone to war with the Austrians to prevent the Protestant princes of Germany being altogether subjugated by the Imperialists, they felt grateful to him; for of course Scotchmen are all on the side of the princes, and nigh half the army of Gustavus Adolphus was composed of my countrymen."

"I do not suppose," Chavigny laughed, "that the cardinal would have cared very much for the destruction of all the Protestant princes of Germany, had it not been that their ruin would make Austria more formidable than ever. As long as Gustavus lived and the Swedes were able to hold their own against the Imperialists, France troubled herself in no way in the matter; but when the Swedes were finally routed at Nördlingen, and it seemed that the Imperialists would triumph everywhere—for most of the Protestant princes were leaving the Confederacy and trying to make the best terms they could for themselves—Richelieu stepped in; and now we see France, which for the past hundred years has been trying to stamp out Protestantism, uniting with Protestant Holland and Sweden to uphold the Protestant princes of Germany, and this under the direction of a cardinal of the Church of Rome. And here are we riding behind a Huguenot general, who perhaps more than any other possesses the cardinal's confidence."

"It seems strange," de Lisle said, "but it is assuredly good policy. While fighting Austria we are fighting Spain, for Austria and Spain are but two branches of one empire, Spain is our eternal enemy. True, she is not as formidable as she was. Henry of Navarre's triumph over the Guises half emancipated us from her influence. The English destroyed her naval power. Holland well-nigh exhausted her treasury, and brought such discredit on her arms as she had never before suffered. Still, she and Austria combined dominate Europe, and it is on her account that we have taken the place of the Swedes and continued this war that has raged for so many years."

CHAPTER 11
CHOOSING A LACKEY

THE policy of the great cardinal had for its objects the aggrandizement of France, as well as the weakening of the power of Austria. So long as the struggle between the Protestant princes and the Swedes against the Imperialists had been maintained with equal successes on both sides, he had been well content to see Germany watering its soil with the blood of its people. Nearly a third of the population had been swept away during the terrible war. Many hundreds of towns and villages had already disappeared, while large tracts of country lay uncultivated, and whichever party won a victory France gained by it. Her interest, however, lay with the Protestant confederation. So long as Germany was cut up into a number of small principalities, divided by religion and political animosity, she could count for little against a foreign enemy.

France had for centuries suffered from the same cause. The families of Lorraine, Bouillon, Enghien, Burgundy, the Guises, Longueville, the Counts of Armagnac, and other powerful vassals of France, paid but a nominal allegiance to the crown, and were really independent princes. Louis XI. had done much to break their power. Richelieu continued the work, and under him France for the first time became consolidated into a whole. Had he lived, the work would doubtless have been completed, but his death and that of the king postponed the work for years. The long regency, controlled by a minister possessing none of the courage and firmness of Richelieu, and personally obnoxious alike to the nobles and to the population of Paris, again threw the power into the hands of the great nobles, plunged France into civil strife, and the wars of the Fronde, like those of the Roses in England, so weakened the nobles that the crown under Louis XIV. became absolutely dominant.

Had Austria succeeded in crushing the Protestant princes, that empire, with all Germany under her control, would have become a power greatly superior in strength and population to France. It was principally to prevent this result that Richelieu after the battle of Nördlingen threw himself into the struggle, but his aim was also to carry the frontier of France up to the Rhine. Here the territories of the Dukes of Lorraine, and Bouillon Prince of Sedan, not only cut France off from the Rhine and the Moselle, but opened a door by which she could at any time be invaded from Germany. The Dukes of Lorraine had always borne themselves as independent princes, giving, indeed, a nominal allegiance to France, but as often allying themselves with German princes as with her. The Duc de Bouillon, on the north of Lorraine, and the Duke of Savoy, farther to the south, also regarded themselves as independent. The former, as Huguenots, had a strong leaning towards the Protestant Hollanders, and both were ready to furnish asylums to French nobles who had incurred the wrath of their kings or ministers.

The Duc de Bouillon, father of Turenne, had fought bravely on the side of Henry of Navarre through the wars of the League. He died when the viscount was but ten years of age, and, his elder brother being but six years older, his mother became regent of the little state. After having greatly weakened the strength of the Huguenot nobles by the siege and capture of La Rochelle, which had long been the stronghold and bulwark of that religion, Richelieu obtained from the duchess a treaty by which she engaged to remain always attached to the interests of France, while the king undertook to protect the house of Bouillon. The Duke of Savoy was next compelled to hand over to France the town and province of Pignerol, and Richelieu then turned his attention to Lorraine. The reigning duke had entered into an alliance with Austria, and the invasion of his territory was therefore the first step by which France entered into the terrible struggle known as the Thirty Years' War.

The duke had given Richelieu an excuse for hostilities. He had married his cousin, the nearest heir to the dukedom, but he treated her so badly that she fled to France and begged the protection of Louis XIII. This he gave her, a French army was at once set in motion against Lorraine, and it was in this struggle that Turenne had first fought under the French flag. He had always evinced the strongest predilection for the life of a soldier, and when he reached the age of fourteen, Richelieu being at the time engaged in breaking the power of the Huguenots and in the siege of La Rochelle, the boy's mother sent him to his uncle Maurice of Nassau, who at the death of his father had become the leader of the Dutch people. He was treated by his uncle in exactly the same way as other gentlemen volunteers, carried a musket, and performed all the duties of a private soldier.

Six months later Prince Maurice died, and his brother, Henry Frederick, succeeded him in the government of the United Provinces. He at once promoted his nephew, and the latter speedily rose to the rank of captain of infantry. Here he was indefatigable in his duties, and unlike most young men of good family, who left the internal economy and discipline of their companies to subordinate officers, Turenne saw to everything himself. He drilled and instructed his soldiers, insisted not only upon strict military discipline, but on good manners and conduct in every particular. He won their respect and affection by his personal kindness, and denied himself almost the necessities of life in order to be able to add to their comforts. In the wars in the Netherlands there were few pitched battles, and the operations consisted almost entirely of the sieges of fortified towns or of measures for their relief.

In all these Turenne took much more than his full share, paying attention not only to his own duties but to all that was being done, spending his whole time in the batteries and the trenches, and in learning all that was possible of war carried on under such conditions. In the winter, operations were always suspended, and Turenne spent his time in Paris, where his manner and conduct won for him the favour of all with whom he came in contact. He had been severely brought up under a Calvinist tutor; his habits were simple, his tastes quiet and almost ascetic, and he cared little for the amusements of the brilliant and corrupt court. When the war with Lorraine broke out, Turenne at once sought for employment with the French army.

He recognized that there was comparatively little to be done in the war of sieges in Holland, and longed to enter a wider field. His request was gladly granted, for the presence of the Duc de Bouillon's brother in the French army was in itself some guarantee of the duke's fidelity to his engagements with France, and Turenne was at once appointed to the colonelcy of a regiment. He devoted himself as assiduously to his work as he had done in Holland, and it was not long before his regiment gained the reputation of being the best-disciplined in the king's service. He took part in a short expedition in 1630, but there was on that occasion no fighting, and he first saw real service under Marshal de la Force in 1634. After the siege of La Motte, the success of which was due to the storming of the breach by Turenne and his regiment, and for which exploit he was promoted to the rank of Maréchal de Camp, a rank equivalent to that of major-general, he took part in several sieges, until Lorraine was completely conquered and its duke driven to abdicate and retire to Austria.

The battle of Nördlingen showed Richelieu that if France did not resolutely enter into the conflict the Austrians would become absolute masters of all Germany. He at once signed a treaty with the Swedes, agreeing to grant them large subsidies to carry on the war. By a similar treaty he promised subsidies and the province of Alsace to the Duke of Saxe-Weimar. He entered into an arrangement with the Dutch, who were to aid France to conquer Flanders, which was to be divided between the two powers; while the Dukes of Savoy, Parma, and Mantua agreed to undertake, in alliance with

France, the invasion of Milan, and to receive in return a portion of the territory won from Spain. At the same time France declared war against Spain. It was to the army commanded by Cardinal de la Valette, which was to act with that of Saxe-Weimar against the Imperialists, that Turenne was attached.

The campaign began unfavourably. The impetuosity of Saxe-Weimar, who hoped to recover his own principality, induced Valette to cross the Rhine; but he was forced to retire in all haste, and the army suffered terribly in the retreat. Turenne was in command of the advanced guard, and his courage and activity alone saved the army from complete destruction—seizing upon defiles, overthrowing the enemy who barred the passages, and enabling the army to recross the Rhine with numbers diminished only by sickness, fatigue, and hunger. At the siege of Saverne, Turenne led the French troops to the attack after three repulses, and succeeded in gaining a footing in the town, but received himself a very severe wound in the arm with a musket-ball. During the following year several towns were captured but no decisive operations took place.

In 1638, the Duke of Saxe-Weimar gained some great successes, defeated the Imperialists with heavy loss at Rheinfelden, and besieged Breisach, the key of southern Germany. The Imperialist army marched to relieve the place, but reinforcements were sent from France under the command of Turenne and Longueville. Three battles were fought and the Austrians driven off. After an assault by Turenne, Breisach capitulated, and all Alsace had now fallen into the hands of Saxe-Weimar. Having been promised Alsace he refused, as Richelieu desired, to hand over Breisach to France; but on the death of the duke in the following year, Richelieu bought over his lieutenants, the French flag waved over the towns of Alsace, and the Upper Rhine became the French frontier. Turenne returned to court, where he was received with enthusiasm, and was a short time afterwards ordered to Italy to assist De la Valette, who had been faring but badly there.

WON BY THE SWORD

Matters had not gone there as Richelieu had calculated. The Duke of Savoy remained true to his engagement with France, but he died in October, 1637. The Spaniards had captured Vercelli, and the emperor had bestowed the regency of the duchy on the Cardinal of Savoy and on Prince Thomas, brother-in-law of the duchess. These, supported by the Duke of Modena and the Governor of Milan, the Marquess of Leganez, declared that they were determined to protect the people against the French and to deliver the young duke from French domination. The duchess implored help from France, and la Valette advanced to her aid.

While in Paris, Turenne had obtained from the cardinal permission to raise a regiment of dragoons and also that a company of dragoons should be attached to each regiment of cavalry. These troops were not intended to fight on horseback, but were, in fact, mounted infantry, an arm which, after being in disuse for many years, has lately been recognized as a very valuable one, possessing as it does the mobility of cavalry with the fighting power of infantry. It was at the head of this regiment that the general started for Italy. The position of affairs in Savoy was dark indeed, for the whole of Piedmont had risen against the duchess. Many considerable towns had been captured by the Spanish, others, including the city of Turin, had opened their gates to them, and with the exception of Susa, Carignano, Chivasso, Casale, and the citadel of Turin, the whole country was lost to her. The French forces were, however, too weak to take the offensive, and the ill-health of La Valette deprived him of his former energy and rendered him unwilling to undertake any offensive movement. Nevertheless, Turenne's counsels infused a new spirit into the army, and indeed the news that the young general, whose name was already known throughout Europe, had arrived, and the belief that his coming would be followed by that of large reinforcements from France, at once reanimated the remaining supporters of the duchess and dispirited the Piedmontese, who began to fear that they had been too hasty in siding with Spain.

CHOOSING A LACKEY

But if, for the time, Turenne was not in a position to act in the field, he began at once to take steps to prepare to meet the coming storm. Early in October La Valette died. The general opinion was that Turenne would have succeeded to the command, but his brother the Duc de Bouillon had broken with Richelieu and joined the party opposed to him. When in Paris, the duke had been on terms of intimate friendship with the Count of Soissons and had invited him to stay with him at Sedan. The invitation had been declined, but the count, having been implicated in a plot against Richelieu, had been obliged to fly and had taken refuge at Sedan, where he had been most warmly received by the duke. Richelieu had at first invited, and then in the name of the king commanded, Bouillon to expel his guest. This the duke absolutely refused to do, and becoming deeply offended at the manner in which he was pressed, joined the party opposed to Richelieu.

It was for this reason that the cardinal decided not to appoint Turenne to the command, knowing the warm affection that existed between the brothers, and fearing that Turenne might be influenced by Bouillon, and might, beloved as he was by the soldiers, lead many of the troops away from their allegiance were he to join the party opposed to him. He therefore appointed the Count d'Harcourt to the command. He had proved himself a brilliant officer on many occasions, and Turenne did not feel in any way aggrieved at his being placed over him. He made a rapid journey to Paris to arrange with the cardinal and d'Harcourt the general plan of the campaign, and was now setting out again to make preparations for it.

Hector Campbell enjoyed the journey greatly. His duties were nominal; and the party always halted at towns, where the troops were billeted upon the inhabitants, and the viscount and his suite entertained by the authorities. After crossing the Alps, however, by the pass of Mount Cenis, and arriving at Susa, his work began in earnest. Turenne himself was almost entirely occupied in consultations with the duchess; his three aides-de-camp, however, were kept hard at work carrying messages to the governors of towns that still adhered to the duchess, with orders for the strengthening of the defences and for the collection of stores and provisions in case of siege. Each was provided with three horses, and almost lived in the saddle.

"You seem to be tireless, Campbell," de Lisle said, when it one day happened that all three were together at headquarters. "I feel as if I had not a whole bone in my body; as I have not had a whole night in bed for the last six days, I can hardly keep my eyes open, while you, who have been doing as much as we have, are going about as actively as if you had had nothing to do for a week."

"I have the advantage of riding so much lighter than you do," Hector said; "weight tells both on horse and rider, and when the horse is tired his pace soon adds to the weariness of his rider. If we had had to do this work when we first left Paris, I have no doubt that I should have felt it, but the journey here has been a fine preparation. Another thing is, that every morning I take a dip in the first mountain stream I come to, and that does one almost as much good as a night's sleep."

De Lisle shivered. "It may do good, Campbell, but I would not jump into one of these icy streams for anything. It makes one shudder to think of it."

"I always had a swim in the Seine every morning when it was not closed by ice," Hector said. "I was told that there was nothing braced one up and made one so hardy as that; and I certainly found that even in the coldest weather I never felt the need of a cloak."

"Well, I don't deny that it may be a good custom, and if all Scotchmen do it, it may account for their hardiness; but I like comfort when I can get it."

"But it is not comfort to be always in the saddle, and to feel so sleepy that you fancy that at any moment you may fall off. Even if a dip in snow-water is, to those unaccustomed to it, somewhat sharp, it is better than having to struggle against sleep for hours."

CHOOSING A LACKEY

"Well, possibly I may try the experiment some day when I feel that I must either lie down by the roadside and sleep or take a dip, but until I feel like breaking down altogether I shall postpone the experiment."

Turenne several times spoke approvingly to Hector. On one occasion, when the lad presented himself on being told that an aide-de-camp was required to carry a message, Turenne said to him: "But it is not your turn, Campbell; de Lisle and Chavigny both returned some hours ago, while it is not an hour since you came in."

"They are both asleep, general," Campbell said; "they have been thirty-six hours in the saddle."

"But you have been more than that, Campbell?"

"But I do not feel it, sir," he said. "I am perfectly fresh and ready to go on. I was a little tired when I came in, but I have taken a swim in the river, and am now at your service."

Turenne hesitated. "You see, sir," Hector went on, "being of light weight the horse does not feel it as he does that of a heavier man, his pace continues light and elastic, and his spirit good, and that makes all the difference to the fatigue of his rider. After two days' rest my horses are perfectly ready for another long day's work, while those of Chavigny and de Lisle start heavily, not having recovered from their fatigue."

"Very well, you can go then, Campbell. I am pleased with your spirit, and also with your thoughtfulness for your companions, who, although strong young men, do not seem to have your power of endurance. I find, too, that you always carry out your instructions with intelligence, and that your reports on matters touching which I have sent you to inquire are always clear and full. It may be that ere long I may find employment for you in which courage as well as intelligence is required. There is but one drawback, namely, that you do not speak Italian. I know that there are few officers in our service who do so; but it would be so much the more valuable were you able to master it."

"I had intended to study the language, general, as soon as I got here, but have had no time to begin it."

"That you certainly have not," Turenne said with a smile.

"Do you think that it would be of any use, sir, if I were to take a Savoyard servant? I find that many of them who come from places near the frontier speak French as well as their own language."

"That would be useful, certainly; but you would have to be careful in your choice, and see that you get one whose sympathies are with the duchess; not only for your own safety, but because a chance word heard here, or an order given and conveyed to the Spaniards, might involve the loss of a battle."

"I see that, general, and will be very careful."

Hector had formed the acquaintance of several young officers attached to the household of the duchess, and on the day following his return from his mission he was supping with a party of four of them when he said:

"Can one of you gentlemen recommend a servant to me? He must be able to talk French as well as Italian. He must be active and intelligent. I should like him to be handy and accustomed to camp service, though this is not so important, for I want him as an interpreter before anything else. I should like him to be a light weight, so as to be able to ride with me. He must be accustomed to fatigue, and he must have courage, for some of the journeys on which I may be sent will not be without danger, and of course he must be of the duchess's party."

"And I suppose," one of the young men said, "that this Admirable Crichton of whom you are in search must be sober, honest, and truthful. Are you particular whether he is Huguenot or Catholic?"

"As to the last, not a bit. I should like him to be as sober as soldiers in general are, and if he confined himself to taking his wine when I did not require him, it would not be very important, provided that he is not talkative when in liquor. As to his honesty, he would have no great temptation so far as I am concerned, but I certainly should not wish to lose him by his being strung up by the provost-marshal for robbing citizens. As to his truthfulness, providing he did not lie to me, it is a point on which I should not be particular."

There was a general laugh.

"And as to his age?" the officer asked.

"If I could find all the qualifications that I require, I should not be particular about that; but I think that for choice I would take a lad of from sixteen to twenty."

"In that case I fancy that I know a lad who might suit you," one of the other officers said. "He is a brother of my groom, and I may own that he has been of no little trouble to him. The boy is an orphan, and having no other friends so far as I know, he has attached himself to his brother, and for the past two years, wherever he has gone Paolo has gone too. He earns a little money by doing odd jobs—running messages, and so on, helps his brother to clean the horses; and with an occasional crown from me, and what he earns otherwise, it cannot be said that he costs his brother anything in money; but in other respects he is always getting him into trouble, for he is a very imp of mischief. Two or three times his brother has obtained places for him, but he always comes back at the end of a week, and sometimes sooner, with bitter complaints from his master that he has set the household in a turmoil with his tricks and ill conduct. Many a thrashing has he had, but they do him no good."

The others laughed.

"There is no doubt that Paolo is a perfect young imp," one of them said, "but he is as sharp as a needle. I have no doubt that if he could be tamed he would make a most useful lad. As it is, I certainly would not recommend anyone who cares for his peace of mind to have anything to do with him."

"I will see him anyhow," Hector said. "I think that I would rather have a sharp boy than a man. Being but a boy myself, I could appreciate and put up with more in the way of mischief than a man could."

"I will tell my groom to bring him round to your quarters in the morning," the officer said; "but mind, I in no way recommend your taking him. You won't keep him a week if you do."

The next morning Hector's orderly told him that a man desired to speak to him.

"Has he a boy with him?"

"Yes, lieutenant."

"Bring them in here, then."

In a minute a man entered, followed by a boy. The former was a good-looking young Savoyard of some four-or five-and-twenty years; the latter was a lad of about the same height as Hector but somewhat older. He had black hair which fell over his forehead down to his eyebrows. His face bore an expression of extreme humility, which, however, was marred by the merry twinkle of his dark eyes.

"My master has bid me bring my brother with me, Lieutenant Campbell," the man said, "and I have done so, but I fear greatly that he will hardly suit you as a servant. I have obtained a dozen places for him, but he is always sent back at the end of three or four days, and I told him last time that I would never say a word in his recommendation again, for that it only gets me into trouble with the gentlemen."

"Well, that is honest," Hector said with a smile. "However, I will ask him a few questions. Now, Paolo, in the first place, could you be faithful?"

"I could be faithful to a master I loved," he said.

"In the second place, are you honest?"

"He is honest," the man said, "I will say that for him."

"Are you truthful?"

"I am as truthful as other people," the boy said.

"What do you mean by that?"

"I mean, sir, that if I were asked a straightforward question I would give a straightforward answer, unless it were wiser not to do so. I would tell the truth to my master, but I do not consider it necessary always to do so to others. For instance, sir, if you were my master, and questions were asked about you, there might be times when it would not be convenient for you that I should mention where you had gone, or what you were doing."

"That is so," Hector said with a laugh. "The important thing for me to know is, would you always tell me the truth?"

"I think that I could promise to do that, sir, or at least to be very near the truth."

"You understand horses?"

"I do, sir."

"And you can ride?"

"Yes, sir, I can ride and run too. In a long day's journey I should get to the end on foot nearly as fast as you would on horseback."

"He can make himself useful on a campaign," the brother said. "He has been with my master and myself in the field for the last three years, and knows his work well if he chooses to do it."

The principal point with me is that which I first asked him about, can he be faithful? I may have to ride on dangerous missions for the general. I may have to enter an enemy's town to obtain information. There is another thing, being of the general's staff, and sometimes quartered in the same house with him and chatting freely with his other aides-de-camp, secrets might be picked up by a sharp pair of ears that if repeated would do grievous harm to the cause of the duchess, as you can well understand. Now, the question, Paolo, is, can you be absolutely trusted; can you, as to all matters you may hear, be as one who is deaf and dumb?"

"I could, sir," the boy said earnestly. "I am all for the duchess, and I hate the Spaniards. I once was found out in a bit of mischief in the palace, and should have been whipped for it and turned out of the town, but the duchess herself said that I was only a boy and forgave me, and I would do anything for her. I would indeed, sir, and I swear that I would be always honest and truthful with you. I should like you as a master. You don't speak to me as if I were dirt under your feet, and I am sure by your voice that you would be kind. Try me, sir; my brother will tell you that I have never said as much before to anyone to whom he has taken me, for indeed I never meant to stay with them, preferring my liberty, rough though my fare may sometimes be."

"I will try you, Paolo. I believe that you are in earnest, and that I can trust you; but mind, there must be no monkey-tricks here. The general must not be disturbed by the antics of a servant-boy. You are likely, in my service, to have as much excitement and adventure as you can wish for, and you must behave yourself, for if you do not do so you will be lucky if you escape with a flogging and being turned out of camp. I am younger than you are, and am just as fond of a piece of fun, but I know when it is good to enjoy one's self and when one must put aside boyish pranks. I have my duties to perform, and do them to the best of my power, and shall expect you to do the same."

"I will, sir," the boy said respectfully. "I will give you no cause to complain of me, at least no wilful cause."

"Then that is settled. Here," he said to the boy's brother, "are five pistoles; see that he is decently clad so as to make a fair appearance by my side. When he is so, let him return here. It were best that he should come this evening, for it is likely that I shall be away on duty to-morrow."

"He shall be here, sir," he said, "and I thank you heartily for engaging him; and I do think that he means this time to behave himself."

"I do mean it," the boy said. "You shall have no reason to complain of me, sir."

Shortly afterwards Hector met the officer who had spoken of the boy.

"Well, have you thought anything more of young ne'er-do-well?"

"I have engaged him."

"You have, after the warning I gave you? Well, I hope you will not have reason to repent it."

"I do not think that I shall. I can quite believe that he is a mischievous young varlet, he shows it in his face; but I am sure that he is shrewd, and I believe that he will be faithful. At any rate I think that we took to each other, and that he has made up his mind to try for once to stay in a place. He really seemed in earnest about it, and if he keeps to his promises I think that he will be just the sort of lad to suit me."

"Well, we shall see," the officer said; "but if he turns out badly, please remember that I warned you against him."

"And if he turns out well," Hector said with a laugh, "I shall not fail also to remind you of your prognostications."

That evening when Hector returned to his room after he had finished his meal, he found Paolo waiting outside his door. His appearance had so changed that he would not have known him. His hair had been cut short in the front and left long behind, as was the custom of the day, hanging down on to his collar. He was neat and tidy. He wore a dark-blue doublet reaching to the hips, with a buff-leather belt, in which was stuck a dagger. His leggings, fitting tightly down to the ankles, were of dark maroon cloth, and he wore short boots of tanned leather. A plain white collar, some four inches deep, was worn turned down over the neck of the doublet, and a yellow cloth cap, with a dark cock's feather, was stuck on one side of his head. In his hand he held a bundle containing a leather jerkin and breeches of the same material, and a pair of buff-leather riding boots that would reach to the knee.

"Your brother has laid out the money well, Paolo," Hector said, as he opened the door and led the way into his room. I do not think that I should have known you."

"I am quite sure that I should not have known myself, master, if I had looked into a horse-trough and seen my reflection. It will be a long time before I shall be able to persuade myself that these clothes are my own, and that I really am an officer's lackey. Now, master, you must teach me my duties, of which I know nought when in a house like this, though I know well enough what they are when you are in the field."

"They are few enough at present, Paolo. Monsieur de Turenne's stable-men look after the horses of his staff. When I do not dine with him, I and my two friends, M. de Lisle and M. de Chavigny, dine and sup together at an inn. There is my room to keep tidy, my bed to make, my armour and arms to be polished, and my clothes to be brushed. Hitherto, my orderly has done these things, but it will now be your duty. As I do not eat in my rooms, it is clear that there is no food for you, and when we are in towns I shall give you money to pay for your meals at a cabaret."

"I hope, master, that you will soon find something more useful for me to do, for, in truth, I fear that with so much time on my hands I shall find it sorely difficult to comport myself as is due to your lackey."

"Do not fear, I have little doubt that you will soon find work enough and to spare, and indeed you will often ride with me."

Some few days later, the other two aides-de-camp being away, the viscount requested Hector to accompany him on a tour of inspection that might last two or three days. He was accompanied by his orderly and three other troopers, behind whom rode two of his own lackeys with baskets of provisions. With them rode Paolo, Hector having asked the general if he should take him with him.

"You may as well do so, Campbell, it will accustom him to his work. What made you choose so young a servant?" he asked, as he rode off.

"He is a year older than I am, though perhaps not so tall. He is the brother of a man in the employment of Monsieur de Vevey. He has been through the last two campaigns. I find him very intelligent. He obeys my orders promptly, and as he is heart and soul in the cause of the duchess, I feel sure of his fidelity, especially as he has had a hard time of it up to now, and is, I think, grateful to me for taking him. He speaks French very well, and might certainly be of great use to me in any enterprise that your lordship might be good enough to entrust me with. Being about the same age, I think that we might perhaps go together unquestioned where a man would be unable to pass."

CHOOSING A LACKEY

The viscount rode on for some minutes without speaking. "There is something in what you say, Campbell, and after this journey is over I may be able to employ you in that way when it is necessary to obtain information I can get in no other manner. Has he ridden with you before?"

"Yes, sir, he has ridden behind me each time that I have been away since I engaged him. When I say behind me, he starts behind me, but when out of town I call him up beside me, and we talk, or rather try to talk, in Italian—or rather I should say in Piedmontese, for he tells me that each district of Italy has its own dialect, and that the natives of one can scarce understand the other. I have bought a book printed here and a dictionary, and of an evening when I have no duties to perform he comes into my room, and translates sentence by sentence as I read it to him. I learn it by heart, and hope that ere long I shall be able to make myself understood in it."

"You do well—very well," the viscount said. "If all my young officers were to do the same, instead of spending the evening and half the night in drinking and gambling, things would go on much more smoothly, and there would not be so many blunders in carrying out my orders. You will greatly add to your usefulness by acquiring a knowledge of the language, and it would certainly enable you to carry out with far less danger such commissions as those you were just speaking of; for you might be asked a question, and if it were replied to by your lackey, suspicions would be at once aroused. You have ridden along this road before?"

"Several times, sir."

"Have you noted the features of the country—I mean from a military point of view?"

"I have nothing else to do as I ride along, sir. As I go I notice where an ambuscade might be laid, either by ourselves or an enemy, where we might expect to be opposed on our march forward, or where a rear-guard might check an enemy were we retiring before him."

"Good! the fate of a battle depends in nine cases out of ten upon a knowledge of the ground, and in quickness in utilizing that knowledge. Our journey to-day is only taken for that purpose. I want to see for myself the country across which we shall at first operate, to inspect the various routes by which we might advance, or through which, if we find the enemy in too great a force to be encountered, we should be obliged to retire. As we go you shall point out to me the observations that you have made, and I shall be able to judge whether the spots are well-chosen for the purpose."

CHAPTER III
THE FIRST BATTLE

DURING the three days that were spent in reconnoitring the country Hector Campbell learnt more than he would have done in as many years under ordinary circumstances. Turenne took the greatest pains to point out to him how the nature of the ground could be taken advantage of; how flanks could be protected against attack by comparatively small bodies, occupying positions from which they could be with difficulty expelled; how important was the action of guns, especially when so placed as to be able to sweep the ground across which an enemy must advance in any endeavour to turn the position of an army. Turenne, on his part, took pleasure in instructing a pupil who was at once so eager to learn, and who showed himself so apt in profiting by his teaching.

"You see," he said, "I am concerned rather in defensive positions at present than in seeing how we could best turn an enemy barring our advance. Although the greater portion of the dominions of the duchess has fallen into the hands of the enemy, she is fortunate in that the few places that remain are those that at once enable her to make a defence with comparatively small forces; and at the same time, it is possible for her to receive aid from France, or, if absolutely necessary, for her to fall back across the Alps. Susa, her head-quarters, lying at the mouth of the valley up which the road over Mount Cenis finds its way, at once guards the pass and keeps open communication with France.

WON BY THE SWORD

"It is, as it were, the handle of a fan, and can be approached by three main roads only,—those to Turin, Carignano, and Chivasso. Unfortunately Turin is in the enemy's hands, but as the duchess's troops still hold the citadel, an advance could not very well be made until that has fallen. Chivasso and Carignano are safe from any sudden attack. There are other minor roads, but so long as these towns are in our hands and held by strong garrisons, an enemy advancing by any of these roads towards Susa would be liable to have their communications cut, and their convoys captured by parties from these fortresses. It has long been a fixed idea in military operations that an army cannot advance as long as a town near the line of route is held by the enemy. That idea is an erroneous one, and several times upon the Rhine we have gained successes by neglecting this rule and disregarding the towns, contenting ourselves with leaving a force sufficient to keep the garrison in check.

"The Spaniards, however, are slow to change their tactics, good soldiers as they are. The consequence is that, although greatly superior in force, last year they made no offensive movement against us. We have had several regiments join us since we arrived here, and although I believe the enemy's force to be twice as strong as our own, I have no doubt that the Count d'Harcourt will as soon as he arrives decide upon taking the offensive. You see our position here, guarded as it is on both flanks by the line of mountains, is as favourable for offence as defence, for we can advance either through Carignano on our right or Chivasso on our left; and however the enemy may dispose themselves they are vulnerable on one side or the other."

This anticipation was justified. D'Harcourt arrived three days later. A council of war was held, and it was decided that an advance should at once be made against the enemy. The main body of the Spanish troops were posted in a fortified camp at Villanova, half-way between Asti and Turin. Leaving only a small body of troops to guard the lower valley of Susa from an attack by the Spaniards at Turin, the army advanced to Carignano, and thence towards Villanova. The Spaniards, however, although nearly twice as strong as the French, were so much surprised at the boldness of this proceeding that instead of marching out to give battle they contented themselves with strengthening still further the defences of their camp, and in order to force them to come out d'Harcourt advanced to Chieri called by the French Quiers— a town situated between Villanova and Turin, and about two leagues distant from each.

Turenne was in command of the cavalry, and took post between Chieri and Villanova. The Spaniards, however, made no effort to relieve the town, which capitulated after a resistance of only two or three days. While the siege was proceeding, a large convoy of provisions succeeded, unmolested, in making its way to Casale, and thus placed the garrison there in a position to hold out for several weeks to come. But a very small store of provisions was found in Chieri, and the army was forced to fall back towards Carignano to obtain food from the stores collected there. The Marquis of Leganez, whose head-quarters were at Asti, knowing that the French had sent all the stores they had brought with them to Casale, had foreseen that this would be the case, and advancing rapidly with the troops from Villanova seized Poirino, on the line by which the French would retire, while at the same time Prince Thomas, who commanded at Turin, advanced with the greater portion of his troops, and marched towards the little river Santina, intending to cross there. Thus the French army could not retire on Carignano without exposing both flanks to the attack of the enemy.

During the short campaign Hector had ridden behind Turenne, and shared in the general disappointment of the army when the enemy refused to accept their offer of battle, and still more so when after the capture of Chieri it became necessary to retreat. His two fellow aides-de-camp loudly bewailed the bad fortune that thus obliged them to retire without having effected anything beyond the capture of an insignificant town, which, however, had the advantage of opening a way for them into the heart of the country then held by the enemy.

"You seem to take it rather philosophically, Campbell," de Lisle said to Hector, as he remained silent while they were bemoaning their fate.

"I do not see that it is of any use taking it otherwise. At least we have had the satisfaction of bearding the Spaniards, who indeed seem to me to behave wisely in remaining in their intrenchments and waiting until they can unite all their forces against us. However, we have shown them that we are not afraid of them, and that even in the middle of November we are so eager to meet them that we have hastened to take the field and to strike a blow before winter sets in in earnest; but I think it possible that we may have a fight yet before we get back. Leganez has the reputation of being a good general, and he may yet combine his troops at Asti with those of Villanova and Turin and try to cut us off from Carignano." At this moment Turenne suddenly entered the room.

"To horse, gentlemen! News has come that Prince Thomas is marching at the head of three thousand foot and fifteen hundred horse to cut us off, and that Leganez is moving with all speed towards Poirino with the same object. Carry my orders for a thousand cavalry and as many infantry to be ready to march at once. We must be beforehand with Prince Thomas."

In ten minutes the cavalry and infantry selected were in movement, and Turenne, placing himself at the head of the former, rode on at a gallop, and keeping on at full speed with his cavalry, occupied the bridge before Prince Thomas came up. On his arrival, the latter, having with him three thousand foot and fifteen hundred horse, prepared to attack, but before he did so Turenne's infantry arrived. The Spaniards attacked with fury, but Turenne's troops stood firm and repulsed them, and as soon as they fell back charged in turn, broke the enemy, and drove them in headlong rout towards Turin. Prince Thomas himself was twice unhorsed and thrown into a ditch, but it was now almost dark, his rank was unrecognized, and he succeeded in making his escape and rejoining his scattered troops.

While this fight was going on, d'Harcourt had attacked the Marquis of Leganez and gained a considerable advantage, but not knowing how the fight was going on at Santina did not venture to advance towards the Po. As soon, however, as a messenger from Turenne brought him news that Prince Thomas had been defeated he continued his march towards Carignano. He was speedily joined by Turenne's horse, which took up the duty of rear-guard and checked the Spaniards, who were pressing on in hopes of attacking the French as they crossed the river. He held them at bay until d'Harcourt had got all his guns and baggage-wagons across the river, and then, following him, broke down the bridge and joined him at Carignano. Here the army went into winter quarters.

D'Harcourt, whose health was bad, retired to pass the winter at Pinerolo, leaving the command in the hands of Turenne, who again established himself at Susa, and began to make preparations for throwing a convoy of provisions into the citadel of Turin.

During the fight at Santina Hector, remained behind Turenne, while the two young Frenchmen, carried away by their ardour, joined in the hot pursuit of the enemy. The prince, who had led the charge, had halted.

"Are you alone here, Monsieur Campbell?"

"Yes, sir."

"Where are de Lisle and Chavigny?"

"They rode on with the cavalry, sir."

Turenne frowned.

"You have done well to remain. An aide-de-camp's place is to carry orders, not to fight. Now, sir, ride at once to the count. I hear his battle is still going on. Tell him that I have defeated and scattered the troops of the prince, and that as soon as I can gather my men I shall march to join him."

WON BY THE SWORD

Hector bowed, turned his horse and galloped off, while the general rode on, sending every officer he overtook in search of the cavalry with orders that they were to abandon the pursuit and return instantly. That evening after they had entered Carignano he called de Lisle and Chavigny into his room.

"Gentlemen," he said, "you will have to choose whether you remain with me or join one of the cavalry regiments. If you remain with me, you must bear in mind in future that you are my aides-de-camp, and that your sole duty here is to carry my orders, and not to fight like troopers in a battle. It is through hot-headedness of this sort that battles are lost. A general, without officers to carry his orders, can do nothing towards controlling the movements of his troops in battle, of following up a victory or covering a defeat."

The two young officers hung their heads and murmured their excuses.

"Enough, gentlemen," Turenne said. "I am perfectly aware that it was your ardour that carried you away, but ardour is a bad leader. Over and over again the ardour of cavalry to pursue the troops they have defeated has brought about the loss of a battle. Courage is a virtue, and most soldiers possess it, but steadiness and coolness are rarer and more useful, and on the part of officers on a general's staff are absolutely indispensable. I doubt not that you will remember this in future, and that I shall not have reason to complain of you again.

The next morning it was Hector's turn to be in attendance on the general.

"You behaved as I expected you would do," Turenne said, when he entered his room on hearing the bell sound. "You fought close to me as long as there was fighting to be done, and I observed that you used your sword well. The moment I drew rein you did the same, and took up your post behind me, showing that although this was your first battle you retained your coolness. I will therefore tell you in confidence that Count d'Harcourt has enjoined me to throw provisions, if possible, into the citadel at Turin. It will take me some time to make arrangements, and my only fear is that the garrison, on hearing that we have retired across the Po—of which you may be sure the Spaniards will take care to inform them—may believe that we shall do no more this winter; and as we know that their provisions must be well-nigh exhausted, they will abandon the citadel and march thither.

"It is now well-nigh eighteen months since they were first cut off. It is certain that their investment is a very close one, and that the most vigilant watch is used to prevent news of any kind from reaching them from the outside. We have made several efforts to communicate with them, but without success. Some of the messengers we sent never returned, and were, doubtless, detected and killed. Others came back reported their failure, saying that every avenue to the citadel was so closely watched that it was impossible to get through."

"Have you any objection, general, to my mentioning this matter to my boy? I am absolutely convinced that he is thoroughly faithful and trustworthy."

"You may do so if you like, Campbell, though it is hardly likely that he will be able to suggest any method of communication with the garrison that has not already been tried."

"Thank you, sir."

The general shortly afterwards went out to wait upon the duchess; in two hours he returned, and as soon as he did so Hector entered his room.

"What is it?" Turenne asked.

"I have been thinking about what you said about the garrison of Turin. I have been talking it over with Paolo, and have come to offer to do my best to deliver a letter from you to the garrison if you will do me the great honour to entrust the mission to me. We both think that two boys would be much more likely to succeed than men. No one would regard them with suspicion; and they could creep and crawl more easily. I do not say that we should succeed, but I think that we should have some chance of doing so. At any rate I am willing to try."

"It would be a very dangerous expedition," Turenne said gravely.

"Not more dangerous than going into a battle, viscount. Not a quarter as dangerous as storming a breach."

Turenne smiled. "The idea has passed through my mind," he said, "but I should not have proposed it had you not first spoken. It is the sort of mission in which I thought you could be made useful, but it is a rough adventure to begin with, and you must not minimize the danger. It is the duty of a soldier to run the risk of being killed in battle, but it lies beyond his duty to go into the enemy's camp to obtain news. He may volunteer for it, but with a knowledge that if detected he would assuredly be hanged."

"I do not think, general, that the risk of detection would be great, but the risk of failure would be so. If when we get there we can see no possible means of passing through the line of sentries, there would be nothing to do but to come back, and I own that in talking it over the thought that I might be obliged to return and to tell you that I had failed occupied a much larger portion of my thoughts than the risk of being detected."

"But I shall not expect you to succeed, Campbell; the chances are a hundred to one against it. I should be glad, however, to have the experiment tried once again, so that if the garrison capitulates before we arrive to its succour, I shall not be able to blame myself for not having made one more effort to induce them to hold out for another few weeks. Have you thought of your plans?"

"Only so far, sir, that we shall dress up as two country boys, cross the Po, and enter the city from the other side. After that we must be guided by circumstances and trust to good luck. May I ask, general, if you have a plan of the city and fortress?"

"Yes; at least the duchess has one, which she has placed at my disposal. I can send an officer to the palace to request her to let me have it. No doubt it would be a great advantage to you to study the position beforehand."

"Well, sir, we will see about getting our disguises at once."

"I will give you an order on the paymaster for a hundred crowns for special service," Turenne said. "It is as well to be amply provided with money, as it may be necessary to buy fresh disguises or to bribe someone to conceal you;" and he drew an order on the treasury and handed it to Hector.

"You will find the plan of the town in your room when you return."

Paolo was waiting for him.

"It is settled, Paolo; we are to go."

"This is an adventure after my own heart," the boy said with delight. "It will be great fun to outwit the Spaniards."

"Yes, but we must mind that they don't outwit us, Paolo, which is quite as likely. Now let us talk of our disguises again. I think you had better go and buy them. I would rather get old ones than new. I don't suppose that anyone is likely to take notice of me in the streets, but it would be well at any rate that we should not both have new clothes, and better that neither of us did so."

"I can manage that sir. There are shops here where one can buy old clothes as well as new ones. I noticed one the other day in a narrow street by the wall. I wondered then who would buy some of the garments hung up. They were so old and so often mended that it was difficult to say what was the original colour. The people are very poor up in the mountains; since the war began, doubtless they have grown poorer, and are glad to buy anything that will cover them."

"Well, here are ten crowns."

"They won't cost half that, master, but I will take them."

"Mind and get something warm, Paolo; it is like enough that we shall have to sleep more than once in the open air, and the winds are bitterly cold."

In half an hour the officer came with the plan, which Hector at once set to to study. The citadel stood on ground but little, if at all, higher than that upon which the town was situated. It was pentagonal in form, and was built in 1565, and was the earliest fortification in Europe in this style, and was considered a masterpiece. It was separated from the town by its glacis. A deep fosse ran along the foot of the wall. The town itself was walled, and extended to the foot of the citadel, and was capable of offering a sturdy resistance even after the citadel had fallen, just as the citadel could protect itself after the capture of the town by an enemy. Hector examined carefully that portion of the town facing the citadel, and took notes of the streets that ran through to the walls, specially noting those which extended farthest from the wall before being broken by cross lanes.

It was evident from the width of the streets that this was the poorest quarter of the town, for the wealthy would not care to build their houses in a position where, if the town and citadel were hostile to each other, they would be exposed to the fire of the latter's guns.

In another half-hour Paolo returned with a large bundle. It contained two coarse cotton shirts, two warm garments resembling waistcoats, and fastened by strings closing up to the neck, two red sashes of coarse flannel, and two loose doublets reaching down to the hips. These were worn and patched, but had been newly lined with sheep-skin. The breeches, which reached down to the knee, were of coarse brown cloth; to cover the leg below the knee were bands of gray flannel which were wrapped round and round the leg and foot, while over these were worn wooden shoes. The hats were of conical shape with wide brims, and both, like the clothes, bore signs of long wear.

"It could not have been better, Paolo," Hector said as he examined them. "I have seen scores of boys so dressed, and we shall certainly attract no attention by our garb. They are warm, too, and we sha'n't come to any harm from sleeping out in them."

"They cost more than I expected, master, owing to the doublets being freshly lined, but I thought it would be worth it."

"Quite right! those sheep-skins will be most useful. There is one thing more we shall want, a thin rope, that will bear our weight well, some twenty yards long. You had better go to a smith's and get him to make a strong iron hook, by which we can fix the rope on to the edge of a wall should it be needed. You had better have it made a good nine inches across the hook, and the shank fifteen inches long."

After again studying the map he took it to the general.

"We have our disguises, sir, and shall be ready to start to-morrow morning."

"You have lost no time," the general said approvingly. "You will, of course, ride to Chivasso. I will give you an order to the governor there, to take charge of your horses and clothes, telling him that you are about to proceed on a mission in disguise, and requesting him to send an officer to pass you through the outposts beyond the bridge across the Po, that is if the other side is not guarded by the Spanish troops. I should advise you to make straight south so as to strike the road from Casale two miles west of Turin. I do not like letting you go, lad, and yet I feel it is of such importance that the garrison should know that aid will be at hand before long, that I feel I ought not to prevent you from carrying out your enterprise. When do you think of starting?"

"At eight in the morning, sir. If we do so we shall easily reach Chivasso before dark, and may be near Turin by morning."

"I will have my note for the commandant ready by the time your horses are at the door. I will make it as small as possible, and you had better before you start sew it up in the lining of your coat, so that if you are searched—which I own I do not think to be likely, unless in some other way you excite the suspicions of the Spaniards—it may not be found upon you."

"I think, sir, that I would rather make it into a little pellet which I can swallow. I fancy that if they were suspicious enough to search me they would rip all the linings open."

That would be a better way certainly, Campbell; I see that you have thought the matter over thoroughly. Of course, you will take no arms with you."

"Nothing but a long knife each. Every peasant carries one, and it may be possible that we shall be compelled to silence a sentinel. If you would not mind, sir, I should like to have six copies of your letter to the commandant. I could manage to swallow six as well as one, and as it is not likely that I shall be able to enter the citadel it would be as well to give them a better chance of finding the letter if I have to try to shoot or throw it in."

"That shall be done; we will use the thinnest paper, so that if you have to swallow them you can do so without difficulty."

"If I find that I cannot by any possibility get my message in through the town, sir, I shall try to cross the river and so make my way in on that side."

"That would be even more dangerous than the other," Turenne said. "On that side an even stricter watch is likely to be kept than on that facing the town, for the Spaniards know that the garrison is not strong enough to attempt any enterprise against the city, while it might at any moment attempt to break out and march away on the other side.

"I own that I do not see myself how you can possibly succeed in either case, but assuredly there must be more chance on the side of the town. I have been thinking it over, and will order a troop of cavalry to ride with you to Chivasso, for the Spanish horse from time to time make forays from Turin carry off prisoners, and burn villages. Until we are in a position to make a general advance it is impossible to check these attacks without keeping the whole of our cavalry massed near Turin, and wearing out horses and men by the necessity for perpetual vigilance. And now, good-bye; may fortune attend you! do not be too rash. The letters shall be sent you in an hour's time."

As they issued out from Susa they found the troop of cavalry awaiting them. The officer in command was well known to Hector, and said:

THE FIRST BATTLE

"So it is you that I am to escort to Chivasso, Monsieur Campbell?"

"Yes; I am sorry to give you occasion for so much trouble."

"No trouble at all; we have not been in the saddle for the past week, and a ride to Chivasso will make a pleasant change. Besides, I have a brother in the garrison there, so that altogether I shall be your debtor. You see, we are not allowed to ride beyond St. Ambrogio, or Rivoli at farthest, for once beyond that, we should be liable to be caught by the enemy's scouting parties. Of course we have a strong force at Rivoli, but except to drive off small parties of the enemy who may venture to come up too close, they are forbidden to engage in any affairs. It is annoying, but one can understand that the general is anxious to avoid encounters in which the enemy is sure to be superior in force, until his reinforcements come up and we are able to take the field in earnest."

"I do not think we shall be otherwise than inferior in force even when our last regiment comes up," Hector said. "What with Holland and the Rhine and the frontier of Spain, it is clear that the cardinal must have as much as he can do to enable all our commanders to make head against the enemy, and it is no secret that beyond one more regiment of cavalry that will arrive with Count d'Harcourt, no other reinforcements are likely to reach us for some time to come. But then, you see, we have Turenne as well as d'Harcourt, and each of them ought to count for two or three thousand men."

"Well, I would rather fight against long odds," the officer said, "than be kept here month after month doing nothing. Here is winter coming on, and I suppose that will put a stop to everything."

"I should hardly think so," Hector replied. "I am sure that the viscount is as eager for action as we are, and winter here is not the same thing as in Holland or on the Rhine. From what I hear there is very little snow in the plains; and as the country is generally flat, an army could march almost as easily as in summer, and in some respects they would be better off."

"How do you mean?"

"I mean that in summer the barns would be all empty of food until filled again by the harvest, whereas in winter they would be all well stocked with forage for the cattle and horses."

"You are right, Monsieur Campbell. Certainly there should be nothing to prevent our operating through the winter, and I shall look forward even more eagerly than I did before for d'Harcourt's return. Will you come back with us to-morrow from Chivasso?"

"That will depend upon circumstances. I think it is more probable that I shall not return to Susa for a few days; my orders are to report myself to the governor."

No bodies of the enemy's cavalry were met with on the way, and at four o'clock in the afternoon they rode into Chivasso. They alighted at the commandant's, and on stating that he was the bearer of a despatch from the general Hector was at once shown in. As he had more than once ridden there with despatches from Turenne, he was known to the officer.

"We heard of the victory three days since," the latter said, as Hector handed him the despatch, "and fired a salvo of guns in honour of it. An Italian deserter from the other side brought the news. The two generals were unwounded, I hope?"

"Yes, colonel, and our losses were altogether slight."

The commandant opened the despatch. He looked a little surprised at its contents. "So you are going to endeavour to pass a message into the citadel. It is a difficult undertaking. The enemy's watch is a very vigilant one. Once or twice during the siege men have succeeded in swimming the Po and evading the enemy's guards, but of late these have been doubled, for it is thought that the garrison may attempt to break out. On the town side the firing has all but ceased; they know that the store of provisions is almost exhausted, and regard it as a waste of powder and shot to continue their cannonade, which only results in the citadel answering it, and that with very much more effect than the Spanish guns produce. May I ask if you have any plan of getting in?"

"No, sir, we must decide upon that when we see how matters stand."

"Who is the we?" the colonel asked.

"Myself and my servant, who is a very sharp and intelligent lad whom I can thoroughly trust. Alone I could do nothing, for I have only picked up a few phrases in Italian yet, and should be detected at once; so anything that has to be said must be said by him. May I ask, sir, if the enemy are in force on the other side of the bridge? if so, we must cross by swimming, either above or below it."

"No; there was a regiment there until three days ago, but they marched away, and no doubt formed a portion of Prince Thomas's force. They know well enough that although our garrison can hold the walls, we are not strong enough to undertake any enterprise."

"Then, sir, we have only to ask for an escort for a mile or so beyond the other side of the bridge, in case a company should have been left to watch the road. Beyond that we will dismount and proceed on foot. We will, if you please, put on our disguises here, with the exception of our hats, and perhaps you will lend us a couple of long cloaks, so that our appearance may not be noticed. Although we shall not start until after dark, it is as well to be upon the safe side. Maybe the enemy have spies in the town, and were it noticed that two young peasants rode out under the escort of a troop of cavalry news might be sent to Turin. In that case we might be arrested as soon as we entered the city. I should be obliged if you would give orders to the officer in command that one of the troopers should bring the horses, cloaks, and hats back here with him."

The governor rang a bell, and on an orderly entering said: "Tell Captain Simon to have his troop in readiness to start in an hour's time, in order to form an escort for one of Viscount Turenne's officers, and tell him that when he has the troop ready to start he is to come to me for detailed orders. I have said an hour, Monsieur Campbell," he went on, after the orderly had left the room, "because, in the first place, it is not yet dark, and in the second, it will take some twenty minutes to prepare a meal. You will have a long night's work before you, and I dare say you have had nothing since you halted for breakfast."

"Thank you, colonel, I had not thought of it; but I should certainly have remembered it before to-morrow morning. We halted for breakfast at eleven, and if it had not been for your kind offer we should have had no chance of getting anything till we entered Turin, and even there the less we go into any cabarets the better."

"That is true. I have sent a message to the cook that twenty minutes is the utmost we can give for the preparation of a meal."

CHAPTER IV
SUCCESS

A LTHOUGH the governor apologized to Hector for the poorness of the repast and the haste with which it had been prepared, it was really excellent, consisting of soup, some fish fresh from the river, a cutlet, and an omelette, with a bottle of good wine of Asti. Paolo's wants had been attended to in the kitchen. It was six o'clock when they started. The officer in command had already received his instructions, and the governor accompanied Hector to the door, where two horses were standing saddled.

"They are not your own," he said, "but are two of mine. I thought that yours had made a sufficiently long journey to-day."

Thanking him for his kindness, Hector mounted, and took his place by the side of Captain Simon, while Paolo fell in with the orderlies riding close behind.

"I presume, monsieur, that you are going to obtain some information for Viscount Turenne. I don't want to ask any questions as to the nature of your mission, but as I have orders to bring back with the horses your cloaks and hats, I presume that in the first place you are going on foot, and in the second, you are going in disguise."

"Your judgment is correct, captain. The viscount wishes to obtain certain information, and I am going to fetch it for him, if I can."

"I hope that you will be successful, sir. It is a good night for travelling, the stars are bright and the moon down, so that you will have light enough to keep the road, and time enough to step aside should you meet any party who might be inclined to question all passers-by."

"Do you know the roads well about here?" Hector asked.

"I was stationed in Turin before the enemy came with too great a force to be resisted."

"I want to strike across the country, and to come into the road from Turin to Casale at a distance of three or four miles from the city."

"A mile or so away a road branches off from this which keeps by the river. It is a mere country road, and except in two or three small villages that you will pass through, you are not likely to meet with anyone upon it. It is about eight miles to the main road from the point where you turn off, and you will then be five miles from Turin. It is just possible that you may meet patrols, but I should think it very unlikely; now that our army has gone into winter quarters at Carignano, they are not likely to be very vigilant."

As they rode along Hector related some of the incidents of the late battle. No signs of the enemy were met with, and the officer presently said, "I am sorry to say that this is the point where you leave us, monsieur. I wish it had been a little farther, so that I could hear more of the fight."

Hector and Paolo dismounted. Two troopers were called up and took charge of their horses, while the cloaks and hats were given to the officer's orderly, then the two lads put on the Savoyard hats they had carried under their cloaks. The officer took two packets from his holster.

"The colonel bade me give this to you at starting," he said. "He thought that after a long walk on foot you would want some slight refreshment before the inns were open in the morning."

"Will you please give him my hearty thanks for his thoughtfulness," Hector said, "and accept the same yourself for your courtesy in escorting me."

"Now we are fairly on our way, Paolo," he went on as he turned down the lane, for it was little more; "this package is a bottle of wine, and the one that I have handed to you contains the eatables."

"That is good, master. We shall find it pretty cold before morning, and there is nothing like a good meal to warm one up again."

"Did you get the bow and arrows at Chivasso?"

"Yes, sir. I went out and bought them as soon as we got there. I wanted them, I told the man, for a boy of ten years old, but all he had were a good deal too long, which I was glad of, for a child's bow would hardly have been strong enough, so I made him cut one down until it was not more than three feet long. That way I shall be able, as we agreed, to carry it under my doublet. Of course it will make me walk stiffly, and there will be no possibility of sitting down, but that matters not at all. It is all the stronger, and will send an arrow a good distance. I have got six arrows as you ordered me. They are regular arrows, but I made the man shorten them so as to suit the bow, and then re-point them. I have got them inside my doublet. I tied them together, made a hole in the lining under the arm, and put them in."

"You have not forgotten the cord, I hope, Paolo?"

"Not I, master. I should have deserved having my ears cut off if I had done so."

They were in no hurry, and walked only fast enough to keep themselves warm. In two hours and a half they arrived at the main road and turned to the right. "Now we will go another couple of miles, Paolo, and then look out for a sleeping place. An empty barn or stable or a stack of fodder is what we want. We may as well sleep warm as cold. We shall not want to be moving on till seven o'clock."

After walking three miles they came upon a small village.

"Do you stay here, master, I will go round and see if I can find a place. I am more accustomed to these villages than you are."

In five minutes he returned. "I have found a capital place," he said. "It is a stable, but it is empty. No doubt the Spaniards have taken the horses, and are using them in their transport wagons."

"It is enough for us that the place is empty, Paolo."

The door stood ajar. They entered and closed it behind them, and they then felt about until they found a pile of rough fodder. They pulled some of this aside, lay down and covered themselves up with the stalks they had removed, and in three minutes were fast asleep, for they had had a long day's work. Hector slept until he was awakened by Paolo, who said, "The day is breaking, and the village will be astir in a few minutes." The weather had changed, and as they stepped out fine flakes of snow were drifting through the air, and the ground was already whitened. They regained the road and walked along until they came to a wood.

"We may as well wait here and breakfast, Paolo." The parcel was opened and found to contain a cold capon and some bread, and on these and the wine they made a capital breakfast, each taking a long sip at the bottle to the health of the colonel. "The market people are beginning to come along, and we may as well buy something from them going in. If we have not something to sell it is not unlikely that we shall be asked questions." It was now broad daylight, and they saw several peasants pass along the road, some with baskets, others driving a pig or a goat.

"Either of these would do," Hector said; "but we don't know where the market is, and it would never do to seem ignorant of that." The snow had stopped suddenly some minutes before, and the sun was now shining.

"That is lucky," Hector said as they walked down towards the road, "we may hope that there will be no more snow and that the sun will soon melt what has fallen. It would be fatal to us if the ground were white, for the most careless sentry could not help seeing us upon it."

They reached the road just as a peasant came along. He was an old man, and was dragging behind him a pile of faggots, which were placed upon two rough poles. He was walking between these, holding two ends in his hands, while the others trailed along on the ground behind.

"Bargain with him, Paolo."

"That is a heavy load, father," the latter said.

"Ay, it is heavy."

"How much do you expect to get for your faggots in the town?"

"I shall get a crown," the man said. "I would not take under, and they ought to be worth more than that now the snow has begun to fall."

"We are going into the town," Paolo said. "We are younger than you, and between us we could drag it along easily. I have got a crown in my pocket to buy some things with. I don't mind giving it to you for your load. If I can sell the faggots for a few soldi over that we shall be able to buy something for ourselves."

"It is a bargain, lad," the old man said. "I am getting old and the rheumatism is in my bones, and I shall be very glad to be spared the journey; so give me your money and take the poles. I hope you will be successful, and sell them a little higher. You had better ask a crown and a half. The women are sure to beat you down, but you will make ten or twelve soldi for yourselves."

Paolo handed the crown to the old man.

"How had we better take this, Paolo?" Hector asked, as the old man, chuckling with satisfaction at having escaped a toilsome journey, turned to retrace his steps.

"There is room for us both between the shafts," Paolo said, "one behind the other. It would be much easier to walk holding both poles than for us both to take one, as in that way the weight will be balanced on each side of us."

WON BY THE SWORD

There was indeed just room between the ends of the poles and the pile of brushwood for them to walk close behind each other, and as the greater portion of the weight rested on the other ends of the poles they did not find the burden a heavy one.

"How are we going to sell these, Paolo?"

"We shall have no difficulty in selling them, master. This frost will set every housewife on the look-out for wood, and you will find that we sha'n't have to go far before we are accosted."

It was two miles from the spot where they had bought the faggots to the gates of Turin.

"I sha'n't be sorry to get rid of this load," Hector said. "It is not the weight but the roughness of the poles. My hands are quite chafed by them."

"Loose your hold for a bit, master. My hands have been accustomed to rough work, and many a load of faggots have I drawn in my time."

"I will hold on, Paolo. It is not more than a quarter of a mile farther. My hands have done plenty of work too, but it has been done with smooth-handled weapons. It is well that they should become accustomed to harder work."

They passed without a question through the gate, and following the example of other vendors of wood, of whom they saw several, Paolo began to shout, "Large faggots for sale!"

It was not long before a door opened and a woman beckoned him.

"How much do you want for the whole?"

"A crown and a half," Paolo said.

"I have been offered as many for a crown," the woman replied.

"Then, signora, you did wrong to refuse. It took two days' work to cut them, and we have dragged them here for miles. Two crowns would not pay for the labour. Not one scudo would I take under the price that I have named. Why, if the town is besieged these faggots would be worth twenty crowns before the winter is over."

"Well, I will give you the money," the woman said. "It is extortionate. Generally I can buy them at half that price."

"I do not say no to that," Paolo laughed, "but with two armies wanting firewood and cutting down the copses without even taking trouble to ask leave of their owners, I think that you will see firewood very scarce in the city before long."

"Well, carry it in and pile it in the yard."

This was soon done, the poles were thrown on to the top of the heap, and the boys went off along the street again.

"We have made half a crown for ourselves," Paolo laughed; "now we must decide how we shall spend it."

"It would be a good plan to spend some money anyhow," Hector said. "What kind of things would you be likely to buy for your family in the country?"

"Well, I should say a cooking-pan to begin with, and a few yards of warm stuff for making my mother a skirt."

"Well, buy the cooking-pan first and sling it across your shoulder, and then as we wander about we can look in the shops and it will seem as if we were on the search for articles that we had been told to purchase; it would be better than sauntering about without any apparent object. But first let us walk briskly towards the side of the town facing the citadel. The Strada Vecchia is the one that I want to examine first."

The knowledge that he had gained from the plan of the city enabled Hector to find the street without their having to ask any questions.

"Now, buy your cooking-pan at the next smith's shop you come to, and then we can go slowly along making our observations."

They soon found that the street they had entered was, for the most part, deserted by its inhabitants. The shops were all closed, the road was strewn with fallen chimneys and balconies, and here and there were yawning holes showing how severely the street had suffered when the artillery duel was going on between the guns on the walls and those of the citadel. A short distance down the street a chain was stretched across it, and here a musketeer was pacing up and down on guard. Two others could be seen at the farther end of the street, where there was a gateway in the wall, now closed up with sand-bags piled thickly against it.

"We will see if the other streets are similarly guarded."

This was found to be so, sentries being placed in every street running down to the wall in this quarter.

"So far so good, Paolo. I do not think that matters could have been better for us. The next thing is to buy a tool with which we can wrench open a door or the shutter of a window; but a door will be best, because we could not work at a shutter without running the risk of being seen by a sentinel, while in a doorway we should be screened from observation. These houses in the Strada Vecchia are old, and the doors ought not to give us much trouble."

"Some of these old locks are very strong, master. I should think that it would be easier to cut out one of the panels than to force the door open."

"Possibly it would, but it is not an easy thing to get the saw to work. We should have to bore a hole large enough for the saw to go through before we could use it. However, we will buy both a saw and a crowbar; as they are both things that are useful to wood-cutters, your buying them will not appear suspicious, nor will the purchase of an auger, but we had better get them at different shops."

Leaving that part of the town they re-entered the streets where business was being carried on as usual.

"We won't buy the things until late in the afternoon, Paolo. There would be no advantage in dragging them about all day."

They sauntered about the streets for some hours, then Paolo went into a small baker's and bought two loaves of coarse bread. At another shop he purchased some cheese, and with these they sat down on a stone bench in the principal square and leisurely ate their food and looked on at the crowd, which consisted principally of soldiers, Spanish veterans, stiff in carriage and haughty in manner, together with others, horse and foot, belonging to the contingent of the Duke of Milan, an ally of the Spanish. Among these were townspeople, the younger ones chatting with each other or with ladies of their acquaintance; the middle-aged and older men talking gravely together as they walked up and down.

Among these there was an air of gloom and depression. The state of panic in which the troops of Prince Thomas, who had marched out confident that they were about to annihilate the French, had returned, and the knowledge that the Marquis of Leganez had also failed, had created a feeling of the deepest disquiet among that portion of the population who had taken a leading part in throwing off the authority of the duchess and in acknowledging that of Prince Thomas. They had regarded her cause as lost, but the vigorous steps that France was taking to assist her had caused uneasiness; and if, while as yet a comparatively small force had arrived, these had shown so bold a front, had captured Chieri in the face of a powerful army, had revictualled Casale, had defeated Prince Thomas and forced their way past the army of Leganez, it might well be that in the spring, when reinforcements reached them, they might even defeat the Spaniards and lay siege to Turin itself. The boys remained where they were until it began to grow dusk, when, after buying at three shops a saw, a crowbar, and an auger, they went and sat down on a doorway in a quiet street until eight o'clock. Then they took their way to the Strada Vecchia. It was entirely deserted. Lights showed in one or two of the windows, but, except that they could hear the tread of the nearest sentry, all was silent. Taking off their wooden shoes they moved cautiously along, keeping close to the houses. The fourth they came to had an unusually deep doorway, and they decided at once that this would suit their purpose. First they tried with the crowbar, but the lock held firmly.

"We will try another way, Paolo. If the door yields, it will go with a crash, and the sentry might come down to see what had caused the noise. We had better take out this lower panel; we shall want four holes bored touching each other to make one large enough for the saw to enter."

The wood was of oak, and it took Paolo fully five minutes to make the holes.

"Now give me the auger," Hector said when it was found that the hole was large enough for the saw to pass through.

"I will begin at the bottom of the panel while you saw away at the top."

Paolo had done his share by the time the holes along the bottom were ready for the saw.

"Now you take the auger again," Hector said. "We have not done half our work yet. The holes must be made on each side. There is no turning the saw."

It took them an hour and a half of hard work before the last cut was completed and the panel fell forward.

"You go in first, Paolo. I will follow you, and will wedge the panel into its place again with some of the chips that the auger has cut out. No one has passed since we began, and if anyone did come along before morning he would not be likely to notice that the panel was gone. Still it is as well to avoid all risk."

As soon as the panel was replaced they mounted the stairs. Before beginning they had seen that there were no lights in any of the windows, and feeling sure that the house was deserted they groped their way upstairs without hesitation until they reached the attics in the sloping roof. They entered one of these facing the street, opened the casement, in which oiled paper took the place of glass, and stepped down on to the parapet. Their course was now easy. The divisions between the houses were marked by walls some six feet high extending from the edge of the parapet over the roof. They were able to climb these, however, without having to use their cord, one helping the other up and then being assisted by him. They had left the cooking-pan and their tools, with the exception of the crowbar, behind them, and had fastened their wooden shoes round their neck. The sun during the day had melted the snow that had fallen in the morning, but light flakes were again beginning to come down fast.

SUCCESS

"I don't care how hard it snows as long as it keeps on," Hector said in a low voice in answer to an exclamation from Paolo when the first flake fell upon his face. "The harder the better, for in that case no sentry could see us half a dozen paces away. There is another advantage. The wind is from the north, and we have only to keep the driving snow on our right cheeks to make our way straight to the fortress, whereas with an overcast sky on such a dark night as this we should very soon lose all idea of the direction that we were going in."

Being obliged to use great caution to avoid noise while getting over the walls, it took them half an hour to reach the end of the street. They had, while waiting before commencing their operations, twisted one of their sashes, and then wound it round the hook so thickly that this would fall almost noiselessly upon the ground. The snow prevented them from seeing six feet below them, but they felt sure that there must be a narrow lane between the house and the wall. They had during the day bought a length, equal to that of their rope, of strong string.

"I have got it as you ordered it, master," Paolo said as they came out of the shop, "but it would never bear our weight."

"I think it might do in case of necessity," Hector said. "In fact, I am sure it would. It does not require a great thickness of new cord to hold a man's weight; but I don't want it for that."

Paolo walked silently along for some time, and then said:

"If it is not wanted to carry our weight, master, I cannot think what it is wanted for."

"It is wanted to get the hook down with. You see when we get down into the street there would be little chance of getting the hook off its hold. We shall most likely want it again, and certainly we shall want the rope. I have been puzzling over it, and I think I have found a way at last. My idea is to fasten this thin rope to the point of the hook, then, on pulling upon it the point will rise until it gets level with the top of the wall on which it is fixed, and we can then shake it down without difficulty. I don't know whether it will act, but I think that it ought to do so; an upward pull at the point must, I should think, lift it as far as the edge."

"I should think that it must," Paolo agreed. "I should never have thought of that."

"We will try it on this last division-wall. I have no doubt about it myself, because even if it did not pull it quite to the top the thing would be so canted over that I think it would fall from its own weight."

They now attached the string to the point, fixed the hook to the top of the wall, and then pulled upon the string. The hook at once fell to their feet.

"That is capital," Hector said. "Now we can go to work. We need carry this crowbar no farther. In the first place we will cross this roof and other roofs as far as we can go; the sentry at the corner is probably standing up for shelter in a doorway, and we may as well get as far as we can from him, and at the same time not go far enough to get near the one at the next corner."

After one or two attempts the hook became fixed on the ridge of the roof, and they at once climbed up, unfastened the hook, and slid down on the now snow-covered tiles. Two more roofs were crossed in the same way, and then they prepared to descend. They had, when they put on their disguises, tied knots in the rope at a distance of a foot apart. They now adjusted the hook on the parapet.

"Shall I go first, master, or will you?"

"I will go first, though in fact it matters little which of us does it; but first I must warm my fingers. I don't think that I could trust to them at present."

He gathered a handful of snow, made it into a ball, and held it in his hands until the cold pained him, then he dropped the snow and thrust his hands up the sleeves of his doublet. Paolo looked on in astonishment, but having great faith in his master imitated his example.

"That is a curious way of warming the hands," he said.

SUCCESS

"I daresay you have made snow-balls in your time, Paolo, and if you have you will remember that, although it made your hands bitterly cold at first, after you had done they soon became almost as hot as fire."

"I do remember that, master, but I should never have thought of it as a way of warming our hands."

For a minute or two there was a sharp pain as the blood began to rush into the fingers, and when this passed off their hands were in a glow. Hector took the rope, lowered himself over the parapet, and then began to descend. When half-way down the darkness became more intense than before, and he knew that he was now below the level of the outer wall. When he reached the ground he shook the rope as a signal, and then, stretching his arms before him, crossed the lane. It was but a step, for the house stood but five feet back from the wall. He waited until Paolo joined him, then he drew on the thin rope and, to his satisfaction, he felt it yield.

"Stand aside," he said, "it is heavy enough to give one a nasty thump."

Paolo withdrew a few paces, then Hector gave another pull. The rope gave way at once. He flattened himself against the house, and the hook fell with a dull thud a foot or two away.

"Coil up the rope, Paolo, and then feel along the wall to the right; don't go too far. I will go to the left, there may be some steps up to the rampart."

This proved to be the case, and together they made their way up quietly, but even had they had their shoes on, the snow was already sufficiently deep to deaden their footsteps. On reaching the top they stood silent for a minute or two. Presently they heard the sound of heavy stamping of feet. They turned at once to descend, if necessary, the steps they had mounted, then Hector put his hand upon the other's shoulder and whispered, "It is the sentry trying to warm his feet; no doubt he is standing up somewhere to shelter himself from the snow; let us go on at once."

They crossed the rampart, fastened the hook on the top of the wall, and descended, and were again successful in bringing the rope down after them.

"Go carefully, Paolo; no doubt there is a moat somewhere here." There was, however, no necessity for caution, for the white surface of the snow was soon broken by a black line.

"It will be awfully cold," Paolo said, with teeth that chattered at the prospect.

"Of course you can swim, Paolo?"

"Not very well, master."

"Then I will go first. You fasten the rope under your arms, and I will haul you across. Be sure you do not make a noise in getting into the water. But first of all take off your doublet, I will carry it and mine across on my head. It cannot be many yards across. The wind will soon dry the rest of our things, and once our work is done we can warm ourselves by running. I would say strip altogether, but we may have to do another swim; for, as we agreed, there is no chance of our being able to return by the way we came."

Fastening the two doublets on his head, Hector lowered himself into the water, which was three feet below the level on which they stood. He had fastened the rope across his shoulder. As he expected, he found the water out of his depth, and at once struck out to the opposite side. It was about forty feet across. He found, on reaching the other side, that the wall was there nearly five feet above the water. He undid the rope and threw up the hook. At the second attempt it caught, and he climbed the side, and then in a low voice told Paolo to start. Presently he heard a slight splash, followed by a gasp. He hauled away rapidly on the rope, and in a couple of minutes Paolo stood beside him, shivering and gasping.

"Put your doublet on. Now let us go forward as fast as we can." They climbed the steep slope to the top of the glacis, and then ran down until they were brought to a standstill by another moat. "This is the one marked in the plan as dividing the fortifications of the town from those of the citadel. Now we have another swim before us. It is wider than the last, but is really no distance. Give me your doublet again."

"I don't mind this so much," Paolo said. "I cannot be colder than I am."

"Don't try to swim, Paolo; lie on your back, with your mouth just out of water. I will have you over in no time."

It was fully fifty yards across; but, accustomed to bathe in almost icy cold water, the swim was nothing to Hector, who was soon across, and who then towed Paolo over as before. They mounted another glacis, and presently reached the edge of a third moat.

"We need go no farther. I know that this moat is but some fifteen yards from the foot of the fortifications. Now, get the arrows out. Cut off a foot or two of the thin cord, and unravel it. I must warm my fingers again first, I cannot use them at all."

"Mine are pretty cold too." And both lads warmed them as before. Paolo then set to work to string the bow, which required all his strength to accomplish. While he was doing so, Hector drew from his pouch the six little pellets, and taking the arrows, straightened out each pellet, wrapped it round an arrow, and secured it firmly with a small strand from the string. When he had done this, he took the bow from Paolo, fitted an arrow to the string, drew it with his full strength, and then, pointing the arrow high, loosed it. The six arrows were sent off. Just as the last was discharged there was a shout of "Who is there? Speak, or I fire!" It was a sentry on the wall, who had caught the sound of the twang of the bow.

"I am a friend, a messenger from the French general," Hector replied. "I have just shot six arrows into the fortress; a message is attached to each for the governor. Report to the officer, and have a search made for them in the morning. That is a piece of good luck," he went on as they turned away. "I thought of shouting, but we might have got a shot in reply, and I made sure that one or other of the arrows would be picked up. Still, this makes certain of it."

Hector seized the disengaged wrist of his opponent.

SUCCESS

"I think I would rather stop out here until morning," Paolo said, "then they will take me in. I am afraid I shall never get across the river."

"Nonsense! the water is low, and we are not likely to have to swim farther than we did in crossing the last moat. Getting through the part of the town between us and the river is a more serious matter. However, it is not very far across, and they are not likely to be very vigilant."

They turned to the right, and kept along at the edge of the moat, until Hector considered that they had made a fourth of the circuit of the walls, and were now facing the river. They had decided before that this would be the easiest side on which to leave the town. The sentinels would not expect that anyone attempting to enter or leave the citadel would try to do so here; as, in addition to passing the wall facing the fortress and that bordering the river, they would be obliged to swim the river itself. The snow was falling as quickly as ever, and the wind blowing fiercely.

"There is no fear of their seeing us, unless we happen to run into the very arms of the sentry," Hector said encouragingly; "we shall only have the moat to swim; and as, according to the plan, it is nothing like so wide as that we passed before, we shall have no trouble with it."

"Ah! here it is," Paolo groaned.

"Nonsense!" Hector said. "One cold bath more or less makes no difference now. There, give me your coat again, and I will take it over."

The moat was indeed but some twelve yards across, and in two or three minutes Paolo stood shivering on the other side.

"The edge is not far from the wall, not much more than the breadth of the moat. Give me the cord."

A few steps and they reached the wall. After two attempts the hook caught, and Hector climbed up. He was looking back to watch Paolo when he was suddenly seized from behind, and a deep voice in Italian said, "If you move I will kill you. Who are you?"

WON BY THE SWORD

With a sudden effort Hector twisted himself round and seized the disengaged wrist of his opponent, which he doubted not held a dagger. The man loosened his hold of his doublet and tried to grasp his neck, but Hector in a moment leapt forward and threw his arm round the man's waist. They wrestled backwards and forwards, but the soldier was a powerful man, and Hector found that he could not long retain a grasp of his wrist. Suddenly he felt his antagonist collapse; the dagger dropped from his hand, the other arm relaxed its hold, and he fell a lifeless mass.

"Thank you, Paolo. You were but just in time. The fellow was too strong for me. Now let us slip down the inside of the wall as quickly as possible."

A minute later they both stood at the foot of the wall, the hook was shaken off, and they proceeded along the wall until they came to a street.

"It is not more than two or three hundred yards to the outer wall," Hector whispered.

Whether there were sentinels or not in the street they knew not. If so, they had withdrawn themselves into deep doorways to avoid the blinding snow, and the wind drowned the slight sound made by their feet on the soft snow.

In a short time they reached the outer wall, crept along it until they found the steps leading up, crossed it in safety, fixed their hook, and rapidly descended. A run of fifty yards brought them to the edge of the river bank.

"We will try to find a boat," Hector said. "There are sure to be some along here."

They walked across the dry bed of the river till they reached the water's edge, and then followed this. In a few minutes, to their delight, they came upon a boat. The bow was hauled a few feet out of water, and a rope, doubtless attached to a heavy stone anchor, stretched from its bows. This they cut, put their shoulders to the gunwale, and soon had her afloat. Then they scrambled in, put the oars out cautiously, and began to row. Both had had some practice at the exercise, and it was not long before the boat grounded on the opposite shore.

SUCCESS

"Pull it up a bit," Hector said. "No doubt it belongs to some poor fisherman to whom its loss would be serious. Now we must keep along the bank for some distance, until quite sure that we are well beyond any patrols the enemy may have on the road. Let us get into a run, Paolo, and see if we can't get our blood in motion again, for I own that I feel half-frozen."

They set off at a brisk trot, which they kept up for half an hour, and then they struck off from the river and soon found the road. Following this, after an hour's walking they came upon a little shed by the roadside, and in one corner found a pile of old sacks.

"We are in luck again!" Hector exclaimed joyfully. "Tired as I am, I don't think that I could have slept in these wet clothes, if one can call them wet—at present they are frozen stiff. These sacks are the very thing. We can strip now and wring out our clothes thoroughly. There are enough sacks here to lay under us and cover us too. After wringing out the shirts we will put them in under the sacks next to us. The heat of our bodies will dry them to some extent, and they will be warm to put on in the morning. The other things we can pile over us. There is no chance of their getting dry; but I am so pleased with our success that I am not disposed to grumble at trifles."

CHAPTER V
THE RELIEF OF THE CITADEL

As soon as the first gleam of daylight showed itself Hector and his companion were on their feet again. The operation of dressing was by no means a comfortable one, for the frost had set in in earnest during the night, and their clothes, with the exception of the shirts, were as stiff as boards. The snow had ceased and the sky was clear.

"It is going to be a fine day, master," Paolo said as they left the hut.

"That is better than battling with a snow-storm such as that of yesterday evening. Come on, Paolo, let us trot for a bit. The snow is four inches deep, and we shall soon get warm running through it."

In a quarter of an hour they broke into a walk again, panting from their exertions.

"I am as warm as a toast now, Paolo. There is a village half a mile ahead. I expect that lies on the road. The sun will be up before we get there, and no doubt we shall be able to get some hot spiced wine and some bread at a wine-shop."

This turned out to be the case. They had settled what story to tell; and when the landlord asked what brought them there so early, Paolo said that they had been on the road a couple of hours, as they were going to see an aunt who was ill at Chivasso, and their father wanted them back again that night. The explanation satisfied the host and he asked no further questions, and in ten minutes they were on their way again, greatly warmed and comforted by their meal, and after walking for another hour and a half they arrived at the bridge of Chivasso. There was a strong guard at the bridge head, for at any moment the garrison of Turin, aided by a force from Leganez's army, might endeavour to carry the town by a sudden assault. The lads passed the bridge unquestioned, entered the gate of the town, and made their way to the commandant's house.

"What do you want?" the sentry at the door asked as they came up.

The regiment was French, and Hector answered at once:

"We want to see the governor, we have important news for him."

The soldier was greatly surprised, for he had not expected his question to be understood by these peasant boys.

"Sergeant," he called out, "here are two peasant boys who speak French. They want to see the governor, and say that they have news of importance to give him."

A sergeant came out.

"Sergeant," Hector went on quietly, "you will please tell the governor that the two persons he sent out under an escort the evening before last, wish to see him."

By the tone of assurance in which the lad spoke, rather than by his words, the sergeant saw that there was something more than appeared on the surface, and at once took up the message. He returned almost immediately. "Please to follow me," he said, and led the way up to the governor's room.

"Welcome back again, Monsieur Campbell! You have returned sooner than I expected. You found, of course, that the difficulties were insuperable?"

"On the contrary, sir, we have been successful, and have communicated with the garrison of the citadel."

"You have!" the governor exclaimed in astonishment. "How on earth did you manage it? I heard that the watch was so strict that it was absolutely impossible for a message to be sent through."

"It was not very difficult after all, and we were greatly favoured by the snow-storm." He then gave an account of how they had managed it.

"Pardieu!" he exclaimed, "that was admirably done; but I am keeping you talking while you are sitting in your wet clothes."

"I think they are quite dry now, sir; and we have walked so fast that we are both thoroughly warm. Still, I own that I shall not be sorry to change them for my own."

The governor rose and opened the door. "Your clothes are all hanging up in that closet. I will have some hot water sent up at once. I shall be breakfasting in half an hour, so you will have time to change comfortably."

Hector was even more glad of a thorough wash than of a change of clothes, and went down to join the governor at breakfast, feeling greatly refreshed.

"Shall I wait on you, master?"

"No, it is not necessary, Paolo; you had better go into the kitchen at once. I have no doubt the governor has ordered them to attend to your wants as he did before."

Four other officers had just arrived on the invitation of the governor to breakfast; one of these was the captain who had commanded the escort.

"Gentlemen," the commandant said, "let me introduce to you Monsieur Campbell, a lieutenant on the staff of Viscount Turenne. He has just returned after having successfully carried out a most dangerous and difficult mission, namely, that of communicating with the garrison of Turin."

The officers gave an exclamation of surprise, while Captain Simon stepped forward and shook hands warmly with Hector.

"You did not tell me exactly what you were going to do," he said. "I thought that it was to see some of the duchess's adherents in Turin, but I never dreamt that you were going to attempt to communicate with the citadel. Had I known that, I certainly should not have expected to see you again, for from what we have heard it is next to impossible to get through the enemy's lines."

THE RELIEF OF THE CITADEL

"We will not trouble Monsieur Campbell until he has finished his breakfast," the commandant said. "He has already told me briefly how he managed, but I shall be as glad as you will to have the details."

Accordingly, after breakfast Hector related at much greater length the story that he had told the governor of the manner in which the mission had been carried out.

"Ma foi!" the colonel said, "I would rather have faced a battery than swum those moats in such weather. Well, gentlemen, I think that you will agree with me that Monsieur de Turenne is fortunate in having so brave and enterprising an officer on his staff."

The officers cordially assented.

"I wonder that you did not enter the citadel and stay there till the convoy arrived."

"In the first place, colonel, I had received no orders to do so, and the general might require me for other service. And in the second place, had I not returned he would not have known whether his message had reached the garrison, and so might have hurried on his preparations more hastily than he otherwise would have done, and might, in his fear that the garrison would surrender, have made the attempt before he had collected sufficient food to last them until he was in a position to raise the siege."

"Your reasons are good ones; but certainly, with shelter and warmth close at hand—for the sentry would speedily have passed the word along, and as soon as it was ascertained that you were indeed a French officer, and alone, the gates would have been opened for you—it must have required no small effort to turn away and to face the danger of passing the sentries and scaling the walls, of possibly having to swim the Po, and of certainly having no chance of getting a change of clothes until you arrived here, for you could not have calculated upon finding the shed, much less those sacks, with the snow falling heavily."

"That was a piece of good fortune indeed. If we had not found it, we should have gone on walking until we got here. Still, we had had little sleep the night before, and were heartily glad that we had no farther to go. And now, sir, with your permission we will start for Susa at once."

"Your escort returned yesterday, but I will send a troop of cavalry with you."

"Thank you, sir, but I do not think that there is any necessity for it. We are very well mounted, and should we see any party of the enemy's cavalry I think that we ought to be able to outdistance them. I shall be glad, colonel, if you and your officers will say nothing about the manner in which I communicated with the garrison, as doubtless the enemy have spies here; and if the story comes out and reaches the ears of the authorities at Turin, I should have no chance whatever of making my way in, in the same manner, should the general entrust me with another mission to communicate with the citadel."

A quarter of an hour later Hector and Paolo mounted and rode out of the town. They kept a vigilant look-out, and travelled by by-roads, but they saw none of the enemy's parties, and reached Susa late that afternoon. On sending in his name to Turenne, Hector was at once shown into his room.

"I did not expect you back for another three or four days, Campbell," the general said, "and I am heartily glad to see you again safe and sound. I blamed myself for letting you go. Of course, as I expected, you found the task an altogether impossible one. Had it been otherwise you would not have been back so soon."

"On the contrary, general, for I should have tried many plans before I gave it up. As it is, I have only to report that I have carried out your instructions, and that your despatches are in the hands of the garrison of the citadel."

"You do not say so!" Turenne said, rising from the table at which he had been sitting writing when Hector entered, and shaking him warmly by the hand. "I congratulate both you and myself on your having performed a mission that seemed well-nigh hopeless. But by what miracle did you succeed in passing through the enemy's lines? All who have tried it before have either died in the attempt or have returned to tell me that it was an absolutely impossible one."

"It would have been very difficult, general, had not the weather favoured us. The snow-storm drove the sentries into shelter, and even had they remained at their posts they could not have seen us five yards away."

"No, I can understand that once beyond the wall you might in such a storm make your way unnoticed up to the fortress; but I understood that not only were there guards on the walls and down near the great moat, but that there were also sentries in all the streets leading to the walls, and that none were allowed to pass along those leading to the walls facing the citadel. Tell me how you managed it."

"The story is a long one, sir."

"Never mind how long it is; give me all details. I am not particularly busy at present, and I would fain know exactly how this feat has been accomplished."

Hector told his story at length. Beyond asking a question now and then, Turenne remained silent until he had brought it to a conclusion.

"I have never heard a story that interested me more," he said, "and I do not know which to admire more, your ingenuity in planning this affair or the hardihood and courage with which you carried it out. Even had there been no enemy to get through, the adventure of letting yourself down by a rope from the house-top and then from the battlements, swimming three moats, crossing the river in such terrible weather, and finally making your way to Chivasso in your frozen clothes, is no slight feat of endurance. The service that you have rendered is a great one, the manner in which you have carried it out is worthy of the highest praise, and I shall at once make out your commission as captain. You are still a year behind me," he added with a smile, "but if you go on in this way, you bid fair to obtain a regiment as soon as I did. You have nearly four years to do it in. To-morrow you will dictate your story in full to my secretary. I shall be sending a messenger with despatches on the following day. I shall mention that I have promoted you to the rank of captain, and that the story of the action that you have performed, which I shall inclose, will fully explain my reason for so speedily advancing you. No, I require no thanks; you have to thank yourself only. I may consider that you have not only done me but the state a service. Your servant deserves a reward also. Here are twenty pistoles; tell him not to throw them away, but to lay them by where some day they will be useful to him."

Paolo was astonished indeed when Hector handed him the general's present. He could at first hardly believe that it was meant for him.

"Why, master," he said, "it would buy me a farm up in the hills!"

"Not a very large one, Paolo, but I daresay that you will add to it; still, this is a good beginning, and some more opportunities may come in your way."

"What shall I do with them, master?"

"That I cannot say. Certainly you cannot carry them about with you. Do you know anyone to whom you could entrust them?"

Paolo shook his head. "There is never any knowing who is an honest man and who is not," he said. "I will bury them, master."

"But somebody might find them."

"No fear of that, sir. I will go a bit up the valley and bury them under a big rock well above the river, so that it will not be reached in the highest floods. They might lie there a hundred years without anyone finding them, even if every soul in Susa knew that they were hidden somewhere and went out to search for them."

"Very well; but be sure you take notice of the exact position of the stone, or you may not be able to find it again yourself. One big stone is a good deal like another. Choose a stone with a tree growing near it, and make a cross with your knife on the bark. That will serve as a guide to you, and you would recognize the stone by it even if you could not find it in any other way."

"Thank you, master. I will go out to-morrow morning and choose my stone, and then when it begins to get dark I will go out and bury my money there. It would not do to hide it in the daytime, for even were there no one on the road someone upon the hills might catch sight of me and come down afterwards to see what I was disposing of."

"Well, I think that that is the best thing that you can do, Paolo. There is certainly a danger in leaving it in anyone's hands, for when you return to claim it, perhaps some years hence, you might find that he was dead, or the place might be captured and burned down. Yes, I think that hiding it is the safest way. You will be pleased to hear that the general has given me a commission as captain."

"That is good news, indeed," the boy said. "I was just going to ask, master, what he had done for you, because, though I went with you, it was you who planned the business, and I only did as you told me."

"You had something to do with the planning too, Paolo. However, I think that we may both feel well content with the rewards that we have obtained for two days' work."

As Hector went out he met de Lisle and Chavigny.

"Well met!" the former exclaimed. "We have just left the general, and he has told us what you have done, and that he has made you a captain in consequence. We were just coming to look for you to carry you off to supper in honour of your promotion."

"You deserve it, if anyone ever did, there is no doubt of that," Chavigny said heartily. "We are quite proud of our comrade."

"It seems absurd that I should be a captain."

"Not absurd at all," Chavigny said. "Turenne was a captain when he was a year younger than you are, and there is many a noble who has been made a colonel before he ever drew sword in battle."

Hector was much pleased at the evidently genuine congratulations of his companions. He had indeed rather feared that they would take his promotion ill; being nearly five years his senior, and having served in two previous campaigns, they might well feel hurt at his being promoted while they still remained only lieutenants. The young nobles indeed felt no shade of jealousy. It was but of late that there had been a regular army, for the nobles still brought their tenants and retainers to the field and supported them at their own expense.

To de Lisle and Chavigny these grades of military rank were of no account whatever. The rank of colonel would add in no way to their position as members of noble families. They fought for honour, and against the enemies of France. They were always addressed by their family name, and would both have resented being called lieutenant. They were proud of being Turenne's aides-de-camp, but had no thought of remaining in the army after the war was over, as they would then resume their place at court. They had both taken a strong liking to their young comrade, whose manner of thought differed so widely from their own. They appreciated the merits of the action of which their general had spoken in such warm terms, and the fact that in point of military rank he was now above them concerned them in no way. It was a merry supper at the best hotel in Susa.

"You see now, de Lisle," Chavigny said, "the advantage of taking a morning dip in snow-water. Neither you nor I would have swum across those moats, and remained all night long in our wet clothes, for a thousand crowns."

"No, no, nor for five thousand," the other laughed. "Pass me the wine; it makes me shiver to think of it. I fancy we may as well admit at once that if the mission had been entrusted to us, we should have made a mess of it. We should have been shot by the guards in the first street we entered. As to climbing along the roofs of houses till we had passed the first line of sentinels, the idea would never have entered our heads. Of course we might have disguised ourselves, and might have got into the town by harnessing ourselves to a load of faggots, but once there we should have had no more chance of getting into the fortress than if we had at once proclaimed ourselves French officers, and had requested a pass into the citadel."

For the next ten days every effort was made to obtain carts and pack-horses from the villages round Susa, and a number of wagons filled with provisions were brought from Carignano, where the principal supplies for the army had been collected. On the fourteenth day all was ready, and late in the afternoon the convoy, with fifteen hundred men from Susa, and four pieces of artillery, marched out. At the same hour the force at Carignano, six thousand strong, leaving only a small body to garrison the city, started for Turin along the farther bank of the Po, and just as day broke a heavy cannonade was opened by them against one of the city gates.

Astonished and alarmed, the troops in the city flew to arms, and hurried to repulse the attack. A quarter of an hour later the dim light of the morning showed the astonished sentries at the end of the town surrounding the citadel a considerable force advancing to the attack of the gate there, opposite which, at a distance of two hundred yards, four cannon were placed, and scarcely had they made out the enemy when these opened fire. A few rounds and the gate was in splinters, and the infantry rushed forward. The sentries on the walls took to flight, and the assailants pushed forward to the inner gate. Access was obtained from that side to the citadel, and then, under the direction of their officers, the assailants occupied all the side streets. At once the procession of carts was allowed to pass along. Some of the garrison ran down and lowered the drawbridge across the moat, and amid exultant shouts a store sufficient for many months was conveyed into the citadel. The carts as quickly as they were unloaded returned through the gates and passed out into the country beyond. By this time a fierce fight had begun. As soon as the firing was heard opposite the citadel, Prince Thomas and his military advisers guessed at once that the attack had been but a feint, made with the object of effecting the relief of the citadel, and calling several regiments to follow them they hastened in that direction. On their way they met the fugitives, and hurried on with all speed. As they approached the street through which the wagons were passing out, they were checked by a heavy fire. The four guns had been placed in pairs at the end of the streets, and the houses near them filled with troops who kept up a murderous fire from the windows, on the head of the columns, and held them completely in check until the last wagon had been taken out. Then the cannon were removed, and when these too were fairly outside the city, a bugle-call summoned the defenders of the houses, and the infuriated Italians and Spaniards, when they rushed down into the street between the gates, found that the last of their foes had escaped them. The artillerymen ran up to the walls, only to find that the guns had been spiked, and they were powerless to inflict any serious damage upon the retiring force.

Prince Thomas ordered a sally, but at this moment a regiment of cavalry from Chivasso was seen dashing across the plain, and being without artillery or cavalry the order was countermanded. Indeed, the prolonged roll of artillery at the other end of the city seemed to show that the French were converting their feigned attack into a real one. Turenne had himself accompanied the column from Carignano, for he knew that the sound of firing might bring up Leganez from Asti, and that he might find his retreat to Carignano intercepted. The moment, however, that the sound of four guns at equal intervals showed that the other column had achieved its object, he at once fell back, his fire ceasing a few minutes before Prince Thomas and his horse arrived at the walls. He had not been accompanied by Hector, who was with the force from Susa.

"You carried my message to the garrison," he said, "and it is but right that you should have the honour of leading the party to its relief."

THE RELIEF OF THE CITADEL

On arriving near the city Hector had dismounted, and, giving his horse in charge of Paolo, had placed himself at the head of the company that was first to enter the town, its captain being transferred to another company.

"Now, men," he said, as they stood waiting for the dawn to break, "the moment we enter the gates half the company will mount the wall to the right, the other half to the left, and each will push along to the next angle of the wall. Lieutenants, one of you will go with each wing of the company, and you will oppose to the last any force that may march along the rampart to attack you. I want one soldier to keep by me."

As day began to break, each man grasped his firelock and awaited the signal with impatience. A cheer broke from them as the four cannon roared out at the same moment, and at so short a distance that every shot told on the gate. Another salvo and both halves of the gate were splintered.

"Aim at the centre where the lock is," an officer shouted. "Get ready, men," Hector said. "Another round and the gate will fall."

As the cannon rung out there was a shout of triumph. One of the gates fell to the ground and Hector dashed forward, followed closely by his company. Not a single shot was fired from the walls, and the men burst through the gates cheering. The leading wing of the company turned to the right, and, led by Hector, ran up the steps close to the gateway on to the rampart.

"Take them on to that bastion at the angle of the wall, lieutenant. I do not think that you are likely to be attacked at present. The enemy must all have been drawn off to the other end of the city. Now, my man, open that bag."

In it were a couple of dozen large nails and a hammer.

"Drive one of those right down the vent of this gun. That is right. One more blow. That will do. They won't get that nail out soon."

He went along the wall spiking each gun until they reached the half-company drawn up in the bastion. No enemy in sight, lieutenant?"

None, sir, at least not on the wall. We heard them running away in the streets below."

"Remember, lieutenant, whatever force may come along you must withstand them. It will not be for long. You will be at once supported if we hear firing."

Then he retraced his steps along the ramparts, passed over the gateway, and saw to the spiking of each gun as far as the next angle of the wall. Here he repeated his instructions to the lieutenant there.

"I do not think," he said, "that there is much chance of your being attacked. The enemy would have to make a detour right round the citadel to come here, and certainly they will return by the shortest way, as soon as they discover that the other attack is but a feint."

Then he returned to the first party.

"Get the two guns," he said, "out of their embrasures and wheel them here. It is likely enough that we may be hotly attacked presently."

They waited half an hour, by which time the wagons were beginning to pour out of the town.

"We have done our business, lieutenant; the citadel is revictualled. Ah! here come the enemy, just too late."

A strong body of troops were seen marching rapidly towards them, and almost at the same moment a heavy fire broke out in the street. The guns had been loaded from a small magazine in the bastion, and had been trained to fire along the rampart. When within a hundred yards the enemy opened fire. Hector ordered the men to lie down and not to reply until he gave the order. They lay in two lines, the first were to fire and the second to reserve their fire until ordered. He took his post at one gun and the lieutenant at the other. A messenger had been sent along the wall to bring up the twenty-five men of the other wing. When the enemy were within fifty yards he asked quietly, "Does your gun bear well on the centre of the column?"

"Yes, captain."

"Then fire!"

The ball cut a way through the dense column.

"When they were within twenty paces, Hector fired."

"Load again!"

The four men, told off to the duty, leapt to their feet. There was a halt for a moment, and then the Spaniards came on again. When they were within twenty paces Hector fired, and at the same time shouted, "First line give fire!" and twenty-five muskets flashed out, every ball taking effect on the head of the column. The Spaniards recoiled, the leading ranks being swept away and many of those behind wounded, for three balls had been rammed down the mouth of the cannon fired by Hector, and these and the musketry volley had done terrible execution. At this moment the twenty-five men sent for ran up.

"Second line give fire!" Hector shouted; and the discharge added to the confusion in the column, and many ran down some steps into the lane by the side of the wall.

"Have you loaded again, lieutenant?"

"Yes, sir, with three balls,"

"Then form up, men, and deliver your fire," Hector said to the new-comers. "Now, lieutenant, touch it off."

As the discharge rang out, mingled with the roar of the guns, Hector shouted, "Fix bayonets, and charge!" The wooden shafts of the bayonets were thrust down the barrels of the fire-locks, and with a cheer the seventy-five men rushed upon the shattered head of the column. The charge was irresistible, and the enemy at once fled at full speed along the rampart or leapt from the wall into the lane below.

"Well done, men, well done!" Hector shouted. "Do not pursue. Reload your cannon, though I do not think there is much fear of their returning."

A few minutes later the soldier who had carried the spikes, and who had been left on the wall, ran up to say that the last cart had passed out.

"Go and tell the other party to fall back to the gate," Hector said; "but first give me two spikes and the hammer.

They might run these cannons into the places of those disabled." So saying, he spiked the two guns that had done such good service, and then retired to the gate, where he was joined by the remainder of the company. As the bugle rung out after the last wagon had passed, and he saw the troops issuing from the houses at the corners of the cross streets, he marched his company across the drawbridge, out into the country, and followed the guns. When he reached the spot where Paolo was holding the horses, he resigned the command of the company and mounted.

"Men," he said, "you have played your part well, and I am proud to have commanded soldiers so steady and courageous."

At this moment the general, who was in command of the force, and who had been the last to leave the town, rode up, the men coming along at a run.

"You had better hurry your men on," he said to the colonel with whom Hector had acted; "the enemy will be on the ramparts in a minute, and you may be sure that they won't let us off without trouble from their guns."

"I beg your pardon, general," Hector said saluting, "but the guns all along this side of the wall are useless; I have spiked them."

"You have, sir! That was well done indeed. Who gave you the orders, and how did you come by spikes?"

"I had no orders, general; but I was appointed to command the first company that entered, and was told that we were to turn right and left along the ramparts. It struck me that as, when we had left, the enemy would be sure to turn their guns upon us, it would be as well to silence them, so I brought the nails and a hammer with me for the purpose."

"It would be well, sir, if we had a good many officers as thoughtful as you are. You have saved us from heavy loss, for, as the country is perfectly level for a mile round, they would have swept our ranks as we marched off. Were you attacked, sir?"

"Yes, general, by a force of about four hundred men, but I turned two of the guns against them. My men fought well, and we repulsed them with a loss of fully a hundred men."

"Bravo, sir, bravo! I shall not fail to mention the service that you have rendered in my report of the affair. Have you lost many men?"

"No, sir; they lay down until the enemy were within twenty paces of us, and their volleys and the two cannon created such a confusion among the Spaniards that when we went at them with the bayonet they fled at once, and I have not a single man killed, and only two or three slightly wounded."

"We have only lost twenty," the general said, "and most of those were killed while serving the guns. That was a small price indeed to pay for our magnificent success."

CHAPTER VI
A CHANGE OF SCENE

ECTOR gained great credit from the report of the manner in which the force had been enabled to draw off without loss from the enemy's guns, owing to his forethought in bringing with him the means of spiking them, and also for his success in checking the advance of the enemy along the ramparts.

"You see, messieurs," Turenne said to the members of his staff, who, with the exception of Hector, were together on the day after his return to Susa, "how important it is for officers, before setting out on an expedition, to think seriously over every contingency that may happen. Now the vast proportion of officers consider that all the thinking has to be done by the general, and that they only have to obey orders. No doubt that is essential, but there may be numerous little matters in which an officer may render great service. This young captain of ours did not content himself with leading the company to which I appointed him through the gateway. Before leaving Susa he must have thought over every incident likely to occur. As the leading company he would know that it would be his business to clear the ramparts, to check any parties of the enemy coming along that way, and it would be only natural for him to determine to use the enemy's cannon to keep them at bay.

"This would probably have occurred to most officers placed as he was. But he did not stop there—he must have thought over the events that would probably follow the entry. He knew, of course, that our feint at the other end of the town would draw off the greater portion of the garrison, but would be sure also that as soon as the attack began, and it became evident that our real object was to revictual the citadel, they would come pouring back again. He would have said to himself, 'We shall be able to keep them at bay until our work is done, then we shall have to fall back. What then? The enemy will mount the ramparts, and while their main force pours out in pursuit, their guns on the walls will play havoc with us. To prevent this I must silence them before my company retires.'

"It is all very simple when we look at it after it is done, and yet probably it did not occur to a single officer of that force except to Captain Campbell. I admit that it did not occur to myself. Had it done so, I should have ordered that some of the artillerymen should carry spikes and hammers, and that upon entering the town they should immediately take steps, by rendering the guns harmless, to enable the force to draw off without heavy loss. In the same way he showed a cool and calculating brain when he carried out that most dangerous service of bearing the news that we should speedily bring aid to the citadel. It is difficult to imagine a better laid plan. He thought of everything—of his disguise, of the manner in which it would alone be possible to approach closely to the wall.

"I think that few of us would have thought of making our way up through a house a hundred yards away, working along the roofs and descending into the lane by the wall itself. I asked him how he got the rope down which it was necessary for him to use four or five times afterwards, and he showed me the plan by which he contrived to free the hook; it was most ingenious. It did not seem to me that it would have acted as he told me, and I asked him to have another one made so that I might understand how it was worked, for such a contrivance would be extremely useful in escalades, when the troops, after descending into a deep fosse, need the rope for climbing a wall or bastion. There it is, gentlemen, and as you see, by pulling this thin cord the hook is lifted from its hold, and the slightest shake will bring it down.

A CHANGE OF SCENE

"The contrivance is an excellent one. The line he took was well chosen. He accomplished the most dangerous part first, and made his way out by the side where the watch was most likely to be careless, as anyone leaving or entering the town there would have to swim the river. The feat shows that he has not only abundance of courage of the very highest order, but that he has a head to plan and leaves nothing to chance. You will see, gentlemen, that if this young officer lives he is likely to gain the highest rank and position. Already I have every reason to congratulate myself upon having, almost as it were by chance, taken him under my protection."

The winter passed quietly, but as soon as spring set in and the roads were sufficiently good for the passage of wagons, d'Harcourt prepared to attempt to raise the siege of Casale, before which Leganez with twenty thousand men had intrenched himself. The roads were still, however, far too heavy for cannon, and as the garrison were becoming hardly pressed he left his guns behind him and started at the end of April with seven thousand foot and three thousand horse. The position occupied by the Spaniards was a strong one, and their general did not for a moment think that the French, with a force half the strength of his own, would venture to attack him. D'Harcourt, however, resolved upon doing so. He divided his force into three parts; two of these were composed of French soldiers, the third comprised the forces of the Duchess of Savoy. The attack was successful on all sides—although d'Harcourt for a time could make no way, and Turenne was repulsed three times before he entered the intrenchments—the Spaniards were completely defeated, and lost their guns, ammunition, and baggage, three thousand killed, two thousand prisoners, and great numbers were drowned in endeavouring to cross the river.

A council of war was held, and Turenne's advice that Turin should be besieged was after much debate accepted, although it seemed a desperate enterprise for an army of ten thousand men to besiege a town garrisoned by twelve thousand, while the Spaniards, after recovering from their defeat and drawing men from their various garrisons, could march to relieve the town with eighteen thousand men. No time was lost in carrying Turenne's advice into effect. The army marched upon Turin, seized the positions round the town, threw up lines facing the city to prevent sorties being made by the enemy, and surrounded themselves by similar lines to enable them to resist attack by the Spaniards, who were not long in approaching them. Thus there were now four bodies of combatants—the garrison of the citadel, which was surrounded and besieged by that of the town; the town was besieged by Turenne, and he himself was surrounded by the Spaniards. Each relied rather upon starving the others out than upon storming their positions, but Leganez managed to send a messenger into Turin telling Prince Thomas that he intended to attack the French and calling upon him to fall upon them with his troops at the same time.

In pursuance of this design he retired some distance up the Po, and proceeded to cross the river at Moncalieri. D'Harcourt despatched Turenne to oppose the passage, but before he could arrive there some five thousand men had crossed the bridge. Without hesitating a moment, although his force was a much smaller one than that of the Spaniards, Turenne attacked them at once, carried the intrenchments they had begun to throw up, killed a large number, and drove the rest into the river, where hundreds were drowned. Then he set fire to the bridge, which was of wood, and intrenched himself on the banks of the river, occupied all the fords higher up, and completely checked any advance of the Spaniards in that direction. He was, however, wounded in the shoulder, and was obliged to leave the army and to be carried to Pinerolo. While he was away Leganez attacked the French line from without, and Prince Thomas from within, and the former succeeded in passing twelve hundred horse and one thousand foot into the town.

The French were now closely beleaguered, and began to suffer severely from famine. In the meantime fresh troops had arrived from France, and although not yet recovered from his wounds, Turenne took the command, and escorted a great convoy of provisions into the camp in spite of the enemy's efforts to prevent him. The townspeople were suffering even more severely. Sorties were made in great force, but were always repulsed, as were the attacks made by Leganez, and on the 17th of September the garrison surrendered, being allowed to march out with their arms. The Count d'Harcourt returned to France, and Turenne again assumed the command of the army for the winter.

Hector conducted himself to the satisfaction of his general throughout the campaign, but was severely wounded in the last sortie made by the besieged, having been thrown down in a charge of Prince Thomas's cavalry and trampled upon by the horses, and being taken up for dead when the enemy fell back.

Directly he heard the news Turenne sent his surgeon to examine him. He reported that he still breathed, but that several of his ribs and his left arm were broken. He mended but slowly, and Turenne, a month after the surrender of the town, came in one day to see him, and said, "The surgeon tells me that it will be some months before you are fit for service again, and that you will need a period of perfect rest to recover your health. There is a convoy of invalids returning to France to-morrow, and I think it were best that you should accompany them. There is no rest to be obtained here, and I know that you will be fretting at being unable to ride, and at your forced inactivity. I shall give orders that you are conveyed in a horse-litter to Sedan, where my brother, the Duc de Bouillon, will gladly entertain you for my sake, and you must remain there until entirely restored to strength.

"I do not think that there will be much doing on this side of the Alps in the next campaign. Unhappily France has troubles of her own, and will find it difficult to spare more troops in this direction, and without reinforcements we can but act on the defensive. Though we may capture a few towns, there is small chance of any great operations. Indeed, methinks that it is by no means unlikely that Prince Thomas, seeing that his effort to rule Savoy in place of his sister-in-law, the duchess, is likely to end in discredit and loss to himself, will before long open negotiations with her.

Therefore you will be losing nothing by going. It is to the duchess that I shall commend you rather than to my brother, who is unfortunately occupied by public matters, and is at present almost at war with Richelieu.

"He is a man of noble impulses, generous in the extreme, and the soul of honour, but he knows not how to conceal his feelings; and in these days no man, even the most powerful, can venture to rail in public against one who has offended him, when that man happens to be the cardinal. I love my brother dearly, but I have mixed myself up in no way with his affairs. I am an officer of the king, and as such I stand aloof from all parties in the state. The cardinal is his minister; doubtless he has his faults, but he is the greatest man in France, and the wisest. He lives and works for the country. It may be true that he is ambitious for himself, but the glory of France is his chief care. It is for that purpose that we have entered upon this war, for he sees that if Germany becomes united under an emperor who is by blood a Spaniard, France must eventually be crushed, and Spain become absolutely predominant in Europe. If he is opposed, Richelieu strikes hard, because he deems those who oppose him as not only his own enemies but as enemies of France.

"As a prince of the church it must have been bitter for him to have to ally himself with the Protestant princes of Germany, with Protestant Holland, and Protestant England, but he has done so. It is true that he has captured La Rochelle, and broken the power of the Huguenot lords of the south, but these new alliances show that he is ready to sacrifice his own prejudices for the good of France when France is endangered, and that it is on account of the danger of civil broils to the country, rather than from a hatred of the Huguenots, that he warred against them. Here am I, whom he deigns to honour with his patronage, a Huguenot; my brother, Bouillon, was also a Huguenot, and strangely enough the quarrel between him and the cardinal did not break out until my brother had changed his religion.

A CHANGE OF SCENE

"He was more rigorously brought up than I was, and was taught to look upon the Catholics with abhorrence; but he married, not from policy but from love, a Catholic lady, who is in all respects worthy of him, for she is as high-spirited and as generous as he is, and at the same time is gentle, loving, and patient. Though deeply pious, she is free from bigotry, and it was because my brother came to see that the tales he had been taught of the bigotry and superstition of the Catholics were untrue, at least in many instances, that he revolted against the intolerance of the doctrines in which he had been brought up, renounced them, and became an adherent of his wife's religion.

"Nigh four years ago the Duke of Soissons, a prince of the blood, incurred the enmity of Richelieu by refusing, with scorn, his proposal that he should marry the Countess of Combalet, Richelieu's niece. The refusal, and still more the language in which he refused, excited the deep enmity of the cardinal. Soissons had joined the party against him, but as usual Richelieu had the king's ear. Soissons was ordered to leave the court, and went to Sedan, where he was heartily received by my brother, who had a warm affection for him. Bouillon wrote to the king hoping that he would not be displeased at his offering a retreat to a prince of the blood, and the king wrote permitting the count to stay at Sedan. After a time Richelieu again endeavoured to bring about the marriage upon which he had set his heart, but was again refused, and, being greatly exasperated, insisted on Bouillon obliging the count to leave Sedan. My brother naturally replied that the king having at first approved of his receiving Soissons, he could not violate the laws of hospitality to a prince of the blood.

"Richelieu then persuaded the king to refuse further payments to the garrisons at Sedan, although the latter had confirmed the agreement entered into by his father, whereupon my brother openly declared against Richelieu, and still further excited the cardinal's anger by furnishing an asylum to the Archbishop of Rheims, second son of Charles of Lorraine, who had also quarrelled with Richelieu.

95

So matters stand at present. What will come of it, I know not. I doubt not that the cardinal's hostility to Bouillon does not arise solely from the Soissons affair, which but serves him as a pretext. You see his object for the past four years has been to strengthen France by extending her frontiers to the east by the conquest of Lorraine. He has already carried them to the Upper Rhine, and by obtaining from the Duke of Savoy Pinerolo and its dependencies has brought them up to the foot of the Alps.

"But my brother's dukedom stands in the way of his grand project, for it is a gate through which an enemy from beyond the Rhine might invade France; and, moreover, the close family relationship between us and the Prince of Holland would add to the danger should Holland, at present our ally, fall out with France. Thus the possession of Bouillon's dukedom, or at any rate its military occupation for a time, is a consideration of vital importance to the kingdom. Such, you see, is the situation. Were I not an officer in the French army doubtless my feelings would be on the side of my brother. As it is, I am a faithful servant of the king and his minister, and should deem it the height of dishonour were I to use my influence against what I perceive is the cause of France. I tell you this in order that you may understand the various matters which might surprise you at Sedan.

"You go there as a patient to be nursed by the duchess, my sister-in-law, and having no influence, and at present not even the strength to use your sword, there is little fear that any will seek to involve you in these party turmoils. I shall write to my brother that you are a soldier of France and that you have done her good service, that you are a protégé of mine, and being of Scottish blood belong to no party save my party, and that I entreat that he will not allow anyone to set you against the cardinal, or to try and attach you to any party, for that I want you back again with me as soon as you are thoroughly cured."

A CHANGE OF SCENE

Hector would much rather have remained to be cured in Italy, but he did not think of raising the slightest objection to Turenne's plans for him, and the next day he started for Sedan, taking, of course, Paolo with him. The convoy travelled by easy stages over the passes into France, and then, escorted by a sergeant and eight troopers, Hector was carried north to Sedan. Though still very weak, he was able to alight at the entrance of the duke's residence, and sent in Turenne's letters to him and the duchess. Three minutes later the duke himself came down.

"Captain Campbell," he said heartily, "my brother has done well in sending you here to be taken care of and nursed. In his letters to me he has spoken of you more than once, especially with reference to the manner in which you carried a message for him to the citadel of Turin. I shall be glad to do anything that I can for so brave a young officer, but I fear that for the present you will have to be under the charge of the duchess rather than mine."

The duke was a tall, handsome man with a frank and open face, a merry laugh, and a ready jest. He was extremely popular, not only in his own dominions, but among the Parisians. His fault was that he was led too easily. Himself the soul of honour, he believed others to be equally honourable, and so suffered himself to become mixed up in plots and conspiracies, and to be drawn on into an enterprise wholly foreign to his nature.

"I will take you at once to the duchess, but I see that you are quite unfit to walk. Sit down, I beg you, until I get a chair for you."

Three or four minutes later four lackeys came with a carrying chair, and Hector was taken upstairs to the duchess's apartments.

"This is the gentleman of whom Turenne has written to me, and doubtless, as I see by that letter upon the table, to you also. He has been a good deal damaged, having been ridden over by a squadron of Prince Thomas's horsemen, and needs quiet and rest."

"Turenne has told me all about it," the duchess said. "I welcome you very heartily, monsieur. My brother says that he has great affection for you, and believes you will some day become a master in the art of war. He says you have rendered him most valuable services, which is strange indeed, seeing that you are as yet very young."

"I was sixteen the other day, madam."

"Only sixteen, and already a captain!" she exclaimed.

"I was made a captain nine months ago," he said, "for a little service that I performed to his satisfaction."

"Turenne would not have promoted you unless it had been an important service, I am sure," she said with a smile. "He does great things himself, and expects great things from others."

"It was the affair of carrying the message to the garrison of the citadel of Turin urging them to hold out, as he would come to their relief soon," the duke said. "Do you not remember that he wrote us an account of it?"

"I remember it perfectly. Turenne said a young officer, but I did not imagine that it could have been but a lad. However, Captain Campbell, I will not detain you here talking, or you will begin by considering me to be a very bad nurse. Directly I received the letter I ordered a chamber to be prepared for you. By this time all will be in readiness, and a lackey ready to disrobe you and assist you to bed."

"I do not need," he began, but she held up her finger.

"Please to remember, sir, that I am head-nurse here. You will go to bed at once, and will take a light repast and a glass of generous wine. After that our surgeon will examine you, and remove your bandages, which have been, I doubt not, somewhat disarranged on your journey; then he will say whether it will be advisable that you should keep your bed for a time, which will, I think, be far the best for you, for you will be much more comfortable so than on a couch, which, however good to be sat upon by those in health, affords but poor comfort to an invalid. Have you brought a servant with you?"

A CHANGE OF SCENE

"Yes, madam. He is a very faithful lad, and accompanied me on that enterprise that you have been speaking of. He is a merry fellow, and has proved himself a good and careful nurse. He sat up with me for many nights when I was first hurt, and has ever since slept on the floor in my room."

"I will give him in charge of my major-domo, who will see that he is well taken care of, and we can have a pallet laid for him at night on the floor of your room."

She herself led the way to a very comfortable apartment where a fire was burning on the hearth; a lackey was already in waiting, and after a few kind words she left him.

"I have fallen into good hands indeed," Hector said to himself. "What would Sergeant MacIntosh say if he knew that I was lodged in a ducal palace, and that the duke and duchess had both spoken to me and seen after my comfort as if I had been a relation of their own?"

In spite of the care and attention that he received, Hector's recovery was slow, and even when spring came the surgeon said that he was unfit for severe work. However, the letters that he received from time to time from de Lisle and Chavigny consoled him, for not only had the winter passed without any incident save the capture of three or four towns by Turenne, but it was not at all likely that any events of great importance would take place. All accounts represented the Spaniards as being engaged in adding to the strength of three or four towns in the duchy of Milan, so that evidently they intended to stand upon the defensive.

The palace of Sedan was the centre of a formidable conspiracy against Richelieu. Messengers came and went, and Bouillon, Soissons, and the Archbishop of Rheims were constantly closeted together. They had various allies at court, and believed that they should be able to overthrow the minister who had so long ruled over France in the name of the king.

As Hector was now able to move about, and was acquainted with all the members of the duke's household, he learned much of what was going on; and from a conversation that he accidentally overheard, he could see that the position was an extremely serious one, as a treaty had been signed with Ferdinand, son of the King of Spain, and the Archduke Leopold-William, son of the Emperor of Austria, by which each agreed to assist the duke and his friends with a large sum of money for raising soldiers, and with seven thousand men. In order to justify themselves, the heads of the movement issued a manifesto, in which they styled themselves Princes of Peace. In this they rehearsed the cardinal's various acts of tyranny and cruelty towards his rivals, the arbitrary manner in which he carried on the government, and declared that they were leagued solely to overthrow the power that overshadowed that of the king, plunged France into wars, and scourged the people with heavy taxation.

As soon as this manifesto was published in Sedan, Hector went to the duke.

"My lord duke," he said, "I cannot sufficiently thank you for the hospitality and kindness with which you and the duchess have treated me. Nevertheless, I must ask you to allow me to leave at once."

"Why this sudden determination, Captain Campbell?"

"If, sir, I were but a private person I should have no hesitation, after the kindness that you have shown me, in requesting you to give me employment in the force that you are raising; but I am an officer of the king, and what is of far greater importance at the present moment, an aide-de-camp of the Viscount Turenne, your brother. Were it reported that I was with your army, or even indeed that I was here, the cardinal would at once conclude that I was representing the viscount, and was perhaps the intermediary through whom communications between you and your brother were being carried on. Therefore I should not only compromise myself, which is of no importance, but I might excite suspicion in Richelieu's mind against your brother, which might result in his recall from the position in which he has so distinguished himself, and grievously injure his prospects. The viscount himself warned me against mixing myself with any party, saying that a soldier should hold himself free from all entanglement, bent only on serving, to the utmost of his power, the king and France."

"You are right," the duke said heartily. "Turenne has no grievances against king or cardinal, and has acted wisely in holding himself aloof from any party; and badly as I am affected towards Richelieu, I will own that he has never allowed my brother's relationship towards me to prevent his employing him in posts of honour. I have never sought to influence him in the slightest, and am far too proud of the credit and honour he has gained to do aught that would in any way cause a breach between him and the cardinal. What you have said is very right and true. Doubtless Richelieu has spies in this town, as he has elsewhere, and may have learned that a young officer on my brother's staff was brought here last autumn grievously wounded. But it is certainly well that now, as the time for action is at hand, you should retire. You are not thinking, I hope, of returning at once, for it was but a day or two ago that the surgeon assured me that it would need another three or four months of quiet before you would be fit to resume your duties."

"I feel that myself, my lord, and moreover I think that it would be as well that I should not join the viscount at present, for it might well be supposed that I was the bearer of some important news from you to him; therefore I propose to go to Geneva, and remain there until I have completely recruited my strength. In the Swiss republic I should pass unnoticed, even by the cardinal's agents. And the fact that, although being but a comparatively short distance from Piedmont, I abstained from joining the general, would, if they inquired, show that I could not have been entrusted with any private communication from you to him."

"It could not be better," the duke said. "When you leave here you should no longer wear that military scarf. Of course, when you enter Switzerland there is no reason why you should disguise the fact that you are a French officer, and having been severely wounded, have come there to repair your health. Doubtless many others have done so; and, dressed as a private person, you would excite no attention. But the Swiss, who strive to hold themselves neutral and to avoid giving offence, might raise objections to a French officer wearing military attire staying among them."

That evening Hector bade his adieu to the duchess and to the friends he had made during his stay, and the next morning, attended by Paolo, he started for Geneva.

"I am glad indeed that we are off, master," the latter said. "In truth, had I stayed here much longer I should have become useless from fat and idleness, for I have had nothing whatever to do but to eat and sleep."

"I am glad to be off too, Paolo. I am convinced myself, in spite of what the surgeon says, that actual exercise will do more for me than the doctor's potions and rich food. I am stiff still, but it is from doing nothing, and were it not that coming from here my presence might be inconvenient for Turenne, I would journey straight to his camp. You saw the prince's manifesto?"

Paolo nodded. "I did, master. Not being able to read or write, I could make nothing of it myself, but a burgher coming along read it aloud, and it made me shake in my shoes with fright. I made my way as quickly as I could from so dangerous a spot, for it seemed nothing short of treason to have heard such words read against the cardinal."

"I fear that the duke has made a terrible mistake, Paolo. Hitherto all who have ventured to measure their strength with the cardinal have been worsted, and many have lost everything and are now fugitives from France. Some have lost their lives as well as honours and estates. Bouillon is an independent prince, and so was Lorraine, and although the latter could put ten men in the field to every one the duke could muster, he has been driven from his principality. Soissons could not help him except with his name, nor can the Archbishop of Rheims. Not a few of the great nobles would join the duke did they think that he had a prospect of success. None have so far done so, though possibly some have given him secret pledges, which will count for nothing unless it seems that he is likely to triumph.

A CHANGE OF SCENE

"It is rumoured, as you know, that he has made an alliance with Spain and Austria. Both will use him as an arm against France, but will throw him over and leave him to his fate whenever it suits them. Moreover, their alliance would assuredly deter many, who might otherwise range themselves with him, from taking up arms. No Huguenot would fight by the side of a Spaniard; and although the Guises and the Catholic nobles allied themselves with Spain against Henri of Navarre, it was in a matter in which they deemed their religion in danger, while this is but a quarrel between Bouillon and the cardinal; and with Spain fighting against France in the Netherlands, they would not risk their lands and titles. Bouillon had better have stood alone than have called in the Spaniards and Austrians. We know whose doing that is, the Archbishop of Rheims, who is a Guise, and, methinks, from what I have seen of him, a crafty one.

"I am sure that neither the duke nor Soissons would, unless won over by the archbishop, have ever consented to such a plan, for both are honourable gentlemen, and Soissons at least is a Frenchman, which can hardly be said of Bouillon, whose ancestors have been independent princes here for centuries. However, I fear that he will rue the day he championed the cause of Soissons. It was no affair of his, and it is carrying hospitality too far to endanger life and kingdom rather than tell two guests that they must seek a refuge elsewhere. All Europe was open to them. As a Guise the archbishop would have been welcome wherever Spain had power. With Spain, Italy, and Austria open to him, why should he thus bring danger and misfortune upon the petty dukedom of Sedan? The same may be said of Soissons; however reluctant Bouillon might be to part with so dear a friend, Soissons himself should have insisted upon going and taking up his abode elsewhere. Could he still have brought a large force into the field, and have thus risked as much as Bouillon, the case would be different, but his estates are confiscated, or, at any rate, he has no longer power to summon his vassals to the field, and he therefore risks nothing in case of defeat, while Bouillon is risking everything."

"I daresay that that is all true, master, though in faith I know nothing about the matter. For myself, it seems to me that when one is a noble, and has everything that a man can want, he must be a fool to mix himself up in troubles. I know that if the King of France were to give me a big estate, and anyone came to me and asked me to take part in a plot, I would, if I had the power of life and death, have him hung up over the gate of my castle."

"That would be a short way, no doubt, Paolo, but it might not keep you out of trouble," Hector said, smiling. "If the person who came to you were also a noble, his family and friends would rise in arms to avenge his death, and instead of avoiding trouble you would bring it at once upon your head."

"I suppose that would be so, master," Paolo said thoughtfully; "so I think that it would be best for me that the king should not take it into his head to give me that estate. And so we are going to Geneva, master?"

"Yes."

"That pleases me not," the other one said, "for I have heard of it as a terribly serious place, where a man dares not so much as smile, and where he has to listen to sermons and exhortations lasting half a day. My father was a Huguenot, and I suppose that I am too, though I never inquired very closely into the matter; but as for exhortations of four hours in length, methinks I would rather swim those moats again, master, and to go all day without smiling would be a worse penance than the strictest father confessor could lay upon me."

"I own that I am somewhat of your opinion, Paolo. My father brought me up a Protestant like yourself, and when I was quite young I had a very dreary time of it while he was away, living as I did in the house of a Huguenot pastor. After that I attended the Protestant services in the barracks, for all the officers and almost all the men are Protestants, and, of course, were allowed to have their own services; but the minister, who was a Scotchman, knew better than to make his discourses too lengthy; for if he did, there was a shuffling of jack-boots on the stone floor and a clanking of sabres that warned him that the patience of the soldiers was exhausted. In our own glen my father has told me that the ministers are as long-winded as those of Geneva; but, as he said, soldiers are a restless people, and it is one thing for men who regard their Sunday gathering as the chief event in the week to listen to lengthy discourses, but quite another for soldiers, either in the field or a city like Paris, to do so. However, if we do not find Geneva to our taste, there is no reason why we should tarry there, as Zürich lies on the other end of the lake, and Zürich is Catholic, or at any rate largely so, and Calvinist doctrines have never flourished there. But, on the other hand, the sympathies of Geneva have generally been with France, while those of Zürich are with Austria; therefore I think that if we like not Geneva we will go to Lyons, where, as an officer of Viscount Turenne's, I am sure to be well received."

"Why not go there at once, master?"

"Because I think that the fresh air of the lake will brace me up, and maybe if I find the people too sober-minded for me we will go up into the mountains and lodge there in some quiet village. I think that would suit both of us."

"It would suit me assuredly," Paolo said joyfully. "I love the mountains."

Such was indeed the course eventually taken. The strict Calvinism of Geneva suited neither of them; and after a fortnight's stay there they went up among the hills, and in the clear brisk air Hector found his blood begin to run more rapidly through his veins, and his strength and energy fast returning. Sometimes he rode, but soon found more pleasure in climbing the hills around on foot, for the mountain paths were so rough that it was seldom indeed that his horse could break into a trot.

CHAPTER VII
THE DUC D'ENGHIEN

FROM time to time news came up of what was passing in the world. The Spaniards had afforded no assistance in men to the duke, for Richelieu had sent a powerful army into the heart of Flanders, and so kept them fully occupied. An Austrian force, however, joined that of the duke, and a battle was fought with the royal army which, under Marshal Chatillon, lay encamped a league from Sedan. The Austrian general commanded the main body, the Duc de Bouillon the cavalry, while the Count de Soissons was with the reserve. At first Chatillon's army had the advantage, but Bouillon charged with such vehemence that he drove the cavalry of the royalists down upon their infantry, which fell into confusion, most of the French officers being killed or made prisoners, and the rest put to rout. The duke, after the victory, rode to congratulate Soissons, whose force had not been engaged. He found the count dead, having accidentally shot himself while pushing up the visor of his helmet with the muzzle of his pistol.

Bouillon soon learned the hollowness of the promises of his allies. The Spaniards sent neither money nor men, while the Austrians received orders to march away from Sedan and to join the Spaniards, who were marching to the relief of Arras.

The duke, deserted by his allies, prepared to defend Sedan till the last. Fortunately for him, however, the position of the French at Arras was critical. The place was strong, two armies were marching to its relief, and it would therefore have been rash to have attempted at the same time the siege of Sedan. The king himself had joined the army advancing against Bouillon, while the cardinal remained in Paris. Many of those round the person of the king, foremost among whom was the Marquis of Cinq-Mars, his master of horse, spoke very strongly in favour of the duke, and represented that he had been driven to take up arms by the persecution of the cardinal. The king was moved by their representations, and gave a complete pardon to Bouillon, who was restored to the full possession of all his estates in France, while on his part he released the prisoners, baggage, and standards taken in the late battle.

This was welcome news to Hector, who at once prepared to cross into Italy; but when they reached Chambery he heard that Turenne had been ordered to join the army that was collected near the Spanish frontier, in order to conquer Roussillon, which lay between Languedoc and Catalonia. The latter province had been for three years in a state of insurrection against Spain, and had besought aid from France. This, however, could not easily be afforded them so long as the fortress of Perpignan guarded the way, and with other strongholds prevented all communication between the south of France and Catalonia. As it was uncertain whether Turenne would follow the coast route or cross the passes, Hector and his companion rode forward at once, and arrived at Turin before he left.

"I am glad to see you back again," the general said as Hector entered his room, "and trust that you are now strong again. Your letter, giving me your reasons for leaving Sedan, was forwarded to me by a messenger, with others from my brother and his wife. He speaks in high terms of you, and regretted your leaving them; but the reason you gave for so doing in your letter to me more than justified the course you took, and showed that you were thoughtful in other than military matters. You served me better by leaving Sedan than you could have done in any other way. In these unhappy disputes with my brother, the cardinal has never permitted my relationship to Bouillon to shake his confidence in me. But after being engaged for many years in combating plots against him, he cannot but be suspicious of all, and that an officer of my staff should be staying at Sedan when the dispute was going to end in open warfare might well have excited a doubt of me while, had you travelled direct here at that moment, it might, as you said, have been considered that you were the bearer of important communications between my brother and myself.

"Now, I hope that you are completely restored to health; you are looking well, and have grown a good deal, the consequence, no doubt, of your being so long in bed. You have heard that I am ordered to Roussillon, of which I am glad, for the war languishes here. The king, I hear, will take up his head-quarters at Narbonne, and Richelieu is coming down to look after matters as he did at Rochelle. So I expect that things will move quickly there. They say the king is not in good health, and that the cardinal himself is failing. Should he die it will be a grievous loss for France, for there is no one who could in any way fill his place. It has been evident for some time that the king has been in weak health. The dauphin is but a child. A regency with the queen as its nominal head, and Richelieu as its staff and ruler, would be possible; but without Richelieu the prospect would be a very dark one, and I cannot think of it without apprehension. However, I must continue to do as I have been doing ever since Bouillon fell out with the court; I must think only that I am a soldier, prepared to strike where ordered, whether against a foreign foe or a rebellious subject.

"Happily my family troubles are over. I hear that there is a probability that, now Bouillon has been restored to favour, he will obtain the command of the army in Italy, which will just suit his active spirit."

Three days later Turenne with his staff crossed the Alps, and journeying across the south of France reached Perpignan. The Marquis of Mielleraye was in supreme command, and Turenne was to act as his lieutenant; the latter at once took charge of the operations of the siege of Perpignan, which had already been beleaguered for some months by the French. The fortress was a very strong one, but as the efforts of the Spanish to reinforce the garrison by a landing effected on the coast failed altogether, and as the operations of Mielleraye in the field were successful, and there was no chance of any relief being afforded to the besieged town by a Spanish army advancing through Catalonia, it was certain that the fortress must in time surrender by hunger. As it could not be captured by assault unless with a very heavy loss indeed, Turenne contented himself with keeping up so vigilant a watch round it that its communications were altogether cut off, and the garrison knew nothing whatever of what was passing around them.

The Duc de Bouillon had received the command of the army in Italy, and Turenne hoped that henceforth his mind would be free from the family trouble that had for the past four years caused him great pain and anxiety. Unfortunately, however, Cinq-Mars, the king's master of horse and personal favourite, had become embroiled with the cardinal. Rash, impetuous, and haughty, the young favourite at once began to intrigue. The Duke of Orleans, the king's only brother, one of the most treacherous and unstable of men, joined him heart and soul, and Bouillon was induced to ally himself with them, not from any political feeling, but because Cinq-Mars had been mainly instrumental in obtaining terms for him before, and appealed to his sense of gratitude to aid him now. He insisted, however, that this time there should be no negotiating with Spain and Austria, but that the movement should be entirely a French one.

Unknown to him, however, the others entered into an alliance with Spain, who engaged to find money and an army. The conspirators had gained the ear of the king, Cinq-Mars representing to him that their hostility was directed solely against the cardinal, and the latter was in great disfavour until he obtained a copy of the treaty with Spain. The disclosure opened the king's eyes. The Duke of Orleans, Cinq-Mars, Monsieur de Thou, his intimate friend, and de Bouillon were at once arrested. Orleans immediately turned traitor to his fellow-conspirators, revealed every incident of the plot, and was sentenced to exile. Cinq-Mars and de Thou were tried and executed. De Bouillon saved his life by relinquishing his principality to France, any hesitation there may have been in sparing him on those terms being removed by the receipt of a message from the duchess, that if her husband were put to death she would at once deliver Sedan into the hands of the Spaniards. De Bouillon was therefore pardoned, and in exchange for the surrender of his principality, his estates in France were to be enlarged, and a considerable pension granted to him.

All this was a terrible trial to Turenne, who was deeply attached to his brother, and who mourned not only the danger he had incurred, but that he should have broken his engagements, and while commanding a royal army should have plotted against the royal authority.

At the end of November the cardinal's illness, from which he had long suffered, took an unfavourable turn, and the king, who had returned to Paris, went to see him. Richelieu advised him to place his confidence in the two secretaries of state, Chavigny and de Noyers, recommended Cardinal Mazarin strongly as first minister of the crown, and handed the king a document he had prepared barring the Duke of Orleans from any share in the regency in case of the king's death, the preamble calling to mind that the king had five times pardoned his brother, who had yet recently engaged in a fresh plot against him. On the 2nd of December, 1642, Richelieu died, and the king, on the following day, carried out his last advice, and appointed Mazarin to a place in his council.

The year had passed quietly with Hector Campbell. His duties had been but slight during the siege, and as during his stay at Sedan and in Switzerland he had continued to work hard at Italian, at the former place under a teacher, who instructed him in more courtly dialect than that which he acquired from Paolo, so during the six months before Perpignan he had, after taking the advice of Turenne, set himself to acquire a knowledge of German. Working at this for eight hours a day under the tuition of a German gentleman, who had been compelled to leave the country when his native town was captured by the Imperialists, he was soon able to converse as fluently in it as in Italian.

"It is in Germany that the next great campaign is likely to take place," Turenne said to him, "and your knowledge of German will be of infinite utility to you. Fortunately for myself, Sedan standing on the border between the two countries, I acquired German as well as French without labour, and while in Holland spoke it rather than French; the knowledge of languages is of great importance to one who would rise high in the army or at the court, and I am very glad that you have acquired German, as it may be of great use to you if we are called upon to invade that country again, that is, if the new council of the king are as kindly disposed towards me as Richelieu always showed himself to be; but I fear that ere long there may be changes. The king's health is very poor. He may not live long, and then we have a regency before us, and the regencies of France have always been times of grievous trouble.

"Even had Richelieu lived he might not have been able to avert such disasters. He and the queen have never been friends, and he would not have had the support from her that he has had from the king, who, although he no doubt fretted at times under Richelieu's dictation, yet recognized his splendid genius, and knew that he worked heart and soul for the good of France. However, his death is a sore misfortune. A regency needs a strong head, but where is it to come from? The Duke of Orleans is a schemer without principle, weak, easily led, ambitious, and unscrupulous. The Prince of Condé is equally ambitious, even more grasping, and much more talented. There is no one else, save men like Chavigny, the father of our friend here, de Noyers, and some others of good family, honest and capable business men, but who would speedily become mere ciphers; and Cardinal Mazarin, who has just been appointed to the council."

"Do you know him, sir?" Hector asked.

"I have seen him more than once. He is said to be very clever, and it is no secret that he is nominated to the council on Richelieu's recommendation, which speaks volumes in his favour, for Richelieu was a judge of men, and must have believed, when recommending him, that Mazarin would render good service to France. But however clever he is he cannot replace the great cardinal. On him was stamped by nature the making of a ruler of men. He was tall, handsome, and an accomplished cavalier. Seeing him dressed as a noble among noblemen, one would have picked him out as born to be the greatest of them. No doubt this noble appearance, aided by his haughty manner and by his ruthlessness in punishing those who conspired against him, had not a little to do with his mastery over men.

"Mazarin is a man of very different appearance. He is dark in complexion, handsome in a way, supple, and, I should say, crafty; an Italian rather than a Frenchman. Such a man will meet with difficulties far greater than those which assailed Richelieu. The latter, personally fearless, went straight to his end, crushing his enemies if they stood in his way, possessed of an indomitable will and unflinching determination. Mazarin, if I mistake not, will try to gain his end by other means—by intrigues, by setting those who oppose him against each other, by yielding rather than by striking. He is said to stand high in the queen's favour, and this will be a great aid to him; for those who might rebel against the authority of a cardinal will hesitate to do so when he has at his back the protection and authority of a queen. However, we must hope for the best. It is probable that Richelieu acquainted him with all his plans and projects, and urged him to carry them into effect. I sincerely trust that he will do so; and in that case, if he comes to the head of affairs, I should assuredly serve him as willingly and faithfully as I served Richelieu, knowing that it will be for the good of France."

It was, indeed, but a short time after the loss of his great adviser that the king followed him to the tomb. He had for long suffered from bad health, and now that the statesman who had borne the whole burden of public affairs had left him, he felt the weight overpowering. He had always been devoted to religious exercises, and saw his end approaching without regret, and died calmly and peacefully on May 14, 1643. By his will he left the queen regent. He had never been on good terms with her, and now endeavoured to prevent her from having any real power. The Duke of Orleans was appointed lieutenant-general, but as the king had rightly no confidence in him, he nominated a council which, he intended, should override both. It was composed of the Prince of Condé, Cardinal Mazarin, the chancellor, Seguerin, the secretary of state, Chavigny, and superintendent Bouthillier.

The king's will prohibited any change whatever being made in the council, but this proviso was not observed. The queen speedily made terms with the ministers; and when the little king was conducted in great state to the parliament of Paris, the Duke of Orleans addressed the queen, saying that he desired to take no other part in affairs than that which it might please her to give him. The Prince of Condé said the same; and that evening, to their astonishment, the queen having become by their resignation the sole head of the administration, announced that she should retain Cardinal Mazarin as her minister, and shortly afterwards nominated Turenne to the command of the army in Italy. Prince Thomas had now broken altogether with the Spaniards, finding that their protection was not available, for the King of Spain had been obliged to recall a considerable proportion of his troops from Italy to suppress an insurrection in Catalonia. Hector did not accompany Turenne to Italy, for early in April Turenne had said to him:

"There seems no chance of employment here at present, Campbell, while there is likely to be some heavy fighting on the Rhine frontier.

"The death of Richelieu has given fresh courage to the enemies of France, and I hear that de Malo, the governor of the Low Countries, has gathered a large army, and is about to invade France. Our army there is commanded by the young Duc d'Enghien, the Prince of Condé's son. He is but twenty-two, and of course owes his appointment to his father's influence. The king has, however, sent with him Marshal de l'Hôpital, who will be his lieutenant and director. I know Enghien well, and esteem his talents highly. He is brave, impetuous, and fiery; but at the same time, if I mistake not, cautious and prudent. I will give you a letter to him. I shall tell him that you have greatly distinguished yourself while on my staff, and being anxious above all things to acquire military knowledge and to serve with honour, I have sent you to him, begging him to give you the same post on his staff as you have had on mine, asking it as a personal favour to myself. This, I have no doubt, he will grant. He has affected my company a good deal when I have been in Paris, and has evinced the greatest desire to learn as much as he can of military matters from me."

"I am grateful indeed for your kindness, sir, of which I will most gladly avail myself, and shall indeed be pleased at the opportunity of seeing a great battle."

"I wish to show my approbation of the manner in which you have, since you left me in Italy, endeavoured to do all in your power to acquire useful knowledge, instead of wasting your time in idleness or gambling, to which so many young officers in the army give themselves up."

The next day Hector and Paolo joined the army of Enghien as it was on the march to Eperney. The former was now within a few months of seventeen, of middle height, strongly built, his hard exercise and training having broadened him greatly. He had a pleasant and good-tempered face, his hair, which was brown with a tinge of gold, clustered closely round his head, for he had not adopted the French mode of wearing it in long ringlets, a fashion unsuited for the work of a campaign, and which de Lisle and Chavigny had in vain urged him to adopt. He was handsomely dressed, for he knew that Condé would be surrounded by many of the young nobles of France. He wore his broad hat with feather; his helmet and armour being carried, together with his valises, on a sumpter mule led by Paolo.

Putting up at an hotel, he made his way to the house occupied by Enghien and the marshal. It was crowded by young officers, many of whom were waiting in an ante-room. On one of the duke's chamberlains approaching him Hector gave his name, and requested him to deliver Viscount Turenne's letter to the prince. In a few minutes his name was called, to the surprise of those who had been waiting for some time for an interview. Enghien was seated at a table, from which he rose as Hector entered.

"I am glad to see you, Captain Campbell, both for your own sake and for that of Turenne, whom I greatly love and admire. As I was with Mielleraye during the campaign in the south, while you were with Turenne, we did not meet there, for though he once rode over and stayed for a few days you did not accompany him. But he has told me of your adventure at Turin, and has spoken of your diligent studies and your desire to learn all that is known of the art of war. I shall be glad indeed to have you riding with me, for I, too, am a diligent student in the art, though until last year I had no opportunity whatever of gaining practical knowledge. I envy Turenne his good fortune in having been sent to begin to learn his duty when he was but fourteen. He tells me that you were but a year older when you rode to Italy with him. It humiliates me to think that while I am sent to command an army simply because my father is a prince of the blood, Turenne gained every step by merit, and is a general in spite of the fact that his brother was an enemy of the cardinal and defied alike his power and that of the king. However, I hope to show that I am not altogether unworthy of my position; and at least, like Turenne, I can lead my troops into battle, and fight in their front, even if I cannot always come out victorious. Where have you put up your horses? With the best will in the world, I cannot put either room or stable at your disposal to-day, for I believe that every cupboard in the house is occupied; but at our halting-place to-morrow we shall be under canvas, and a tent shall be assigned to you."

"I thank you, sir. I have fortunately been able to find quarters at an inn."

"At any rate, I hope that you will sup with me. I will then introduce you to some of my friends."

Enghien was at the age of twenty-two of a striking rather than a handsome figure. His forehead was wide, his eyes sunken and piercing, his nose very prominent and hooked giving to his face something of the expression of an eagle's. He resembled Turenne in the eagerness with which in childhood he had devoted himself to his studies, and especially to military exercises; but except that both possessed a remarkable genius for war, and both were extremely courageous, there was but slight resemblance between their characters. While Turenne was prudent, patient, and thoughtful, weighing duly every step taken, bestowing the greatest pains upon the comfort and well-being of his troops, and careful as to every detail that could bring about success in his operations, Condé was passionate and impetuous, acting upon impulse rather than reflection. Personally ambitious, impatient of opposition, bitter in his enmities, his action and policy were influenced chiefly by his own ambitions and his own susceptibilities, rather than by the thought of what effect his action might have on the destinies of France. He was a born general, and yet but a poor leader of men, one of the greatest military geniuses that the world has ever seen, and yet so full of faults, foibles, and weaknesses that, except from a military point of view, the term "the Great Condé" that posterity has given him is but little merited. He had much brain and little heart. Forced by his father into a marriage with a niece of Richelieu's, he treated her badly and cruelly, although she was devoted to him, and was in all respects an estimable woman and a true wife, and that in a court where virtue was rare indeed.

THE DUC D'ENGHIEN

At supper that evening Enghien introduced Hector first to the Marshal de L'Hôpital and then to the young nobles of his company.

"Monsieur Campbell," he said, "is the youngest of our party, and yet he is, as the Viscount of Turenne writes to me, one in whom he has the greatest confidence, and who has so carefully studied the art of war, and so much profited by his opportunities, that he would not hesitate to commit to him any command requiring at once courage, discretion, and military knowledge. No one, gentlemen, could wish for a higher eulogium from a greater authority. Turenne has lent him to me for the campaign, and indeed I feel grateful to him for so doing. When I say, gentlemen, that it was he who saved the citadel of Turin to our arms, by undertaking and carrying out the perilous work of passing through the city and the Spanish lines to carry word to the half-starved garrison that succour would arrive in a fortnight's time, and so prevented their surrendering, you will admit that Turenne has not spoken too highly of his courage and ability. I have heard the full details of the affair from Turenne's own lips, when he paid a short visit to Paris after that campaign closed; and I should feel proud indeed had I accomplished such an enterprise. Captain Campbell is a member of an old Scottish family, and his father died fighting for France at the siege of La Rochelle, a captain in the Scottish regiment. And now, gentlemen, to supper."

It was a joyous meal, and of a character quite new to Hector. Grave himself, Turenne's entertainments were marked by a certain earnestness and seriousness. He set, indeed, all his guests at ease by his courtesy and the interest he took in each; and yet all felt that in his presence loud laughter would be out of place and loose jesting impossible. Enghien, on the other hand, being a wild and reckless young noble, one who chose not his words, but was wont to give vent in terms of unbridled hatred to his contempt for those whom he deemed his enemies, imposed no such restraint upon his guests, and all talked, laughed, and jested as they chose, checked only by the presence of the gallant old marshal, who was nominally Enghien's guide and adviser. Next to Hector was seated General Gassion, one of the finest soldiers of the time. He, like Hector, had no family influence, but had gained his position solely by his own merits. He was enterprising and energetic, and eager to still further distinguish himself; and Hector was not long in perceiving that Enghien had his cordial support in combating the prudent and cautious counsels of the marshal. He spoke very cordially to the young captain. He saw in him one who, like himself, was likely to make his way by merit and force of character, and he asked him many questions as to his past history and the various services in which he had been engaged.

"I hope some day to win my marshal's baton, and methinks that if you have as good fortune as I have had, and escape being cut off by bullet or sabre, you, too, may look forward to gaining such a distinction. You see all these young men around us have joined rather in the spirit of knight-errants than that of soldiers. Each hopes to distinguish himself, not for the sake of advancing his military career, but simply that he may stand well in the eyes of some court beauty. The campaign once over, they will return to Paris, and think no more of military service until another campaign led by a prince of the blood like Enghien takes place, when they will again take up arms and fight in his company.

"Such campaigns as those under Turenne in Italy would be distasteful in the extreme to them. They would doubtless bear the hardships as unflinchingly as we professional soldiers, but as soon as they could with honour retire you may be sure they would do so. It is well for us that they should. Were it otherwise our chances of advancement would be rare indeed, while as it is there are plenty of openings for men of determination and perseverance who will carry out precisely any order given to them, and who are always, whether in the field or in winter quarters, under the eyes of a commander like Turenne, who remains with his army instead of rushing off like d'Harcourt to spend his winter in the gaieties of the court, and to receive their smiles and praises as a reward for his successes."

"I suppose, general, there is no doubt that we shall give battle to the Spaniards?"

"No doubt whatever. It depends upon Enghien, though no doubt the marshal will throw every obstacle in the way. In the first place, there can be no denying that the Spanish infantry are superb, and that Fuentes, who commands them, is a fine old soldier, while our infantry are largely composed of new levies. Thus, though the armies are not unequal in strength, l'Hôpital may well consider the chances of victory to be against us. In the second place, in a battle Enghien will be in command, and though all of us recognize that he possesses extraordinary ability, his impetuosity might well lead to a disaster. Then the marshal must feel that while the glory of a victory would fall to Enghien, the discredit of a defeat would be given to him, while if aught happened to Enghien himself the wrath of Condé and his faction would bring about his disgrace.

"I doubt not that he has received instructions not to hazard a battle except under extraordinary circumstances, while Enghien would, if possible, bring one about under any circumstances whatever. Lastly, the king is desperately ill, ill unto death, some say, and none can foretell what would take place were we to suffer a heavy defeat while France is without some great head to rally the nation and again show face to the Spaniards. At the same time, I may tell you at once, that in this matter I am heart and soul with Enghien. I consider that did we shrink from battle now, it would so encourage Spain and Austria that they would put such a force in the field as we could scarcely hope to oppose, while a victory would alter the whole position and show our enemies that French soldiers are equal to those of Spain, which at present no one believes. And lastly, if we win, Enghien, when his father dies, will be the foremost man in France, the leading spirit of the princes of the blood, and having behind him the vast possessions and wealth accumulated by Condé, will be a power that even the greatest minister might dread, and I need hardly say that my marshal's baton would be very appreciably nearer than it is at present."

"Then I may take it," Hector said with a smile, "that the chances are in favour of a pitched battle."

"That is certainly so; l'Hôpital's instructions are to force the Spaniards, who have advanced against Rocroi, to raise the siege, but to do so if possible by manœuvring, and to avoid anything like a pitched battle. But I fancy that he is likely to find circumstances too strong for him, and that one of these mornings we shall stand face to face with the enemy. The Spaniards are doubtless grand soldiers, and the army we shall meet is largely composed of veteran troops; but we must remember that for years and years the Dutchmen, by nature peaceable and for the most part without training in arms, and although terribly deficient in cavalry, have boldly withstood the power of Spain."

"They seldom have met them in the open field," Hector said doubtfully.

"Not very often, I grant, though when allied with your countrymen they fairly beat them on the sands near Ostend, and that over and over again they fought them in their breaches on even terms, and, burghers though they were, beat back Alva's choicest troops."

The next morning the army marched forward. Hector rode with the group of young nobles who followed Enghien. Rocroi was a town of considerable strength lying in the forest of Ardennes. It was the key to the province of Champagne, and its capture would open the road to the Spaniards. The siege was being pressed forward by de Malo, who had with him an army of twenty-seven thousand veteran troops, being five thousand more than the force under Enghien. Gassion, who as Enghien's lieutenant had the control of the movements, so arranged the marches that, while steadily approaching Rocroi, the marshal believed that he intended to force the Spaniards to fall back, rather by menacing their line of communications than by advancing directly against them.

THE DUC D'ENGHIEN

After the first day Gassion invited Hector to ride with him, an invitation which he gladly accepted, for the conversation of his younger companions turned chiefly upon court intrigues and love affairs in Paris, and on people of whose very names he was wholly ignorant. Riding with Gassion across from one road to another along which the army was advancing, he was able to see much of the movements of bodies of troops through a country wholly different from that with which he was familiar. He saw how careful the general was to maintain communication between the heads of the different columns, especially as he approached the enemy.

"De Malo ought," he said, "to have utilized such a country as this for checking our advance. In these woods he might have so placed his men as to annihilate one column before another could come to its assistance. I can only suppose that he relies so absolutely upon his numbers, and the valour and discipline of his soldiers, that he prefers to fight a pitched battle, where a complete success would open the road to Paris, and thus lay France at his feet and bring the war to a conclusion at one stroke."

CHAPTER VIII
ROCROI

GASSION conducted the movements of the army so adroitly that he had brought it to within almost striking distance of the Spanish divisions before Marshal l'Hôpital perceived the fact that it was so placed that a battle was almost inevitable. He besought Enghien to fall back while there was yet time, pointing out the orders that had been given that a battle was not to be hazarded, and the terrible misfortunes that would fall upon France in case of defeat. Enghien, however, was deaf to his advice, and refused to acknowledge his authority.

Turenne, under similar circumstances, would have drawn off and forced the enemy to raise the siege by threatening their line of communications; but Turenne thought nothing of personal glory, and fought only for France. Enghien, on the other hand, throughout his career was animated by personal motives, and cared nothing for the general welfare of France. Turenne was wholly unselfish; Enghien was ready to sacrifice anything or everything for his own glory or interest. At present, surrounded as he was by young nobles as eager to fight as he was himself, and backed by Gassion, one of the most able and enterprising soldiers of the day, he declared that he had come to fight and would do so. Even had l'Hôpital known the news that had been received by Enghien, he would have been powerless to check or control him. A courier had indeed the day before brought the young duke a despatch containing the news of the king's death and peremptory orders not to fight. Enghien simply put the letter in his pocket, and the contents were known only to Gassion and a few of his most intimate friends.

De Malo was as anxious to bring on a general engagement as was his fiery opponent. He was kept well informed of what was going on in Paris, and knew that the king's death was imminent. His position on a plain, surrounded on all sides by woods and marshes with but one approach, and that through a narrow defile, was practically impregnable; and by occupying the defile he could have kept the French at bay without the slightest difficulty until Rocroi surrendered. He knew, too, that General Beck with a considerable force was hastening to join him; but he feared that prudent counsels might at the last moment prevail in the French camp, or that the news of the king's death might reach them, and he therefore left the defile open and allowed the French army to gain the plain and form up in order of battle facing him, without offering the slightest opposition or firing a single gun.

It was late in the afternoon by the time the French were in position, and as both commanders were anxious that the battle should be a decisive one neither took any step to bring on the fight, but contented themselves with preparing for the encounter next morning. The night was cold and somewhat thick, and the positions of the two armies were marked by lines of fire. The march had been a long and fatiguing one, and silence soon fell upon the scene. Enghien wrapped himself in his cloak, and, lying down by a watch-fire, was speedily asleep, wholly unoppressed by the tremendous responsibilities that he had assumed, or the fact that he had risked the destinies of France for the sake of his personal ambition, and that in any case the slaughter that must ensue in the morning would be terrible. Gassion, however, with a few of the older officers, sat for hours discussing the probabilities of the battle. Hector, remembering the manner in which Turenne exercised the most ceaseless vigilance, and nightly inspected all the outposts, endeavouring to ascertain the plans and positions of the enemy, had, as night closed in, requested Gassion's permission to go the rounds.

"Certainly, if it so pleases you, Captain Campbell. The watchword to-night is 'Condé', but I will in addition give you a pass enjoining all officers to allow you to go where you please, you being on the staff of the prince. I shall go round myself later on, for de Malo may intend a night attack, by which he would certainly gain advantages. His troops are fresh, while ours are weary. He has had every opportunity of studying the ground, while it is all new to us. Still, I hardly think that he will move till morning. Enterprise is not the strong point of the Spaniards, they love to fight in solid bodies, and hitherto their infantry have never been broken by cavalry. At night they would lose the advantage of their steadiness of formation. It is clear, by his willingness to allow us to pass the defile and take up this position, that de Malo is absolutely certain of victory and will wait, for daylight would permit him to make his expected victory a complete one, while at night great numbers of our army would be able to make their escape through the woods."

Hector returned to the spot where his horses were picketed with those of Enghien's staff. He found Paolo lying down under a tree where he had been ordered to take up his post, so that Hector could find him if required.

"Are you asleep, Paolo?"

"No, master; I have been thinking about the battle to-morrow, and where I had best bestow myself."

"As to that, Paolo, I should say that you had better keep with the prince's servants here. You will, of course, have your horse saddled and be ready to ride on the instant. If we are victorious there will be no occasion for you to move, but if you see that we are beaten, my orders are that you are not to think of waiting for me. I must keep with the others. Doubtless the cavalry would cover the retreat, and it would be a serious inconvenience for me to have to come here to look after you, therefore as soon as you see that the day has gone against us mount and ride. You can wait at our halting-place of last night until you see the prince's party come along. If I am alive I shall be with them; if not, my advice to you is to ride south and to report yourself to Turenne. He will, I doubt not, either take you into his own service, or give you such strong recommendations that you will have no difficulty in obtaining a post with some officer of distinction should you wish to continue with the army. Now, I am going along our line of outposts, and I intend to reconnoitre the ground between us and the enemy. That is what Turenne would be doing were he in command here."

"I will go with you, master; when it comes to reconnoitring, methinks that I am as good as another. I can run like a hare, and though a bullet would go faster, I am quite sure that none of these heavily-armed Spaniards would have a chance of catching me."

"I intended to take you with me, Paolo. We shall need as much care and caution here as we did in getting into the citadel of Turin."

"I think, master, that it would be well for you to leave your armour behind you. It will be of small avail if you fall into the midst of a band of Spanish spearmen, while it would be a sore hindrance in passing through these woods, and the lighter you are accoutred the better."

"That is so, and I will take your advice. I will give it into the charge of the horse-guard. I will, of course, take my sword and pistols, and you may as well take yours."

"I like a knife better than a sword, master, but I will take them both. I think it would be as well for you to lay aside your helmet also, for the light from one of these watch-fires might glint upon it and catch the eye of a Spaniard."

"You are right, Paolo; have you got the hat?"

"Yes, sir, it is here with your valises."

"That is certainly more comfortable," Hector said as he put it on. "Now, you had better carry the things across to that fire where the prince's staff are sitting. There is no fear of anyone interfering with them there."

As soon as this had been done they started, picking their way carefully through numbers of sleeping men, and stopping once or twice to exchange a word with the groups still gathered round the fires. First they passed along the whole line of outposts, answering the challenges by the words, "Officer of the prince's staff on duty." They found the sentries fairly vigilant, for with so powerful an enemy within striking distance every soldier felt that the occasion was one for unusual watchfulness. At each post Hector questioned the sentinels closely as to whether they had heard any sounds indicating the movement of troops in the interval between the two armies, and in only one case was there an affirmative answer.

"I heard a sound such as might be made by the clash of armour against a tree or by an armed man falling, I have listened attentively since, but have heard nothing more."

"From which direction did the noise seem to come?"

"From across there, sir. It seemed to me to come from that copse in the hollow."

"That is just what I thought might be likely, Paolo," Hector said as he walked on. "That hollow ground between the armies, with its wood and low brushwood, is just the place where an ambush might be posted with advantage. Turenne would have taken possession of it as soon as darkness closed in, for it would not only prevent the possibility of the army being taken by surprise during the night, but it might be invaluable during the fight to-morrow, for a force ambushed there might take an advancing enemy in the rear. We will go farther on till we get to a point where the brushwood extends nearly up to our line. We will enter it there, and make our way along until we see whether de Malo has taken advantage of our failure to utilize the wood."

As soon as they reached the point he indicated they moved forward, crouching low until they reached the bushes; then they crawled along, keeping outside but close to them. In this way they would be invisible to any sentries posted near the edge of the wood, and would also avoid the risk of drawing the enemy's attention by accidentally breaking a dried branch or even snapping a twig. In ten minutes they entered the wood that extended along the greater portion of the hollow.

"Keep on your hands and knees," Hector whispered, and feel the ground as you go to make sure that there are no broken branches that would crack if you placed your knee upon them. We may come upon the Spaniards at any moment. Keep close to me. Touch me if you hear the slightest sound, and I will do the same to you. The touch will mean stop. Move your sword along the belt till the handle is round at your back; in that way there will be no risk of it striking a tree or catching in a projecting root."

"I will do that, master, and will keep my knife between my teeth. It may be that we shall come upon a Spanish sentinel who may need silencing."

"No, Paolo; only in the last extremity and to save our lives must we resort to arms. Were a sentry found killed in the morning they would know that their position in the wood had been discovered. It is most important that they should believe that their ambush is unsuspected."

Their progress was very slow. When they were nearly opposite the centre of their position Paolo was suddenly touched by his master. They listened intently, and could hear at no great distance ahead low sounds at regular intervals.

"Men snoring," Paolo whispered in his ear.

They moved forward again even more cautiously than before. Presently they stopped, for at the edge of the wood facing the camp they heard a slight movement and a low clash of arms, as if a sentinel on the look-out had changed his position. Feeling sure that the guards would all be placed along the edge of the wood, they moved forward again, stopping every few yards to listen. There was no doubt now that they were close to a large body of sleepers. Occasional snores, broken murmurs, and a sound as one turned from side to side rose from in front of them.

"You go round on one side, I will go round on the other, Paolo. We will meet again when we have passed beyond them. It is important that we should form some estimate as to their numbers."

In half an hour they met again, and crawled along for some distance side by side in silence.

"How many should you say, Paolo?"

"They were lying four deep as far as I could make out, master. I kept very close to the outside line. I could not count them accurately because of the trees, but I should say that there were about two hundred and fifty in a line."

"That was very close to what I reckoned them at. At any rate, it is a regiment about a thousand strong. They are musketeers, for several times I went close enough to feel their arms. In every case it was a musket and not a pike that my hand fell on. Now we will go on till we are opposite our last watch-fire, and then crawl up the hill."

They were challenged as they approached the lines.

"A friend," Hector replied. "An officer of the prince's staff."

"Give the countersign," the soldier said.

"Condé"

"That is right, but wait until I call an officer."

"Good ! but make no noise; that is important."

The sentinel went to the watch-fire, and an officer sitting there at once rose and came forward.

"Advance, officer of the staff!" he said in low-tones. That is right, monsieur," he went on as Hector advanced close enough to be seen by the light of the fire.

"I have a special pass signed by General Gassion," he said.

The officer took it, and looked at it by the light of the fire.

"That is all in order," he said as he returned it; "but the sentry had the strictest orders that no one coming from the side of the enemy was to be allowed to enter our lines, even if he gave the countersign correctly, until he had been examined by an officer."

ROCROI

"He did his duty, sir. One cannot be too careful on the eve of battle. A straggler might stray away and be captured, and be forced under pain of death to give up the countersign, and once in our lines much information might be obtained as to our position. However, I hardly think that any such attempts will be made. The Spaniards saw us march in and take up our position, and must have marked where our cavalry and artillery were posted. Good-night!"

The greater part of the night had already gone, for in May the days are already lengthening out. After the troops had fallen out from their ranks wood had to be collected and rations cooked, and it was past ten o'clock before any of them lay down, and an hour later, before Hector left on his expedition. The examination of the outposts had taken more than an hour; it was now three o'clock in the morning, and the orders were that the troops should all be under arms before daybreak. Hector returned to the spot where he had left General Gassion. All was quiet there now, and he lay down until, somewhat before five, a bugle sounded. The signal was repeated all along the line, and almost at the same moment the Spanish trumpets told that the enemy, too, were making preparations for the day's work. General Gassion was one of the first to spring to his feet. Hector at once went up to him.

"I have come to report, general," he said, "that I have reconnoitred along the whole line of wood in the hollow in front, and have found that a regiment of musketeers about a thousand strong have been placed in ambush there."

"Then, by heavens, you have done us good service indeed, Captain Campbell! They might have done us an ill turn had we advanced knowing nothing of their presence there. Nothing shakes troops more than a sudden attack in the rear. Please come across with me and repeat the news that you have given me to the prince himself."

There was bustle all along the line. The troops were falling into their ranks, stamping their feet to set the blood in motion, swinging their arms, and growling at the sharp morning air. At the head-quarters bivouac the young nobles were laughing and jesting as they prepared to mount.

"Where is the prince?" Gassion asked.

"There he lies under his cloak, general. He is still fast asleep. It is evident that the thought of the coming battle does not weigh heavily upon him. I acknowledge that I have not closed an eye; I do not think that many of us have done so."

So sound, indeed, was the prince's sleep that Gassion had to shake him almost roughly to rouse him.

As soon, however, as his eyes opened he leapt to his feet. "I have had a wonderful night," he laughed; "never have I slept more soundly on a down bed than on this hard ground, which, however, as I find, makes my bones ache wonderfully. Well, it is a fine day for a battle. What is your news, Gassion?"

"It is important, monseigneur. Captain Campbell has spent the night in reconnoitring on his own account, and has discovered that a thousand Spanish musketeers are lying in ambush in the copse in the hollow."

"Is that so?" the duke said shortly. "Well, Captain Campbell, you have rendered us a vital service indeed, and one that I shall not forget. However, now we are forewarned, we shall know how to deal with them. If I should fall, Gassion, and you should survive, see that Captain Campbell's service is duly represented. Now, to horse, gentlemen!"

The morning sun rose on the 20th of May on a brilliant scene. The two armies were disposed along slightly elevated ridges, between which lay the hollow with its brushwood and copses. Enghien commanded the cavalry on the right wing, with Gassion as second in command. In place of his helmet the prince wore a hat with large white plumes, remembering, perhaps, how Henri of Navarre's white plumes had served as a rallying point. Marshal l'Hôpital commanded the cavalry on the French left, Baron d'Espenan commanded the infantry in the centre, and Baron Sirot the reserves. The right of the Spanish army was composed of the German horse led by de Malo, the Walloons on the left were under the Duke of Albuquerque, while in the centre were the veteran Spanish infantry under the command of General Fuentes, who had often led them to victory. He was too old and infirm to mount a horse, but lay in a litter in the midst of his hitherto unconquerable infantry.

All being ready on both sides, the trumpet sounded, and simultaneously the cavalry of both armies moved forward. Enghien moved farther to the right, and then dashing down the slopes led his cavalry along the bottom, fell suddenly upon the musketeers in ambush and cut them to pieces. Then galloping forward he fell upon the Spanish left in front and flank. The impetuous charge was irresistible; the Walloons broke and fled before it, and were speedily scattered over the plain, pursued by the victorious French. But upon the other wing de Malo's charge had proved equally irresistible. L'Hôpital's horse was broken and scattered, and, wheeling his cavalry round, de Malo fell upon the flank and rear of d'Espenan's infantry, shattered them at once, captured the whole of the French artillery, and then fell upon the reserves. Baron Sirot, an officer of great courage and ability, held them together and for a time repelled the attack of the German cavalry; but these, inspirited by their previous success, continued their attacks with such fury that the reserves began to waver and fall back. Enghien was still in pursuit of the Walloons when an officer rode up with news of the disaster that had befallen the rest of the army. Enghien grasped the situation instantly, and his military genius pointed out how the battle might yet be retrieved. His trumpets instantly recalled his scattered squadrons, and galloping round the Spanish centre he fell like a thunderbolt upon the rear of de Malo's cavalry, already exulting in what appeared certain victory.

Astounded at this unlooked-for attack, they in vain bore up and tried to resist it; but the weight and impetus of the French assault bore all before it, and they clove their way

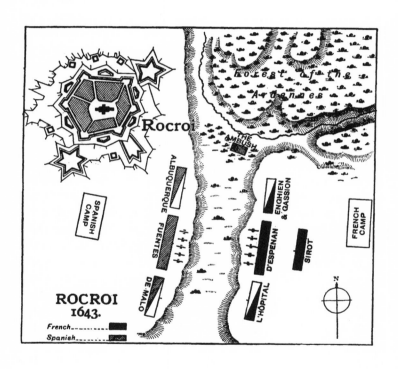

through the confused mass of cavalry without a pause. Then wheeling right and left they charged into the disorganized crowd of German horsemen, who, unable to withstand this terrible onslaught, broke and fled, de Malo himself galloping off the field with his disorganized troopers. Never was a more sudden change in the fate of a great battle. The French cause had appeared absolutely lost; one wing and their centre were routed; their reserves had suffered heavily, and were on the point of giving way. Humanly speaking, the battle seemed hopelessly lost, and yet in ten minutes victory had been converted into defeat, and the right and left wings of the Spanish army had ceased to exist as collected bodies. There remained the Spanish infantry, and Enghien, recklessly courageous as he was, hesitated to attack the solid formation that had hitherto proved invincible.

While still doubting whether, having defeated the rest of the army, it might not be best to allow this formidable body to march away unmolested, news reached him that General Beck, with his reinforcements, would be on the ground in an hour. This decided him, and he ordered the whole of the guns that had been rescued from their late captors to be turned on the Spanish square, and then, collecting his cavalry into a mass, dashed at it. The Spaniards remained motionless till the French line was within twenty yards of them, then men stepped aside, a number of guns poured their contents into the cavalry, while a tremendous volley swept away their front line. So terrible was the effect, so great the confusion caused by the carnage, that had the Walloon cavalry been rallied and returned to the field, the tide of the battle might again have been changed; but they were miles away, and Enghien rallied his men without a moment's delay, while the French artillery again opened fire upon the Spanish square. Again the French cavalry charged and strove to make their way into the gaps made by the artillery, but before they reached the face of the square these were closed up, and the guns and musketry carried havoc among the French squadrons, which again recoiled in confusion. Once more Enghien rallied them, and, when the French artillery had done their work, led them forward again with a bravery as impetuous and unshaken as that with which he had ridden in front of them in their first charge; nevertheless for the third time they fell back, shattered by the storm of iron and lead. Enghien now brought up his artillery to close quarters, Baron de Sirot led up the infantry of the reserve, and the attack was renewed.

The aged Spanish general, though streaming with blood from several wounds, still from his litter encouraged his soldiers, who, stern and unmoved, filled up the gaps that had been made, and undauntedly faced their foes. But the struggle could not be long continued. The square was gradually wasting away, and occupied but half the ground which it had stood upon when the battle began. And Fuentes, seeing that further resistance could only lead to the annihilation of his little band, felt that no more could be done. There were no signs of Beck coming to his assistance. Indeed the troops of that general had been met by the cavalry in their flight; these communicated their own panic to them, and such was the alarm that the division abandoned its baggage and guns and fled from the field, where their arrival might still have turned the tide of battle.

Fuentes at last ordered his officers to signal their surrender. Enghien rode forward, but, the Spanish soldiers believing that, as before, he was but leading his cavalry against them, poured in a terrible volley. He escaped by almost a miracle, but his soldiers, maddened by what they believed to be an act of treachery, hurled themselves upon the enemy. The square was broken, and a terrible slaughter ensued before the exertions of the officers put a stop to it. Then the remaining Spaniards surrendered. The battle of Rocroi was to the land forces of Spain a blow as terrible and fatal as the destruction of the Armada had been to their naval supremacy. It was indeed a death-blow to the power that Spain had so long exercised over Europe. It showed the world that her infantry were no longer irresistible, and while it lowered her prestige it infinitely increased that of France, which was now regarded as the first military power in Europe.

ROCROI

The losses in the battle were extremely heavy. The German and Walloon cavalry both suffered very severely, while of the Spanish infantry not one man left the battlefield save as a prisoner, and fully two-thirds of their number lay dead on the ground. Upon the French side the losses were numerically much smaller. The German cavalry, after routing those of l'Hôpital, instead of following up the pursuit hurled themselves upon the infantry, who broke almost without resistance. These also escaped with comparatively little loss, de Malo leading the cavalry at once against the French reserves. Among the cavalry commanded by Enghien the loss was very heavy, and included many gentlemen of the best blood of France. There was no pursuit; half the French cavalry were far away from the field, the rest had lost well-nigh half their number, and were exhausted by the fury of the fight; indeed, the fugitive cavalry were miles away before the conflict ended. The gallant old general, Fuentes, expired from his wounds soon after the termination of the battle.

Hector was with the body of young nobles who followed close behind Enghien in the three first desperate charges. In the third his horse was shot under him just as the cavalry recoiled from the deadly fire of the square. He partly extracted his foot from the stirrup as he fell, but not sufficiently to free him, and he was pinned to the ground by the weight of the horse. It was well for him that it was so, for had he been free he would assuredly have been shot down as he followed the retreating cavalry. This thought occurred to his mind after the first involuntary effort to extricate his leg, and he lay there stiff and immovable as if dead. It was a trying time. The balls from the French cannon whistled over his head, the musket-shots flew thickly round him, and he knew that ere long the attack would be renewed.

Fortunately the fourth advance of the French did not come directly over him, the commanders purposely leading their troops so as to avoid passing over the ground where so many of the young nobles had fallen. Not until the last musket had been discharged and the cessation of the din

"His horse was shot down under him."

told that all was over, did he endeavour to rise. Then he sat up and called to two dismounted soldiers, who were passing near, to aid him. They at once came up, and soon lifted the horse so far that he was able to withdraw his leg. His thick jack-boot had protected it from injury, although it had been partly the cause of his misfortune, for the sole had caught against the side of the horse and so prevented him from withdrawing it. Nevertheless, his leg was so numbed that it was some time before he could limp away. He retraced his steps towards the spot where he had mounted at starting. He had not gone far when he saw Paolo galloping towards him. The young fellow gave a shout of joy as he recognized him, and a minute later drew rein by his side and leapt off his horse.

"Thank God I see you alive again, master! Are you wounded?"

"No; my horse was killed and fell upon my foot, and has no doubt bruised it a bit, otherwise I am unhurt."

"It has been terrible, master. I climbed up into that tree beneath which we halted yesterday and watched the battle. I shouted with joy when I saw Enghien clear out the ambuscade, and again when he drove the Walloon horse away; then everything seemed to go wrong. I saw the marshal's cavalry on the left driven off the field like chaff before the wind. Then the centre broke up directly they were charged; and as the enemy fell upon the reserve it seemed to me that all was lost. Then I saw Enghien and his horsemen coming along like a whirlwind, bursting their way through the enemy's horse, and in turn driving them off the field. I hoped then that the battle was all over, and that the Spanish infantry would be allowed to march away; but no, my heart fell again when, time after time, our cavalry dashed up against them, and each time fell back again, leaving the slope behind them covered with dead men and horses; and I shouted aloud when I saw the artillery move up and the reserves advancing. As soon as I saw that the square was broken and a terrible mêlée was going on, I knew that all was over, and could restrain my impatience no longer, so I mounted my horse with, I may say, small hope of finding you alive, seeing that you rode behind Enghien, whose white plumes I could see ever in front of the line."

"It has been a marvellous victory, Paolo, and there can be no doubt that Enghien has covered himself with glory. It was his quick eye that saw what there was to be done, his brain that instantly directed the blow where alone it could be effectual, and his extraordinary bravery that roused the enthusiasm of those around him to a point at which no man thought of his life. But for him it was a lost battle."

"Well, master, I am glad that we have won the battle, but that is as nothing to me in comparison that you have come out of it safely, and I think, master, that we have a right to say that we helped in some degree to bring about the victory by discovering that ambuscade down in the hollow."

"That had not occurred to me, Paolo," Hector laughed. "No doubt it was a fortunate discovery, for had the musketeers lain hidden there until we were beaten back after our first charge, and then poured their fire into us, it would doubtless have thrown us into some confusion, and might even have caused a panic for a while."

"Now, master, if you will mount this horse I will be off and catch another; there are scores of them running about riderless, some of them belonging to the marshal's men, but many more to the Germans, and a few that galloped off riderless each time Enghien fell back."

"Don't take one of those, Paolo; it might be claimed by its master's lackeys; get one of the best German horses that you can find. You might as well get two if you can, for I want a second horse while I am here with the prince."

CHAPTER IX
HONOURS

IN half an hour Paolo returned leading two horses. By their trappings and appearance both had evidently belonged to officers.

"Take off the trappings," Hector said, "then put a saddle on one for me; shift your own saddle on to the other, and picket your own with the spare horses of the staff, then we will ride over and get my saddle, bridle, holsters, and trappings. The horse has carried me well ever since I left Paris, and I am grieved indeed to lose it."

"So am I, master; it was a good beast, but I think that either of these is as good, though it will be long before I get to like them as I did Scotty. We shall want housings for this second horse, master."

"Yes; there will be no difficulty about that. There are scores of dead horses on the field; choose one without any embroidery or insignia. You may as well take another pair of holsters with pistols."

Riding across to the spot where Enghien and his officers were forming up the prisoners, talking courteously to the Spanish officers and seeing to the wounded, Hector, leaving Paolo to find his fallen horse and shift his trappings to the one that he rode, cantered up to the spot where Enghien's white plume could be seen in the midst of a group of officers, among whom was General Gassion. He saluted as he came up.

WON BY THE SWORD

"I am glad indeed to see you, Captain Campbell," Enghien said warmly, holding out his hand; "I feared that you were killed. Some of my friends told me that you were struck down in the third charge, and that they had not seen you since and feared that you were slain."

"My horse was killed, prince, and in falling pinned me to the ground, and being within thirty yards of the Spanish square, I lay without movement until you came back again and broke them. Then some soldiers so far lifted my horse that I could get my foot from under it, my servant found and caught a riderless German horse, and here I am unharmed."

"Well, sir, at the time that you came up General Gassion was just telling these gentlemen that had it not been for you things might have gone very differently. Had you not discovered that ambush their fire would have been fatal to us, for we fell back, as you know, farther than the copse, and a volley from a thousand muskets would have played havoc among us, and after so terrible a repulse might well have decided the day against us. For this great service, rendered by you voluntarily and without orders, I as commander-in-chief of this army, with the full and warm approval of General Gassion, appoint you to the rank of colonel, a rank which I am sure will be confirmed by the queen's minister when I report to him my reasons for the promotion. General Gassion reports that the man who accompanied you on this reconnaissance was the same who followed you in the expedition to Turin. As he is not a soldier I cannot promote him, but I will order my chamberlain to hand him a purse of a hundred pistoles. When you return to Turenne, tell him that I owe him my best thanks for having sent you to me, and that, thanks to the aid of his teaching, you have been the means of preventing a great disaster to our forces."

"I thank you, indeed, monsieur, for your kindness, and for promoting me so far beyond my merits, but I hope in the future I shall be able to still further prove my gratitude."

"That is proved already," Gassion said, "for although every man to-day has fought like a hero, you were the only one in camp that suspected that the Spanish might be lying in an ambush, and who not only thought it, but took means to find out whether it was so."

The next morning Enghien informed Hector that he was elected as one of the three officers who were to have the honour of carrying his despatches to Paris, and that he was to start in half an hour. Paolo, who was in the highest state of delight at the purse that had been presented to him the evening before, was greatly pleased with the prospect.

"Heaven be praised, master, that you are not going into another battle! It was well-nigh a miracle that you escaped last time, and such good luck does not befall a man twice. I have never seen Paris, and greatly do I long to do so. How they will shout when they hear the news we bring!"

"It will not be altogether news to them, Paolo. La Moussaie, Enghien's intimate friend, who acted as his aide-de-camp during the battle, was sent off ten minutes after the fight ended with a paper, on which the prince had pencilled that he had utterly defeated the enemy. He will change horses at every post, and will be in Paris by this evening. We bear the official despatches, giving a full account of the battle, and of the total destruction of the Spanish infantry, with no doubt a list of the nobles and gentlemen who have fallen. Well, I should think now, Paolo, that when we have seen enough of Paris and we have journeyed down to Perpignan again, you will leave my service and buy a farm; you can afford a substantial one now."

"What, master! I leave your service, where gold comes in in showers, and where one serves a master whom one loves? No, sir, I am not such a fool as that. I do not say that when the war is over I may not settle down in a snug home among the mountains of Savoy, but not until then; besides, I am but eighteen, and a nice hand I should make at managing a farm."

"Well, get the horses ready at once and the valises packed. You can put them on my spare horse. The mule will scarce keep up with us, for we shall certainly travel fast, so you had best hand it over to someone who you think will treat it kindly."

Twenty minutes later Hector, and two officers who had distinguished themselves especially in the battle, sat mounted before the tent that had now been raised for d'Enghien.

The young prince himself came out. "Gentlemen," he said, handing them three sealed packets, "you will present these to the queen, who is now Regent of France, for Louis XIII. died a week ago. They contain the despatches and reports of myself and General Gassion. Your packet, colonel," he added to Hector, "is General Gassion's report; it goes more fully into military details than mine. You, Monsieur de Penthière, carry my despatches in reference to the battle of yesterday. You, Monsieur de Caussac, are the bearer of my plans for our future operations. I think that you will all agree with me that, after the battle we have won, we shall be able to make ourselves masters of Flanders with but slight resistance."

The three officers bowed their agreement with the words.

"I know not who is in power or on whom the queen chiefly relies for counsel, but should any questions be put to you, you will, I hope, be able to express the urgency of prompt action in this matter before the Spaniards have time to rally from the terrible blow that this defeat has inflicted upon them. And now, gentlemen, a rapid and pleasant journey. Orders were sent on last night that four sets of fresh horses should be in readiness along the road. They are my own horses, and good ones. Twelve troopers will accompany you; three of these will remain behind at each stage where you change, and the horses that you have used will be brought on at a more leisurely pace after you. They will readily find out in Paris where you are lodged, and I beg that you will retain the horses as a slight proof of my good-will."

Then he waved his hand and went into his tent again. The three lackeys, each holding a spare horse, were sitting in readiness for a start some fifty yards away. After a moment's conversation the officers rode up to them.

"You must follow us quietly," one of them said. "For today you can keep up with us to the end of the first stage. Three fresh horses have been provided for us, for we ride without a stop to Paris. Three soldiers will there take charge of the horses we ride. When we go on you will follow quietly with the horses that you are now leading. It will be impossible for you to keep up with us."

Then they placed themselves at the head of their escort of dragoons, the lackeys fell in behind them, and they started at a fast pace.

"Do you know where the first relays are?" one of the officers asked the sergeant in charge of the escort, after they had ridden three or four miles.

"The first is at Rethel, monsieur, the second at Rheims, the third at Chateau-Thierry, the fourth at Meaux."

"Then we will ride on at once. You have your orders?"

"Yes, sir."

Whereupon the three officers quickened their pace. The distance to be traversed was about a hundred and thirty miles, and as they had five horses, including those they rode, each stage would average about twenty-six miles.

"Now, gentlemen," de Penthière said, "it seems to me that it would be a pity to founder fifteen good horses in order to gain an hour on this journey. The queen has already received news of the victory, or at least she will receive it some time to-day, therefore the details we bring are not of particular importance. It is now eight o'clock. If we were to gallop all the way we might do it in twelve hours. The roads in many places will be bad, and we must stop for meals at least three times; with the utmost speed we could hardly be in Paris in less than fifteen hours. Her majesty will scarce want to read long despatches at that time, and may take it that we ourselves will need a bath and a change of garments, and the services of a barber, before we could show ourselves

143

in court. Had we been bearers of the original despatch, we might have gone in splashed from head to foot. As it is, it seems to me that if we present ourselves with our papers at seven in the morning we shall have done that which is necessary. What do you both say?"

"I agree with you, de Penthière. It would be a sore pity to injure good horses by galloping them at the top of their speed, to say nothing of knocking ourselves up. Had we been sent off from the field of battle I should have said, spare neither the horses nor ourselves. But indeed it seems to me that to-morrow morning will be quite early enough for us to present ourselves and our despatches. To tell you the truth, I have never ridden a hundred and thirty miles or so at the pace of a courier. I should say let us go at a reasonable pace, and get into Paris soon after midnight, which will give us time for some little sleep, and afterwards to make ourselves presentable. What say you, Colonel Campbell?"

"I have no opinion, messieurs. I know nothing of the manners of the court, and if you think that to-morrow morning will be quite soon enough for us to deliver the despatches I am quite willing to fall in with your view. It is certainly a long ride, and as we marched hither we found that the roads were very bad, and certainly where the army has passed they are so cut up by the artillery and wagons that they are sure to be quite unfit for going at racing speed. Therefore I think that if we present ourselves at the palace early in the morning, we shall have done all that can be expected of us."

It was indeed two o'clock in the morning when they arrived at the gates of Paris. Accustomed though they all were to horse exercise, the journey had been a very fatiguing one. Until night fell they had ridden briskly, talking as they went on the probable state of affairs in France and of the military operations that were likely to be undertaken as the result of the victory, but progress became slow after darkness set in. The roads were in many places detestably bad. In passing through forests it was not possible to travel much beyond a walk, as it was necessary not only to avoid overhanging arms of trees, but to keep the track, for the road in many places was nothing more.

Once or twice they lost it altogether, and it was only when they hit upon the house of a peasant or a little village, and obtained a guide, that they were able to recover their road. Consequently all were thoroughly exhausted when they reached Paris. The gates were opened to them when it was understood that they bore despatches from the army. They made their way to the Hotel Condé. It was illuminated, for the prince had given a great banquet in honour of the victory won by his son; and although most of the guests had left long before, a party of the closest friends and connections of the prince were holding an informal council, when the word came to them that three officers had arrived with despatches from the Duc d'Enghien. The prince came down. Hector had dismounted without assistance, but the other two officers had to be lifted from their saddles.

"Are you bearers of any special news, de Penthière?" the prince asked; for the two young nobles were well known to him. "No, monseigneur, save that our despatches give full details of the battle."

"What is our loss?"

"It is very heavy," de Penthière said. "Fully a hundred men of good blood have fallen. The loss principally fell upon the cavalry commanded by the duke, who three times charged the Spanish infantry, and only succeeded at the fourth attempt in breaking their square."

"And the Spanish infantry?"

"Every man was either killed or taken."

"Glorious!" the prince said. "Well, I will not detain you now, for I see that you can scarce stand, and it would be cruel to keep you up, much as we desire to hear the particulars."

"I think, monseigneur, that this gentleman, Colonel Campbell, is more in a condition to talk to you than de Caussac or myself."

WON BY THE SWORD

"I shall be happy to answer any questions," Hector said, bowing to the prince. "I have been campaigning for the last four years under Monsieur de Turenne, and am accustomed to long journeys and sleepless nights."

"Thank you, colonel. We will not keep you up long."

Some lackeys were ordered to assist the two young nobles to couches, and then Condé and his companions left the court-yard and entered a small saloon where they had supped two hours before. Some fresh bottles of wine and cold viands were at once placed upon the table. Hector drank off a goblet of wine.

"Now, Monsieur le Prince, I will tell you all I know about the fight." And he gave Condé and his companions a brief sketch of the various movements and changes of the battle.

"It was a hard-fought field indeed," Condé said, "and the result is a glorious one for France. Now we will keep you no longer from your couch."

"May I ask, sir, at what time we ought to present ourselves with the despatches at the palace?"

"It will not be necessary for you to present yourselves before ten o'clock, for it was late last night before her majesty retired. Paris was wild at the news of the victory, and the reception at the palace was crowded. Still, I should say that at ten it would be well that you and your companions should attend there, though you may have to wait for an hour or more for an audience."

At ten o'clock Hector and his companions presented themselves at the palace. Seven hours' sleep, a warm bath, and the services of the barber, who curled the hair of the two young nobles and sprinkled them all with perfume, did much to restore them, though they were all somewhat stiff, and every bone seemed to ache. They were kept waiting for half an hour, at the end of which time the door of the ante-chamber was opened and their names were called. The queen, who was still a beautiful woman, was standing talking to a gentleman, in whose attire there were but few symbols that would betray to a stranger that he was an ecclesiastic of high rank.

146

"You are the bearers of despatches from the army, messieurs?"

"We have that honour, your majesty," de Penthière, who was the senior of the party said. "We arrived from Paris at two o'clock this morning, but did not venture to disturb your majesty at that hour."

"You did rightly," the queen said graciously. "We already knew that a great victory had been gained, and could afford to wait for the particulars. Do you each bear a despatch?"

"We do, your majesty," de Penthière said, producing that which he bore. "This, your majesty, is the general report of the Duc d'Enghien of the events of the battle. Colonel Campbell is intrusted with the more detailed description of General Gassion. Monsieur de Caussac's despatch contains the duke's views as to the carrying on of the campaign; these he submits to the judgment of your majesty and the council."

Cardinal Mazarin stepped forward and took the three documents.

"These we will peruse and consider at our leisure," the queen said, "and I shall, I hope, see you at my levée this evening. In the meantime I thank you for your service in having brought the despatches so speedily here, and am well aware that the fact that you have been chosen as the messengers of the commander-in-chief is in itself a proof that your share in the battle was in the highest degree honourable."

She graciously held out her hand, which de Penthière and his companions, dropping upon one knee, raised to their lips, one after the other.

"You are aware of the contents of the despatches, cardinal," the queen said when they were alone.

"Of their general scope, madam. The Prince of Condé did me the honour to call upon me at eight this morning. He had gathered a general account of the battle from the lips of that young Scottish colonel, who was the only one of the party who was capable of relating it, the others being almost speechless with fatigue, for the road from Rocroi hither is long and rough."

147

"You may well say the young Scottish colonel, cardinal. He is but a youth, and it is strange indeed that he should already have attained that rank."

"He has served for four years under the Viscount Turenne," Mazarin said, "and must therefore have had good opportunities of distinguishing himself. Still, it is seldom indeed that any save one of royal blood or of the very highest families obtains such a rank so quickly. Turenne, however, was himself a colonel after less than four years' service."

"Yes, cardinal, but he had the advantage of belonging to the family of an almost independent sovereign."

"Condé said that he had himself asked the young man how it was that he had won it, and he replied that it was solely due to the kindness of the Duc d'Enghien, who had been pleased to consider a small service he had rendered as worthy of recognition. It is like enough, your majesty, that we shall see his name mentioned in one of these documents. It is certain that he would not have been chosen to carry the despatches—a duty which is regarded as a reward of the most distinguished service—unless he had done something of marked importance."

The two French officers on leaving the palace at once went off to pay their respects in the first place to the heads of their families, and afterwards to visit the various circles and coteries with which they were connected, and where they would be sure of a flattering welcome and attentive listeners. Hector, for his part, rode direct to the quarters of the colonel of the Scottish regiment. A soldier came out and took the bridle of his horse as he saluted, while a sergeant asked what name he should announce.

"Then you do not remember me, Sergeant Macfarlane?"

The soldier looked at him earnestly. "Why," he exclaimed suddenly, "it's Hector Campbell!"

"Right enough, sergeant."

"You have changed mightily, sir; you were but a laddie when you went away nigh four years ago. The news came to the regiment that you had been made a captain, and proud we all were. The colonel will be right glad to see you," and he led the way into the house.

"Then the regiment has not been on service just lately?"

"We had two years on the Rhine; but we came back here last autumn. The Red Cardinal was not fond of us, but he knew that he could trust us—which is more than he could have done some of the regiments—so he had us back again; and we were not sorry, for it was but dull work there—sieges and nought else."

He was just going to open the door of the inner room when Hector said, "You can announce me, Macfarlane, as Colonel Campbell."

"Gude Lord," the sergeant ejaculated, "ye dinna say that ye are a colonel?" Then reassuming with a great effort his military stiffness, he opened the door and announced in a loud tone, "Colonel Hector Campbell."

There was an exclamation of astonishment from the colonel and two or three officers who were sitting with him.

"Why, Campbell," the former said, coming forward and warmly shaking his hand, "you are changed indeed, and you have come back to us almost the living image of your father when he first joined."

The officers all shook hands with him warmly, and the colonel went on, "Macfarlane announced you as colonel, Hector, but surely you cannot have gained that rank?"

"I only obtained it two days ago. You see it is a good thing to be a prince's aide-de-camp. Turenne, wishing to give me every opportunity of seeing service, sent me to Enghien with a message asking him to employ me on his staff."

"And you were at Rocroi?" the colonel exclaimed. "What is the real news of the battle? It was given out officially last night that we had won a victory, and there are all sorts of rumours this morning in the town—they say that three officers arrived last night with full details."

149

"I was one of the three, colonel; and I have just now come from the palace after handing my despatches to the queen."

"Then it was Enghien who made you colonel?"

"Yes."

"Well, then, you must have done something marked, or you could never have got the rank. Why, he has half the young nobles of France in his train—he has not made them all colonels, I suppose?"

"No, I suppose not; but we started early the next morning, and therefore cannot say what promotions were made."

"Still they made yours, Campbell. When did they do that?"

"Just after the fight was over."

"Umph! and what for?"

"Well, I luckily discovered that the Spaniards had set an ambush."

"Come, come, let us hear all about it. Tell us the whole story of the fight."

Hector gave all the details.

"Well, it certainly seems to have been an extraordinary battle. Everyone appears to have been beaten in turn."

"Not Enghien's command, sir."

"Well, no; but when cavalry are repulsed three times with a loss, as you say, of nearly half their numbers, it is pretty well equivalent to a beating; and if Enghien had not been able to bring up the artillery and reserves, I take it that the third charge would have been the last. The ambush that you discovered was, I suppose, that of the thousand musketeers Enghien charged at the beginning of the fight."

Hector nodded his assent.

"Well, it is as well they were found out and surprised before the other part of the business began, or there is no saying how the battle would have ended. We heard you had got your company. Turenne himself was good enough, when he came here to confer with Richelieu that summer, to call at the barracks and to give me an account of the service you had rendered. We all agreed that the rank was well earned, and I have no doubt that this new step has been just as honourably gained. And how do you think matters are going?"

"I know nothing about it, sir, beyond the fact that it was not a secret that Enghien and Gassion were both in favour of advancing at once into Flanders, and capturing the Spanish strong places before they could gather another army together."

"No doubt that would be the best way, but I should doubt very much if Enghien will be allowed to carry out his plans. You see, the king's will, appointing a council to act in concert with Condé, Orleans, and the queen, has been set at nought. The queen is absolute regent, and Mazarin is her minister—just as Richelieu was minister of Louis. Of course this victory will put everyone in the best of temper, and make the way easy for Mazarin just at first, but a defeat would set all the cliques at work against him.

"It is quite true that the defeat would not be his fault, but for some mysterious reason or other the French always hold the ministers for the time being, responsible for military disasters. So long as Mazarin checks Enghien, and prevents his running any risks of disaster, things are likely to go on smoothly here, and you may be sure that he will give the prince no chance of either suffering a defeat or achieving a victory. You see, the prince and his father together might be a great deal too powerful for the cardinal. Everyone knows that Condé himself has never cared much for anything but his own interests. Enghien has the character of being the most impetuous and violent young noble of the day, and the fact that he forced this fight when, as is generally known, l'Hôpital had the strictest orders not to risk a battle, makes it clear that Enghien has but little regard for authority.

"You will see that Mazarin will not give him further opportunities of becoming the idol of France until he has assured himself that he can count upon his friendship. Mazarin is not Richelieu. The red cardinal won his way to the leadership of France by proving himself able to defeat all intrigues against him, and crush every enemy, even those of the most exalted position. Mazarin has no such antecedents. He is not even a Frenchman; he does not even look like a noble. That he is clever we may be sure, or Richelieu would not have recommended him as his successor. But I fancy that it is the cleverness of an adventurer, and however adroit, an adventurer, and especially a foreign adventurer, will not hold power in France very long without exciting the hatred of the community and the hostility of the nobles. However, I suppose you are remaining here for a time."

"That I do not know. I would rather return at once to the camp. But I suppose I must wait for some intimation that I may do so. You see, I am altogether out of my element in Paris, and I should feel particularly uncomfortable at the court."

"Whom would you rather go to, Enghien or Turenne?"

"Just at present there is more doing with Enghien than Turenne, and more to learn, otherwise I would far rather be with Turenne. Enghien's camp is too full of young nobles; and I should say that he would take but little trouble in keeping order and repressing license. Turenne is by no means unduly strict, but he enforces order, and sets us such an example of earnestness and attention to work, himself, that he has a right to expect the same, to some degree, of everyone under him."

"Where are you staying?"

"At the Hotel Condé. The prince was good enough this morning to ask me to establish myself there while I remained in Paris, and I could not very well decline his invitation."

"I should think not," one of the other officers laughed. "In these days a powerful friend is of the greatest use. Without that one has not much chance of advancement. Not that I want advancement; I would rather remain as I am, a captain in the Scottish regiment, surrounded by good and loyal friends and comrades, than be made a general. Still, one likes to have a grumble sometimes at any rate."

HONOURS

"Well, Home," the colonel said, "Hector Campbell is a proof that even in France merit will make its way. That Turenne should have taken a fancy to him in the first place was fortunate. But Turenne would surely not have promoted him to be a captain within three or four months of his joining except for the marked bravery and diligence that he told us he displayed at Turin; and I have no doubt that when we hear the particulars we shall find that this promotion now has been equally well deserved, for certainly Enghien is not likely to have gone out of his way to promote one altogether a stranger to him when he had so many young nobles round him, personal friends of his own, belonging to families whom he would wish to oblige. Of course you will, as one of the bearers of despatches, attend at the court this evening, Campbell?"

"Yes, the queen said that she would expect to see us."

"Of course; and you will be envied by every young courtier there. At the present moment Paris is half wild over the victory of Rocroi, and as you three will be the representatives of the army, specially selected for the share you had in the battle, you may be sure that you will be regarded with eyes of favour by every lady of the court."

"Well, I should think it would be a great nuisance," Hector said gruffly. "Hitherto I have had nothing to do with ladies. There were very few with the Duchess of Savoy, and whenever there were receptions or state ceremonies of any kind, I was always ready to exchange with de Lisle or Chavigny, my fellow aides-de-camp. So that during the whole time I was there, I never but once or twice accompanied the general on such occasions."

"Ah, you were younger then," Home laughed. "You have passed eighteen now, and, as you must know yourself, are by no means bad-looking, with a certain air of freshness and simplicity that is so rare here in Paris that it will be regarded as refreshing and delightful after the flippancies of the court gallants."

Hector laughed uncomfortably.

"I could not take up flippancies, I am afraid. But what you say is true, Home; and if I had to remain at court, I suppose I should have to set to work at once to cultivate some affectation or other to counteract this simplicity of which you speak. However, thank goodness, I do not suppose that I shall stay here long. At any rate, it is lucky that I purchased a new court suit before I started to join the Duke of Enghien. Coming from Viscount Turenne I thought that I was bound to make a good figure among the crowd of young nobles round Enghien, but it made a large hole in my savings."

"Do you mean to say that you had savings?" one of the other officers exclaimed. "Who ever heard of such a thing? I never have a pistole left in my pocket a week after I get my month's pay."

"It is a very different thing living in Susa to living in Paris," Hector laughed. "I can assure you that I never spent more than half my pay; but living was dearer down in Roussillon. Things have been in such a disturbed state there for years that the country was well-nigh a desert; and though my two comrades and I messed together, the living cost twice as much as it did at Susa. Shall I see any of you this evening at the palace?"

"I shall be there," the colonel said, "and so will Home and Lesley. It is always expected that three officers from each of the regiments stationed in Paris, and five from the one that happens to be on guard for the evening, should attend the royal receptions. It will be a specially brilliant affair to-night, for the queen has held but few receptions of late. It was only announced yesterday afternoon, after the news of the battle arrived. Had it not been for that, the salons would not have been opened for another month."

"I am very glad that there will be somebody there I shall know."

"Don't flatter yourself that you are going to consort with us," the colonel laughed. "You will have to be presented to at least a score of court dames. However, fortunately, they will not expect the usual amount of compliments. They will be really wanting to hear of the battle, and most of them will be interested in some special friend with the army, and will want to inquire about him."

"It will not be so bad, then," Hector said. "If I only have to talk of military matters I shall not mind, but it will be painful indeed if I have to give news of the death of anyone dear to the lady I am speaking to."

"I don't think that you need fear very much about that. Enghien is pretty sure to have sent a list containing the names of any court gallants that have fallen, and their relatives will at once have been notified of it, and will not be present at the court. As to the others, who have merely lost lovers, they will not break their hearts over it. It is the fashion to change them so rapidly that probably not a few of the ladies will have consoled themselves for their absence already. However, to begin with, I daresay I shall be able to act as your mentor and guide, and point out to you who is who, so that you can avoid falling into serious errors. You see, there are half a dozen parties at court already. There are Mazarin's friends, who, by the way, are not numerous; there are the Duke of Beaufort's clique; there is Condé's party.

"Madame Chevreuse's party consists largely of herself. She is a power, but at present no one can say with whom she will ally herself. Hitherto she has been simply anti-Richelieu, and was his most troublesome and bitter enemy; and I should say that not improbably she will at once begin to conspire against Mazarin as she did against him. She has been the queen's greatest ally; but then the queen was always a bitter enemy of Richelieu, whereas at present it is supposed that she is strongly in favour of Mazarin. In a few months the situation will clear itself, parties will become defined. No doubt Enghien's victory will add to the power and importance of Condé, who is already dangerously strong; then matters will become interesting. At present the situation is somewhat chaotic, and politics will not be openly and generally discussed, simply because no one knows what anyone else's opinion may be."

"Well, then, till the evening I will say good-bye, colonel. I am going to have a chat with Sergeant MacIntosh, and shall then return to Condé's hotel. I suppose I shall be expected to take my mid-day meal there."

"It would be as well to do so certainly, even though it is like enough that he himself will not be there. He is the prince of schemers, and doubtless at present his thoughts are concentrated on the manner in which he and Enghien can best gain advantages from the victory."

CHAPTER X
AN ESTATE AND TITLE

ON entering The Scottish Soldier, Hector found that, as he hoped, the cabaret was deserted, for it was the hour at which the regiment was assembled for drill. It would have been a little embarrassing for him as a colonel to come upon a number of private soldiers at the cabaret. Separately he might have chatted with each, but a general greeting when a number of them were there together would have been embarrassing.

The old sergeant as he entered ran up to him. "Well done, my lad, well done! 'Tis a delight to me indeed to know that you have so grandly made your way, and already won the rank of colonel."

"Why, how did you know, MacIntosh?"

"The guard at the colonel's was changed just after you went into his quarters, and you may be sure that they lost no time in spreading the news that you had returned, and returned a colonel. In ten minutes this place was as full as it would hold, and there was such a crowd outside the door that a sergeant-de-ville came in to inquire what was the matter, thinking, perhaps, that the regiment was in mutiny. I was right glad when I heard the trumpet sound the assembly a few minutes ago, and they had to rush off in a hurry, for I felt that it would be awkward for you were you to come in when they were all so excited."

"Yes, I was glad myself when I found that they were gone. I regard every soldier in the regiment as my friend, and would shake hands with them now as heartily as I did when I went away near four years back, but I myself felt that it would be somewhat embarrassing were I greeted by them wine-cup in hand. Here are twenty pistoles; say that I left them here for them to drink my health on my promotion, but that I shall be so busy during the day or two that I remain in Paris that I shall not be able to pay another visit here. Now let us have a quiet talk together, and give me all the news of the regiment."

"Perhaps, colonel—"

"Oh, you need not call me colonel, MacIntosh, when you and I are together alone. I am what I was—Hector Campbell, the lad to whom you showed so much kindness for his father's sake. Yes, I will tell you one or two of my adventures, and you shall come round to me to-morrow morning at seven o'clock at the Hotel Condé, and we will stroll out together, and sit down in the gardens of the Palais Cardinal, and you shall then tell me about the regiment, who have gone, and what changes there are."

"That will be best," the sergeant said. "We did hear something of how you were made captain. Turenne was good enough to tell the colonel, and so some of it came down to us, but of course it was very little. The men would like to hear all about it and about this battle at Rocroi, at which, of course, you must have in some way distinguished yourself to be appointed colonel at your age."

Hector gave him a full account of the battle. "The special thing for which I was promoted," he said, at the finish, "was that, the night before, it struck me that there might be an ambush set in the copses in the hollow between the two armies. So far as I could see, no efforts whatever had been made either to occupy the woods or to find out if the enemy had done so; so I went with my servant, who is a capital fellow, and we made our way into them, and discovered a regiment of musketeers hidden there. Of course I reported the fact to General Gassion, and he told the prince. So, before attacking the enemy's lines, the prince charged right along the wood and destroyed the musketeers there. If he had not done so, they would have taken him in rear when he was hotly engaged with the Spaniards, and might have changed the fate of the battle."

"Certainly they might," the sergeant said. "A volley from a thousand muskets from the rear would well shake even the best cavalry. It was a happy thought of yours indeed."

"Any merit there is in it was due to Turenne, who had carefully instructed me in everything that could be of importance when two hostile armies faced each other; and as he would never have dreamt of retiring to rest before having every place where an enemy could conceal himself carefully searched, it seemed to me a matter of course that it should be done. However, General Gassion and the prince were both good enough to consider that the service was a vital one, and as soon as the battle was over the prince gave me my promotion."

"And it was well earned, lad, well earned. And now about that affair at Turin."

"It could not have been better done, Hector," the old soldier said in high delight when the story was told. "I used to think that you spent more time than was necessary in reading over accounts of battles and sieges, but I see that the time was well spent. You may be sure that I will be with you at seven to-morrow morning," he added as Hector rose to leave, "though I expect I shall have a heavy night of it here, for there will scarcely be a man in the regiment who won't come round and stay to hear the news. I warrant that by this evening there will not be a sou remaining out of the money you have left for them."

Hector arrived at the hotel just in time for the mid-day meal, and was pleased to find that Condé himself was not present. He and his two companions were placed at different points at the great table, so that as many as possible could hear the story of the battle. After the meal was over, Hector was glad to leave the salon, and in company with a gentleman of the household, who had volunteered to be his guide, spent the afternoon in visiting the principal sights of Paris, of which he had seen but little when a boy in barracks. The hotels of the nobles, each a fortress rather than a private building, interested him greatly, as also the streets in which the principal traders lived; but he was unfavourably impressed with the appearance of the population in all other parts, and could well understand what his guide told him, that it was dangerous in the extreme for a gentleman unattended to pass through these quarters.

At six o'clock he sat down to the evening meal at Condé's, after which, having attired himself in his new suit, he repaired with de Penthière and de Caussac to the Louvre. It was eight o'clock when they entered, the reception rooms were already full, and the brilliancy of the attire, both of the courtiers and ladies, seen by the light of great chandeliers, was impressive in the extreme to one who had never seen any gathering of the kind before. There was a little pause in the buzz of conversation as the three officers entered, and Hector's two companions were at once surrounded by friends, while he himself was joined by Colonel MacIvor and the other two officers.

"You are the heroes of the evening, Campbell," the former said with a laugh. "A dozen ladies have already asked me to present you to them."

"Well, please don't do so just now, colonel; let me look round first."

"That is but fair, Campbell. First, though, I will tell you a piece of news that I have just heard. The queen sent off a messenger two days ago to Turenne, and it is believed that he is to have the command of the army on the Rhine."

"That is good news indeed," Hector exclaimed. "It is high time that he should be given a command, instead of being always put under men less capable than himself. Still, it is unexpected at the present moment."

"I know that the queen always had the greatest liking for Turenne," the colonel said, "but of course until now she has had no power. Moreover, I fancy that the appointment is to some extent dictated by policy. Condé is already dangerously powerful; Enghien's victory will, of course, largely add to his influence. No doubt some large estates will be given to the latter, such a service cannot be ungenerously rewarded, but it will be thought unadvisable to give him at present further opportunities. Condé is old, and his son, who is certainly ambitious and hot-headed now, will be even more powerful than his father has been. Were he to win more victories, and to become a popular idol, his power might well overshadow that of the throne. Therefore it is likely enough that my news is true. Turenne has proved that military duty is with him supreme, for he held aloof from all the troubles in which his brother the duke has involved himself, and he may act as a counterpoise to Enghien. I fancy that the latter's plan, which, as you have told me, would lead to a conquest of Flanders, will not be adopted. It would not have been so in Richelieu's time. The red cardinal would not have lost a moment in ordering him to march into Flanders, thinking only of the good of France, and disregarding the fact that continued successes might lead to his own power being shaken."

"And you do not think that Mazarin will act in the same way?"

"I think not. Of course at present not much is known about him. He affects the greatest humility, is almost obsequious to the great nobles, and even professes to be anxious to return to Italy as soon as his services here can be dispensed with. But I expect that he will in time occupy as great a position as that of Richelieu, but that he will hold it by craft rather than strength is, from the look of the man, likely enough. For myself I should say that it is infinitely better for France that an ecclesiastic like Richelieu or Mazarin should be at the head of affairs, than that the great nobles should all struggle and intrigue for power, ready as they have shown themselves over and over again to plunge France into civil war for the attainment of their aims. Ah, here comes the queen!"

The door at the end of the salon opened and Anne entered. By her side walked the young king, a little behind were Orleans and Condé, Beaufort and Bouillon, while, following them, with an air that was almost humble, came

Mazarin. The queen and the young king were dressed in violet, the mourning colour of the court, and the ladies present all wore shades of that colour relieved by white. All present formed themselves into two lines, through which the queen walked. She acknowledged the deep reverences, and the little king bowed repeatedly. Anne of Austria was one of the most beautiful women of her time, and although the charm of youth had disappeared, her stateliness of bearing made up for this loss, and Hector thought that he had never seen so lovely a woman.

As soon as they had passed into an inner apartment known as the audience chamber the lines broke up, and a buzz of conversation and light laughter followed the silence that had reigned as the procession passed. The court, indeed, felt a general feeling of relief at the death of Louis. Although well meaning and desirous of doing good, the life of the monarch had not been a happy one. His health had never been good, and although he had the wisdom to see that in supporting Richelieu, and in every way adding to his authority, he was acting for the good of France, the knowledge that he himself was little more than a cipher galled and irritated him. His disposition was a jealous one, and as the great minister knew that Anne of Austria was ever his opponent politically, he worked upon this feeling, and embittered the lives of both the king and queen, and the latter was the constant victim of the king's jealousy and caprices.

These things, combined with the ascetic temperament of the king, had rendered the court of France a dismal one, and the royal salons formed a strong contrast to the brilliancy of those of Richelieu. Now the king was gone, and there was a general feeling of relief among the nobles and ladies of the court. It might be that stormy times were ahead, and indeed it was no secret that Condé, Beaufort, and many other nobles were already united against Mazarin. They called themselves "The Importants," a term well suited to their own idea of their power, and of the position they aspired to as the natural leaders of France.

AN ESTATE AND TITLE

"Madame de Chevreuse wishes you to be presented to her," Colonel MacIvor said to Hector. "Everyone knows her reputation; she is the cleverest woman in France, and one of the most intriguing. She is the queen's greatest friend, and has been her main-stay in her struggle with Richelieu. Of one thing we may be sure, that she will not tamely see Mazarin step into his place, and she has, it is whispered, already thrown herself into the arms of 'The Importants,' and if anyone can persuade the queen to throw over the cardinal it is she."

With a slight shrug of his shoulders Hector followed the colonel to a group of three or four ladies seated upon some fauteuils.

The colonel stopped before one of these, and bowing deeply said, "Duchess, I have the honour to present to you my compatriot, Colonel Campbell, who arrived here this morning with despatches from the Duc d'Enghien."

Madame Chevreuse, like the queen, was still a beautiful woman. She was petite, and possessed a face whose fascination few could withstand. She was the most restless of intriguers, and was never so happy as when engaged in conspiracies which might cost her her estates and liberty.

"Why, Monsieur Campbell," she said with a smile, "I had looked to see a fierce warrior, and, lo and behold I find one who, by his appearance, will be far more in his element at court than in the field."

"Then appearances must greatly belie me, madame," Hector said; "for while I may say that I am at home in a military camp, I feel sorely ill at ease here, and I feel I would rather face an enemy's battery than so many beautiful faces."

"That is not bad for a beginner," the lady said with a smile, "but methinks you will soon get over that fear, for there is nothing very dangerous in any of us. The Duchesse de Longueville," and she motioned to the lady next to her, "is as desirous as myself that you should be presented to her, and that she should hear from your lips somewhat more of the doings of her brother than she has yet learned."

Hector again bowed deeply. The sister of Enghien was as ambitious for her brother's sake as he was for his own self, and she was his potent ally in the troubles of the times.

"Enghien was wounded," she said. "Monsieur la Moussaie left the field directly the battle was won, and could tell me little about my brother's injuries."

"He received three wounds, duchess, but happily none of them were severe, and he was on horseback on the following morning. It seemed miraculous to us all that he should so escape, for he rode ever ahead of us in the charges against the Spanish square."

"You were acting as one of his aides-de-camp? I do not remember having seen your face before."

"No, madame. I have been for the past four years on the staff of the Viscount de Turenne, and have not left the army during that time. The general had the goodness, seeing that there was little doing in the south, to send me to learn what I could from the operations of the duke against the Spanish. He sent me a letter of recommendation to your brother, who kindly appointed me to the same position under him that I had occupied under Turenne."

"Did you find the ladies of Italy very lovely?" Madame de Chevreuse asked suddenly.

"In truth, madame, I had but small opportunities of judging, seeing that, unless when sent with some message from the general to the Duchess of Savoy, I do not think that I exchanged a single word with a woman during the whole of my stay there."

Madame de Chevreuse, and the Duchesse de Longueville, and all the ladies sitting round, smiled.

"Then you have very much to learn, Colonel Campbell," Madame de Chevreuse said. "You will find plenty of ladies in the court here who will not object to give you lessons."

"I trust, madame," Hector said bluntly, "that there will be little opportunity for me to take lessons as to the manners of the court, for I hope that my stay here will be short indeed."

"That is a most ungallant speech," the younger duchess said, laughing, "and shows indeed the truth of what you have said as to your ignorance of women. Do you not know, sir, that it is an unwritten law at court that every gentleman here must be at the feet of one fair lady?"

"I suppose that, had I been brought up at court," Hector said, "I should not be more insensible than others; but when one passes three-quarters of one's time on horseback, and that under a commander like Turenne, who sets us all an example in the matter of endurance and watchfulness, one has small leisure indeed for aught else, and indeed is glad enough to seek one's bed as soon as the day's work is done."

"If you are another Turenne," Madame de Chevreuse laughed, "I give you up. He is the most insensible of men. His head contains but one idea, and that is duty; and as to us poor creatures, he is as insensible as was St. Anthony."

At this moment the door that separated the salon from that of the queen opened, and the names of Monsieur de Penthière and Monsieur de Caussac were called. The two officers at once passed into the inner room.

"You are either left out in the cold, monsieur le colonel, or you will have the honour of a separate audience," Madame de Chevreuse said.

"As I have been rewarded far above my merits for any service that I have rendered," Hector said quietly, "it is probable that the queen has nothing to say to me. She was pleased to receive me very graciously this morning, and gave me her hand to kiss, and I assuredly have no right to expect any further favours."

In a few minutes the two officers came out, both looking radiant, the queen having graciously presented them with the titles to two estates. A minute later Hector's name was called, and he went off, with a deep bow to the ladies and a murmured apology for leaving them.

"A loyal spirit, surely," Madame de Chevreuse said; "bizarre, of course, and at present simple as a child. Moreover, I should say that the atmosphere of the court will not infect him as it has the others. It is refreshing to meet with one who, although he must have distinguished himself vastly, is still modest and simple, without a shadow of conceit or of self-consciousness. He spoke as frankly to us as if we were two waiting-maids at a cabaret. However, men of that stamp may always be made useful, and I would rather have the devotion of a young officer like that, who is, I should say, likely to rise to high rank, than that of half a dozen men ready to lay their hearts at the feet of the first comer, and who are as ready to change mistresses as sides."

By this time the door had closed behind Hector. The queen was sitting on a sofa, with the little king by her side. Mazarin stood a pace behind her. Condé and Orleans had a short time before gone out, and had mingled with the crowd in the ante-chamber, and the courtiers present, who were all members of her council, stood some distance in the rear.

"We have had time, Colonel Campbell, to read our despatches, and can now estimate the service that you rendered the Duc d'Enghien and our army. General Gassion, or I should say Marshal Gassion, for he has to-day been raised to that rank, speaks of the value of that service in terms of the highest eulogy, and indeed says frankly, that had it not been for your voluntary expedition and the discovery by you of the Spanish ambuscade, it is probable that we should have suffered a defeat instead of a victory. The duke speaks no less strongly in your favour. I can remember that when the Viscount Turenne was here three years ago, he told us how a young Scottish officer on his staff had saved Turin to us by a most daring enterprise, by which he informed the garrison of the citadel that help would soon reach them, and mentioned that for that service he had appointed Monsieur Campbell a captain. You are Scottish by birth, are you not?"

"I am, your majesty, by birth and descent. My father was a captain in the Scottish regiment, and fell at the siege of La Rochelle. I was, I may say, adopted by the regiment, and had the good fortune to be trained in arms from a child, and the still greater fortune to attract the attention of the Viscount de Turenne, who, young as I was, obtained a commission for me and appointed me to his staff."

Hector before the queen.

WON BY THE SWORD

"Well, young sir, the viscount rewarded you for the great service that you rendered him at Turin; the Duc d'Enghien has similarly rewarded you for your service to him at Rocroi; but it is ours to reward you for your services to France; and Cardinal Mazarin will, in my name, hand you to-morrow the estate of de la Villar, in Poitou, which carries with it the title of Baron de la Villar. A soldier who has rendered such service to us cannot be allowed to remain a soldier dependent on his pay, and I am sure that should need arise you will do me as good service as you have rendered to Turenne and Enghien."

"Your majesty is too good and gracious," Hector stammered, overcome by this sudden and unexpected reward; "but be assured, madame"—and he recovered himself, and his voice was steady—"should there be need, I will willingly lay down my life in your majesty's service, and in that of the king, your son."

"Which means also," the queen said gently, "in that of my minister, who may need faithful friends even more than we do, and under whose advice we have now acted."

"Assuredly, madame. Cardinal Mazarin is your minister, and as long as he possesses your confidence he represents France in my eyes, and I will render as faithful service to him as to yourself."

"Well spoken, baron," the queen said graciously. "Henceforth I shall count you as among my friends." She held out her hand for him to kiss, as did the little king, and after a deep bow to them and to the cardinal, Hector left the audience chamber still almost bewildered by the honours bestowed upon him.

Hector made his way through the crowd to the side of Colonel MacIvor, the general verdict of those who watched him being that he had not met with the same good fortune as those who preceded him, but that for some reason or other he had been reprimanded.

"Well, lad," the colonel said, "what fortune have you met with? judging by your face, either the queen or the cardinal have failed to recognize the service that you have rendered."

"Upon the contrary, colonel, they have so heaped favours upon me that at present I can scarcely realize my good fortune, and feel almost humiliated that so much should have been given for what was a mere matter of duty and attended by no great peril."

"What have they done, then, Campbell?"

"Well, colonel, absurd as it seems even to myself, the queen has graciously bestowed upon me the estate of la Villar, by which gift she says I become as its owner the Baron de la Villar."

"That is fortunate indeed, my dear Campbell," the colonel said, heartily shaking him by the hand. "It shows that the duke and Gassion were of the same opinion that we expressed, namely, that your discovery of that ambush was the chief factor in bringing about the victory of Rocroi."

"But it was such a simple thing," Hector said. "It was merely a reconnaissance, such as I have made scores of times in Italy."

"No doubt, Campbell; but you see the other reconnaissances did not lead to any results, while this did. My dear lad, it is by results that men are judged. That you, a young officer on Enghien's staff, should unbidden, and, as you say, as a matter of duty, have undertaken such a business, shows how thoroughly you have profited by your teaching under Turenne; and as such you deserve what you have gained, though I do not say that you would have obtained your desserts had not your reconnaissance saved Enghien from defeat. Now I will take you to Madame de Chevreuse again. She beckoned to me after you entered the audience chamber, and told me to bring you up again when you came out, as she and the Duchesse de Longueville had taken a great fancy to you. Now, my dear boy, your position is changed. You have become a French noble, and, however unwilling, may find yourself mixed up on one side or the other with the doings of your court. Both these ladies have power, and it is well to keep in with them, for either of them might prove a valuable friend and protector, and the first rule here is make as many friends as possible, for no one can say when you may require them."

Hector again followed the colonel to the group of ladies.

"Madame," MacIvor said, "I have the honour to present you—"

"Why, have you not presented him to us already?" Madame de Chevreuse said with a laugh. "Your memory must be singularly short, colonel."

"My memory is not short, madame, but it is a somewhat different personage that I have now to present to you. Madame, I have the honour to present Colonel Campbell, Baron de la Villar."

Both ladies uttered an exclamation of surprise.

"Why, what has he done, colonel?" the duchess exclaimed. "It must have been some remarkable action, surely, for him to be made colonel by my brother and Baron de la Villar by the queen."

"In the opinion of the Duc d'Enghien and General Gassion, duchess, he performed a service that to a large extent brought about the victory of Rocroi. My young friend is at present not beyond the age of modesty, and therefore if you will allow me I will state the circumstances. Under General de Turenne he was in the habit of constantly visiting the posts at night with the viscount or alone, and endeavouring to discover the position and intentions of the enemy. The night before the battle he started voluntarily to perform the same duties, and, accompanied only by his servant, he crept into a wood that lay between the two armies and there discovered a thousand musketeers who were lying in ambush. He reported the discovery to General Gassion, who on his part informed the duke of this most important intelligence, for it was evident that, had the ambuscade been unsuspected, they would have taken the cavalry in the rear at the critical moment of the battle, and would have opened so heavy a fire that even the bravest of cavalry, thus surprised and shot down by an unsuspected foe in their rear, might have fallen into confusion. Being forewarned, the duke directed his first charge upon the wood, took the musketeers by surprise, and annihilated them, before charging and routing the enemy's horse. Thus you see, ladies, that we have another illustration of the mouse saving the lion, and the lion was generous and noble-minded enough to give the mouse full credit for the service that he had rendered him."

"Then we have good reason to be grateful to you, monsieur le baron," Madame Chevreuse said, laying aside the bantering tone in which she had before addressed the young Scot, "and her majesty has done well to reward your loyalty, for the estate is a fine one, and has remained without a master since Richelieu brought its last owner to the block for having, as he affirmed, conspired against the king—that is to say, against himself. You have begun well indeed, sir. Henceforth the Duchesse de Longueville and myself may be counted upon as your friends. And now," she said, changing the subject abruptly, "as you say that you are anxious to be off, with whom will you serve, with Turenne or with Enghien? for I hear that Turenne has been sent for to take the command of the army of the Rhine."

"I belong to Viscount Turenne," Hector said. "It is to him that I owe everything. He picked me up a rough boy, with no recommendation save that my father died fighting for France, and that I was more addicted to military study than most lads of my age, and that, as he was good enough to say, I reminded him of his own boyhood. It was owing to his kindness and his tuition that I have now made my way, and it was still further to increase my military knowledge that he sent me for a time to serve under the Duc d'Enghien. Therefore, much as I admire the glory that the duke has gained, and recognize his extraordinary genius, I feel that duty and gratitude alike bind me to my great master."

"Quite right," the Duchesse de Longueville said warmly. "I am sure that my brother will approve of your decision. He admires Turenne as much as you do, and regards him as his master in military science, and it may be perhaps that one of these days you will take part in a battle in which my brother and Turenne will both have command."

"If it be so, madame," Hector said, "there can be little doubt of victory, for with the two greatest military geniuses France has produced during the last hundred years it would be hard indeed if victory did not attend their united banners."

The news of the honour that had been bestowed upon this young colonel circulated rapidly through the salon, and many gentlemen came up and begged Colonel MacIvor to introduce him to them. One who had received so marked a proof of the queen's favour, and who had won the praise and good-will of both Turenne and Enghien, might well become in time a man of mark, and so many compliments were showered upon Hector that he was glad indeed when the queen again passed through the room on her way to her apartments and he was at liberty to retire. He walked slowly back to Condé's palace, went up to his room, changed his court suit for that which he had worn during the day, and then went out again, feeling that it would be hopeless to attempt to sleep. He paced backwards and forwards for some hours on the quay, thinking of the changes that three days had brought about.

He could scarcely realize even now, that he who a week ago was but a captain with nought but his pay, was now not only a colonel but a noble of France, with an estate of whose value he was ignorant, but as it carried with it a patent of nobility it was evident that it must be one of dimensions sufficient to support the title. The change excited no feeling of exultation. His whole thoughts so far had been directed solely to his career as a soldier. He had hoped that some day he might win a colonelcy; more than that he had never thought of. High commands in France were matters of birth, interest, and connection. Gassion, who had just earned his marshal's baton, was the sole exception to the rule. Hitherto generals, and still more marshals, had always been men belonging to the first families of France. It had been a matter of course that when an army went to the field it was under the command of a prince of the blood, and the utmost an outsider could look for was the command of a regiment.

The promotion had delighted him, not for the sake of the pay or position, but because, if he obtained the command of one of the regiments that were rapidly being formed to meet the dangers that threatened France, he would have opportunities of doing good service and of earning the esteem of such men as Turenne. His civil dignity, however, oppressed rather than gratified him. He would have heavy responsibilities. When not on active service he would be expected to show himself at court, and would have a difficulty in holding himself aloof from its intrigues and conspiracies. His thoughts turned to Scotland. He had relations there, it was true, both on his father's and mother's side, but they were strangers to him. Moreover, Scotland at present was torn by a civil and religious war. In England a civil war was raging, and the extreme party in Scotland, having got the upper hand, had allied themselves with the English parliamentarians, and the cause of the king was well-nigh lost.

The Scottish officers and men in the French service had for the most part left their homes owing to the bitter religious differences of the times, and, under the easier conditions of the life in France, had come to look with disgust at the narrow bigotry of the Scottish sects, a feeling heightened perhaps by the deep resentment that still prevailed in France at the insolence with which Knox and the Scottish reformers had treated their princess, Queen Mary. Among the French officers the feeling was wholly in favour of the royal cause in England. The queen was French, and had France herself not been engaged in warfare numbers of the young nobles would have gone over and drawn their swords in her cause, and Hector would gladly have done the same.

For the time, at any rate, he had no idea whatever of returning to Scotland. If better times came he had often thought that, if successful in winning a competency, he would return to his native land, for his close connection with the

Scottish regiment kept alive in him his feeling of nationality, and he always regarded himself as a stranger in France. The estates and title now bestowed upon him seemed to put this hope further away than ever, and to fix him permanently in France, a contingency more disagreeable to him the more he saw how completely France was dominated by faction, and how unstable were the conditions of life there. His musings, therefore, as he walked up and down for hours, were very different from those which most young men would have felt at so great and sudden a change in their fortunes.

CHAPTER XI
THE CASTLE OF LA VILLAR

THE next morning he called at eleven o'clock, at which hour the cardinal's secretary had informed him that Mazarin would expect him. He went to the abode of the minister. Mazarin received him with marked courtesy.

"Here are the deeds appointing to you the estate of la Villar and your patent of nobility," he said, pointing to a box upon his table. "You have been singularly fortunate, sir, and from all inquiries that I have made from officers who have served with Monsieur de Turenne, and, I may say, from Colonel MacIvor, I hear nothing but good of you, as a soldier devoted to duty, as a young man free from the vices and dissipations too common among those of your age, and as possessing intelligence as well as courage. Such men, sir, even royalty does well to attach to itself, and for them a splendid career is open. I, high as is the office in which Providence has placed me, may well envy you. You fight against the enemies of France; I am surrounded by enemies open and secret, and the war is no less earnest than that which Turenne and Enghien are waging.

"The great nobles of France are jealous that I, a foreigner, should have the ear of the queen, and be first minister of the country. Gladly indeed would I resign my position and return to my bishopric in Italy, were it not that I promised the great man to whose place I have so unworthily succeeded, that I would do my best for the country on whose behalf he spent every hour of his life, and that I would, unless driven from it by force, hold the seals of office until the young king should be old enough to rule France unaided. You, baron, are like myself a foreigner, and ready to risk your life in the service of France, and you will understand how I am situated and how I feel. You, happily for yourself, are not so highly placed as to excite enmity, although doubtless not a few of those who flocked round you yesterday evening to congratulate you on your good fortune felt a sensation of envy that a young soldier of fortune should be so honoured.

"In my case envy is accompanied by the deepest animosity. The great nobles find me an obstacle in the way of their grasping power, and they would hesitate at nothing to rid themselves of me. Were it not for the support of the queen, my position would be untenable even for an hour. Without me the queen herself would speedily become as much a cipher as she was so long as the weak king reigned. We have need, both of us, of men of heart and devotion such as I take you to be. I ask for no engagements, sir, but I felt that there was a genuine ring in your voice yesterday evening when you promised faithful service to her majesty, and I feel that if such service is needed you will be ready to render it."

"I shall indeed, your eminence. I cannot conceive that any circumstances can occur that would render such aid as I could offer of service to you, but be assured that should such an occasion arise, the queen may count upon me to render it to the extent of my life; and when I say the queen I, of course, include your eminence as her trusted adviser and supporter."

"Well spoken, sir. I believe your words, and it may be that the occasion is not so far distant as you may imagine. Here is the box, sir. By the way, it will, I am sure, be a pleasure for you to know that her majesty has the intention of creating the Viscount de Turenne field-marshal as soon as he arrives in Paris."

"It is indeed, monseigneur; never did a soldier better earn such honour. There, indeed sir, is a true and noble heart, loyal to his duty beyond all things, adored by his soldiers, ready to serve under officers altogether inferior to himself, incapable of jealousy, and devoted to his sovereign and his country."

"You do not speak too warmly of him," the cardinal said; "and among all the difficulties of the situation there seems to be but one fixed point, and that point is that upon Monsieur de Turenne we can at least confidently rely."

Hector felt that his audience was at an end, and taking the box from the table, and again thanking the cardinal for the honour bestowed upon him, he retired. The cardinal's chamberlain met him at the door. "Will you step in here, monsieur le baron?" he said, and led the way into a small apartment. "As a stranger to the court, monsieur, you are probably unaware of the value of the gift that has been granted to you, or of its duties and obligations."

"Altogether, sir; beyond the fact that it is in Poitou, which her majesty mentioned yesterday, I know absolutely nothing about it."

"Without being an estate of the first class," the chamberlain said, "it is one which is of importance in its province. The revenue is punctually paid and is amply sufficient to enable its lord to make a good figure at court, and to rank among the notables in the province. It is a fief held directly from the crown; its owner is bound to furnish feudal service of twenty-five mounted men and twenty-five arquebusiers, or, should he prefer it, fifty horsemen in all. Some of its owners have in times of peril raised a force of thrice that strength. So you will see that the Lord of la Villar is not an unimportant personage. The estate is held at present by a royal intendant. You will find in that box an order for him to place you in possession of the castle and estate whensoever you may present yourself, and as at the present moment your services can be spared from the army, it might be as well to visit it at once, if only for a few days. Possibly the cardinal did not inform you that he has ordered that the regiment that has been just recruited shall bear the name of the regiment of Poitou, and has appointed you to its command."

This news gave much greater pleasure to Hector than did the gift of the fief, or the rank that accompanied it.

"Will you please give my earnest thanks to his excellency," he said, "and assure him that he can depend upon my devotion."

When Hector returned to the Hotel Condé he found that the soldiers who had started with him from Rocroi had all arrived, bringing with them the twelve horses that had been left on the road; four of these were to be handed over to each of the officers. The division was just being made as he entered the court-yard, each officer taking the four he had ridden by the way.

Paolo at once came up to him. "What are we to do with these horses, master?" he asked, with an air of bewilderment.

"We have now seven of them, counting mine, the one I led, and that you rode when you set out."

"I must see where I can bestow them for the present until we think the matter over;" and going up to one of Condé's officers, he asked him if he could recommend a place where he might leave safely four horses for a time.

"The auberge of the Pomme d'Or is but a street from here, monsieur; it has good stables, and the host is an honest man, which is not often the case with men of his class. When the stables here are full the prince often engages extra stalls there for the use of his guests. I will send four men with the horses at once, if such is your pleasure."

"You will greatly oblige me by doing so," Hector replied. Having seen the horses safely and comfortably lodged at the inn, Hector returned to the hotel with Paolo.

"You are not tired, I hope, Paolo?" he asked as they walked back.

"No, master; we have taken three days to do what you did in one, and have fatigued neither ourselves nor our beasts."

"That is well, for I am going to start on a journey this afternoon, that is to say, if I can manage to make my arrangements."

"May I ask where you are going, master?"

"You will be surprised to hear that I am going to visit my estates in Poitou."

Paolo looked sharply up to see whether Hector was joking. Seeing that he looked serious, he said hesitatingly, "But I did not know, master, that you had estates in Poitou. I never heard you speak of them."

"Because I had them not, Paolo. That box that you are carrying holds the titles. The fief was granted to me last night by the queen herself, the Duc d'Enghien and General Gassion having been good enough to make a good deal more of that night adventure of ours than it deserved. The estates carry a title with them, and I am now the Baron de la Villar."

Paolo gave an exclamation of delight. "Well, master, I am glad indeed; but," he went on in a changed tone, "now that you, monsieur, have become a noble, you will no longer require the services of a lad from Savoy."

"Indeed I shall, Paolo, as long as you choose to remain with me. Why, have you not shared with me in the adventures, one of which made me a captain, and the other a colonel and a noble? Of course I shall have other servants, but you will always be my body-servant and companion."

"And are you going to leave the army, monsieur?" Paolo asked, after pouring out his thanks.

"No, I shall still remain in the army. Turenne will be in Paris soon, and will then go to the Rhine to take the command there, and I hope to go with my regiment."

"Then you have a regiment, master?"

"Yes; one of the newly-formed regiments has been named the regiment of Poitou, and I am to have the command. Of course, it may be sent either to him or to Enghien, but I hope that it will be to Turenne; and I should think so, because from what I hear there is scarcely any army left on the Rhine, and therefore it is probable that the new regiments will all be sent there, as Enghien's force is quite sufficient to cope with any enemy he is likely to meet with in Flanders. Now, I am going down to the barracks, and for the next two or three hours you can amuse yourself by taking a look at Paris."

WON BY THE SWORD

It was not to the barracks that Hector made his way, but to The Scottish Soldier.

"I did not expect to see you so soon again, colonel. Your man brought me word that I was not to come this morning, as you would be engaged," the sergeant said when he entered.

"Yes, but our talk was only postponed, sergeant; now I want you to aid me in a matter that I have on hand."

"What sort of matter is it?"

"I want to find four good men to take into my service. The queen has granted me an estate, as if a colonelcy was not an ample and more than ample reward for discovering that ambuscade. It is the fief of la Villar in Poitou, and the most absurd point of the thing is that with it is a title, and I am now Colonel Campbell, Baron de la Villar."

"Well, well," the sergeant exclaimed; "you will be coming and telling me next that you are going to marry a princess of the blood. Did one ever hear of such things! However, Hector, lad, I congratulate you with all my heart, and I am as glad as if it had been a bairn of my own that had had your good fortune. Now, in what can I help you about the four men? What sort of men do you want?"

"I want four good men and true, sergeant, men that I can rely upon. I shall want them to ride with me in the field as orderlies, for I have been appointed to the command of an infantry regiment. Of course, I should like young and active men, but that they should be steady and accustomed to arms is still more important."

"I know but few men outside the regiment," the sergeant said. "The laddies like to have the place to themselves, and I don't encourage others about; but if you can do with good men who have somewhat passed their prime, but are still capable of service and handy with their arms, I know just the men that will suit you. We had a little bit of trouble in the regiment a week since; four of the men—Allan Macpherson, Jock Hunter, Donald Nicholl, and Sandy Grahame—came in after tattoo, and all a bit fu'. It was not here they got it, though; I know better than to supply men with liquor when it is time for them to be off to the barracks.

Captain Muir, who is the only dour carl in the regiment, happened to be on duty, and he spoke a good deal more hardly to them than to my mind there was any occasion, seeing that they are good soldiers and not in the guard-room more often than others. They answered him more freely, no doubt, than they would have done had they not been in their cups.

"They were had up before the colonel the next morning. They had all served their time, and having been greatly angered at their treatment, they at once up and told the colonel that they would take their discharges. The colonel would have pacified them, but Captain Muir stood out strongly, and said that if such insolence as theirs was allowed to go unpunished it would be a bad example indeed for the regiment; so the colonel paid them up to the day and gave them their papers. It has caused a lot of feeling in the regiment, as you may guess, and the men all groaned and booed when Muir came on parade the next day, and it was as much as the colonel himself—whom they all love as a father— could do to silence them. It is said that he spoke very sharply to Muir afterwards, and that it is likely the captain will get transferred to another regiment. However, that is too late for the men who have left. Their comrades are going to get up a subscription to send them back to Scotland, for you may be sure the hot-headed fools have not a bawbee of their pay laid by."

"I know them all, sergeant, and I should say they would be the very men to suit me; they are all strong and hearty fellows, and might have been good for another ten years' campaigning if it had not been for this business. Can you send for them?"

"They will all be here in half an hour for their meal," the sergeant said. "They are lodged upstairs, for you may be sure that they would come to me; and even if I kept them for six months, I should not have lost much when I reckon what they have spent here during their service. I have no doubt they will jump at the offer; for they were mere lads when they came over—it was your father who sent for them—

and I know that they reckon they will find none of the old folk when they return home. And now what are your estates like, lad?"

"I know very little about them at present, beyond the fact that I am bound by my feudal obligations to put fifty men in the field when called upon to do so."

"Then it must be a place of good size," the sergeant said. "And you hold it direct from the crown?"

Hector nodded.

"That is good. When you hold from one of the great lords, you never know whom you may be called upon to fight against—it may be the king, it may be his minister, it may be some other noble—while holding direct, you have only the king's enemies to fight against."

"Or rather, MacIntosh, the chief minister's enemies; for, after all, when a king signs a proclamation, it is usually a minister's signature that ought to be attached to it."

"Well, well, Master Hector, it makes little difference to us Scots whom it is that we fight for, it is no quarrel of ours. We have taken service under the King of France; but when there are two parties, and each claims to be in favour of the king, we have simply to fight for whoever happens to have the king's signature. If they both have it, then it is the general who commands our division who gives us orders, and it matters nought to us whom he takes his orders from."

"At any rate, MacIntosh, it is not for soldiers to inquire too deeply into these matters; if we did, we should have one half of the regiment firing into the other."

"So we should, lad, so we should; therefore we soldiers do wisely in leaving the matter to our officers. If the colonel says 'Charge!' we charge; if he says 'Dismount and take to your musketoons!' we do so, without troubling our heads as to whether it is Germans or Spaniards or Frenchmen whom we have to aim at. Ah, here come your four men!"

182

THE CASTLE OF LA VILLAR

As the four troopers entered the cabaret and saw who was speaking to MacIntosh they hesitated, and would have turned, but the sergeant called out, "Attention! salute!" and they stood as motionless as statues till Hector ordered them to stand easy.

"I have been talking about you men to Sergeant MacIntosh, who tells me that you have taken your discharge and the reason for your so doing. I think that you acted hastily; however, that is your affair. The matter that concerns me is this: —I am appointed colonel of an infantry regiment and I want four good men as orderlies. They will be mounted, and I shall see that they draw rations when there are any rations to be had; but they will be my troopers and not soldiers of the regiment. I want good men, who can be relied upon in any emergency; they will ride behind me in battle, act as scouts if necessary, and they will receive double the pay of ordinary troopers. In peace-time, or when the regiment is in winter quarters, I shall pass my time either in Paris or on my estate in Poitou, and they will of course accompany me. I may tell you that I am now Baron de la Villar, but I should wish to be always addressed as Colonel Campbell. I know you all of old, and that your only failing is somewhat too great a love for the wine-flask; that must only be indulged in at times when you are not only off duty, but when there is no possibility of your services being required. Now, what do you think, men; will my service suit you?"

"That it would, sir," burst from them simultaneously.

"Of course, there will be some other advantages beyond that of pay. When the time comes that you get beyond active service in the field, I shall be able to provide you with easier posts at la Villar, and there you will find a comfortable home in your old age, if you prefer to stay with me rather than to return to Scotland."

"No further word need be spoken, colonel," Allan Macpherson said; "we are your men, and shall be proud to follow you, were there no question of pay at all, but just our rations and a home to look forward to when our arms get weak and eyes dim."

"Then, men, if so say you all, the service begins from the present time. You have your armour and head-pieces, your doublets and jack-boots, so there is not much to buy. I have horses ready for you. You have pistols."

"Yes, we have all pistols and swords, colonel, but the musketoons belonged to the regiment."

"There will be no occasion for you to carry them. Get for yourselves four long cloaks well-lined and serviceable— 'tis best that they should be all of a colour, dark-blue or gray— and broad hats to match the cloaks; have in each a small red feather. I would that you should make a decent show, for we shall start in two hours for Poitou. Here are twenty crowns. See that you have ammunition for your pistols. Be at the Hotel Condé in two hours from the present time. Your dinner here is ready for you, eat heartily, but do not drink too deeply in honour of your new service.

"Now, MacIntosh, I have a word or two further to speak to you."

They went into an inner room.

"Now, old friend, are you tired of this life of keeper of a cabaret? because I shall want you down in Poitou. Your house was mine when I sorely needed it, and mine shall be yours now. You are as yet but fifty-five, and I take it that you can do a man's work still, for you no longer suffer from that wound that disabled you ten years ago. Now, I shall require someone to drill the fifty men who will form my contingent, if all vassals of the king are called upon to take the field. Of course they will not always be under arms; most of them will be the sons of tenants, or substitutes provided by them, and will only give two or three days' service a month. It is probable, however, that half will be regular retainers at the castle. I know nothing about the castle at present, or how large it is, or whether it is defensible or not; still, it was spoken of as a castle, and 'tis, I suppose, one to a certain degree.

"At any rate, I desire that if I do put a troop in the field they shall be as well drilled and as well equipped as are the Scottish regiment of musketeers. I suppose that there must be an official to act as my agent when I am away, and to act as castellan, but in any case the captain of my troop will be in charge of all matters connected with its defence. Now, old friend, the post is yours if you like to take it. As a soldier, none can be better fitted for the post than a sergeant of the Scottish regiment; as a man, there is no one I could rely on better than you. Your duties would not be heavy, your position an honourable one. The castle would be your home as well as mine, and when I am there you would have the four troopers to crack with."

"Your offer is a most kind one," the sergeant said, "but I must think it over in all lights before I answer. I should miss the company of the lads, but already many of my old comrades are gone; most are still in Paris earning with difficulty their bread, some are under the sod, some have returned home. Every year the number who rode with me lessens. They will be countrymen, but no longer comrades. Certainly I have no thought of returning to Scotland, the people are ower gude for me; besides, the country is all in a stir and the folks are flying at each other's throats. I wudna go back, not if they offered me a barony. Then, on the other hand, I misdoubt me how I should feel among strangers—I don't say foreigners, for I have been so long here that as far as tongue goes I am as much French as I am Scottish. Still, I would rather be forming troopers in your service than drawing stoups of wine, and the young soldiers do not regard me as the old ones did, and grumble if I will draw them no more. Most of all, I should like to be with you and in your service, and to know that I had a home in my old age."

"That you will have whenever you come to claim it, MacIntosh, whether you accept my offer or not. However, I think that what you say is best, and that it would be well for you to think the matter well over and give me no answer until I return. I should be sorry indeed if, after giving up your place here and going down to Poitou, you should regret the exchange. Therefore, we will leave it so. And now I must be going; we must postpone our chat over old times and the regiment until I return."

On returning to Condé's hotel Hector found Paolo awaiting him.

"Paolo, you must go out and buy six horse-cloths and five housings; let them be fairly handsome. I have taken four old soldiers into my service, and should wish their horse appointments to be fit for troopers in one of the royal regiments, but without any insignia or cognizance, say maroon with yellow braiding. I shall also want four valises for the men, and bags for carrying forage. You can wrap up the housings that came with the horses; they all bear Enghien's cognizance, and this must be removed before we can use them. The men can strap them behind their valises. Were there pistols in the holsters?"

"Yes, master, they were just as when you rode them."

"It was a princely gift," Hector said, "for the horses are all splendid animals. Have you packed up my things?"

"Yes, master, they are all ready for placing on the sumpter horse. I bought a dozen of good wine, thinking that you might need it on the way, for some of these country auberges keep but poor stuff."

"We are getting luxurious all at once," Hector laughed. "How about my armour?"

"That is also packed up. I thought that you would not care to ride heavily accoutred."

"Certainly not. Which of the horses do you take to be the best?"

"Certainly the one you rode in upon is the best, master, but all four are grand animals. The two I picked up on the battlefield are fine animals also."

"It does not make much matter which I ride now, Paolo; we shall have the opportunity of seeing which has the most fire and endurance as we ride along; and at any rate I shall

keep Enghien's four horses for my own riding, keeping two
with me and leaving two behind at the castle. I shall buy
four strong and serviceable horses for the troopers when I
get my first rents, for in sooth my purse is beginning to run
very low."

"Possibly, master, when you look in the armoire in your
room you may find something to replenish it. One of the
cardinal's servants brought a packet for you. I stowed it away
and locked the door of your room."

"Well, there is no time to lose, Paolo, so see at once
about the matters that I have told you. Here is sufficient
money to buy the other goods."

"Here is the key of the room, sir."

Having seen Paolo hurry away, Hector went up to his
room. In the armoire he found the packet, which was a heavy
one. Opening it, he found a letter and a bag sealed with
wax. The letter was from the intendant-general. It was
directed, "A Monsieur le Baron de la Villar."

"It does not look as if it could be for me," Hector said,
with a merry laugh. Breaking the seal he found:

> *By the order of Monseigneur Cardinal Mazarin, first
> minister of the crown, I enclose the last half-year's rents of the
> estates of la Villar, received by me from the royal intendant in
> charge of the said estates three weeks since, to defray the
> necessary expenses that must be incurred by you between the
> period of your taking possession and, of receiving the next
> half-yearly payment of rents.*

Enclosed with this was a formal permit, giving a month's
leave of absence to visit his estates, "To Colonel Campbell,
Baron de la Villar, commanding the Poitou regiment."

"Very nice and thoughtful on the part of the cardinal,"
Hector said, "and, moreover, very seasonable, for I was
wondering how I should pay the retainers at the castle and
my four troopers until the rents began to come in. By the
time I had paid the usual fees to the servants here, and the
expenses of the journey to Poitou and back, I should have

been almost penniless, and should have been obliged to borrow from someone on the strength of my coming rents, which would have been a very bad beginning."

After bidding farewell to Condé, and thanking him for his hospitality, Hector started immediately the mid-day meal was concluded. His cavalcade made a good show as he rode through the streets of Paris, with the four orderlies behind him, splendidly mounted, followed by Paolo leading another fine horse carrying baggage. The journey was an uneventful one, and on arriving at the castle of Villar, Hector was received by the royal intendant. It was still a place of considerable strength, standing on the crest of a hill. It had been kept in a good state of repair by the intendant, and could offer a stout resistance to anything short of an army provided with a powerful battering train. On making a tour of the estate Hector found that here, as throughout France, an immense amount of distress existed, owing to the crushing taxation rendered necessary by the war; he made minute inquiries of the intendant of the circumstances of the various tenants of the estate.

The officer was about to return to Paris now that his commission was ended, but as he had a son who had acted as his assistant, Hector appointed him in his stead, charging him to press no one unduly. He placed under his care the domestic arrangements of the castle, retaining the servants who had been there under the royal officer. There was only a permanent garrison of twelve men, but this could be raised to a hundred were the tenants of the estates driven to take refuge within the walls. The expenses of keeping up the castle were not large. The rivers afforded an abundance of fish, and the forests on the mountain-sides sheltered an ample supply of game. Considerable numbers of half-wild sheep and two or three herds of cattle grazed on the domain round the castle, and there were eight good horses in the stables, besides a score of others on the hills. Most of the holdings had vineyards, and were bound to furnish a certain amount of wine to the castle, and as the consumption had been small since the estate was confiscated, the cellars were full. Hector told the steward that the command of the castle itself would be taken by an officer whom he would send down from Paris, who would have control in all matters save in the management of the estate.

Before leaving, he called all the tenants together and told them that, seeing how heavily the royal taxes pressed upon them, he should remit half their annual payments until better times came, and also the fine of a year's rent which they would in the ordinary course of things pay on the appointment of a new lord. The news filled the poor people with delight.

"I shall, however," he went on, "expect that you will render fully and willingly the military service you are bound to give according to the tenure of your holdings. In a short time my castellan will arrive here; he will have instructions from me to make the service as little onerous as possible, and that you shall each furnish your quota of men at times when it may be most convenient for you. I shall, however, expect fifteen men added to the strength of the garrison. These can be changed every eight weeks. All the men capable of bearing arms will come up for training one or two days in each month. I trust that you will never be called upon to defend the castle, but I would have it always kept in such a state that were troubles to arise you could all, with your wives and families, find refuge here and be able to defend yourselves against all attacks.

"Next winter I shall have the fortifications strengthened. I know that you are bound to furnish horses and carts for so many days in the year. I shall want this work performed, but you will be paid both for your own work in building, and for your carts and horses; and so, it will be done at a time when there is little farm work on hand, this will be a benefit to you, and the wages will be deducted from the payments that you have to make."

Loud cheers rose from the men, who were overjoyed on learning that their new lord was inclined to deal so generously with them, and especially that the fine, which many of them would have found it impossible to pay, was to be altogether remitted. Having completed all his arrangements Hector returned to Paris, mounting his men on four of the horses he found in the stables, and leaving at the castle two of those which Enghien had given him, and the two Paolo had caught on the field of battle. He arrived on the evening of the day before his leave expired, put up at the auberge of the Pomme d'Or, and early the next morning took his way to The Scottish Soldier.

CHAPTER XII
THE POITOU REGIMENT

WELL, MacIntosh," Hector said as he entered the cabaret, "have you made up your mind? The castle is a strong one, and I mean to make it stronger. The air is good and so is the wine, and I am sure that you will find the duties pleasant.

"If you go I think it would be as well that you should take a couple of your old comrades—you said there were many of them in Paris—with you, to act as your sergeants, drill the tenants, and see that all goes on in order. It will be pleasant for you to have two of your old friends with whom you can talk over past times."

"I had decided to accept your offer, Hector; but certainly this would have decided me had I not already made up my mind. That was the one drawback, that I should be among strangers, but with two of my old friends I should not feel lonely. There is Sholto Macfarlane, he was in my troop. He lost a hand from his musket bursting three years ago, and now makes his living by helping the boatmen unload at the quays. Then there is Kenneth Munroe. He was invalided after a bad attack of fever in Flanders, and now teaches the broadsword exercise at a fencing-master's place at St. Denis. They would both jump at the offer if they only got free lodgings and keep."

"Then that is settled, MacIntosh. I am heartily glad of it. Now the sooner you get down there the better."

A visit to Sergeant MacIntosh.

THE POITOU REGIMENT

"Well, I can go at once. Sergeant Morrison is taking his discharge at the end of the week. He is a married man with a helpful little wife. I was telling him of the offer that you had made me, and he asked me what I would take for the cabaret. It is a good business, and having a wife he could manage it better than I can. I said that if he had a fancy for it I would rather that he took it than another; and he would do better than a Frenchman would, for the lads would not care for the place unless it was kept by one of the regiment. He asked me what were the profits. I told him.

" 'Then I am afraid that you would want a bigger sum than I could pay, MacIntosh,' he said. 'I have been a saving man, especially since I first thought of marrying, and I have laid by half my pay for the last eight years; but that would not go far towards the purchase of the place, for your profits in a year are as much as my savings of eight years.' So I said to him, 'Well, we will get the place valued. You will want half the money that you have saved to stock it well, the other half you shall pay me down; and I will give you five years to pay the rest, you paying me a tenth part every half-year.'

"Well, sir, we struck a bargain on that. The place has been valued, and on Saturday evening Morrison will come straight in and take it over. He is a popular man in the regiment; and as he is only just leaving it he is known to them all, while there are not above a quarter of the men who knew me as a comrade in the old days."

They then had a long talk over the sergeant's new duties, and Hector gave him a plan of the new fortifications that he had drawn out, together with full instructions how they were to be carried out.

"The steward will arrange all about the tenants coming to work, and the proportion of labour that each will have to give. As I have told you, he will manage all details of that kind, look after the indoor retainers, and see to the food. You will have entire control of the garrison, of the tenants who will come to drill, and of the works on the fortifications. You will find the steward a very pleasant and agreeable young man. He will take his meals with you. I have chosen a room for you, and you can have another near it for your two sergeants. You can pay them at the same rate as sergeants of the regiment receive, and I need hardly say that the position will be a good deal better. As commander of the garrison and castellan of the castle you will be called Captain MacIntosh, and as such you will be named in my letter appointing you to the post, and I propose that you shall receive the pay of captain."

"The pay is immaterial, lad, I have been nigh twelve years here, and have laid by enough to keep me comfortably all my life, and as, so far as I can see, there will be nothing to spend down there, I don't know what I should do with pay."

"That is nonsense, MacIntosh. You must draw the pay, and spend it as you like, or save it. You must remember that I may be killed in the next battle I go into, and as I have no heirs the king will give the fief to someone else. The new-comer might like myself have some friend whom he might appoint castellan."

"It would make no difference," the other said. "In addition to what I have saved I shall have the price of the cabaret."

"That is not to the point, MacIntosh. The steward has instructions to hand you your money monthly, while the garrison will be paid weekly. If you choose to throw the money into the fosse, that is your own business, mine is to see that my castellan is paid. I am going over at noon to-day to St. Denis, where my regiment is quartered, but will ride in on Saturday. You must buy three horses for yourself and your sergeants; get good serviceable animals. I have told the steward to repay you their cost when you arrive there; he has monies of mine in hand for all purposes."

Hector then went round and had a chat with Colonel MacIvor, and returned to the auberge, where the troopers and Paolo had the horses already saddled. He mounted and rode with them to St. Denis, putting up at an hotel. He found where the regiment of Poitou were stationed and at once proceeded there on foot. Two or three officers were chatting together in the barrack square, while some sergeants were drilling the companies.

He at once went up to them. "Gentlemen," he said, "I must introduce myself to you. I am Colonel Campbell; I have the honour to command the regiment. I shall be glad if you will order the officer's call to be sounded and send orderlies off at once to the lodgings of the officers and ask them to assemble. To whom have I the pleasure of speaking?"

The senior officer introduced himself and the others. Report had told them that their new colonel was still a young man, and that he had served with distinction under both Turenne and Enghien, but they were not prepared for so young a commander as this. The French regiments had, as a rule, two colonels, the one a veteran soldier, who had won his way to the rank by long service and long fighting, the other a young nobleman who had gained the post solely by family influence, but possessed no knowledge whatever of military matters, and who was never with the regiment except when it went upon a campaign, and even then generally preferred the pleasures of Paris to the hardships of war. Had Hector been appointed to what was called the second no surprise would have been felt at his youth, but that anyone should have gained the position of first colonel at his age by sheer merit was astonishing indeed to them. In twenty minutes the officers were all assembled and introduced by the senior captain to Hector.

"We will not begin business now," the latter said. "My leave of absence does not terminate until to-morrow morning, and I think that it is much more pleasant to talk over matters comfortably round a table than it is to do so in a set manner. Therefore, gentlemen, if you will all sup with me this evening at the Fleur de Lis, after we have finished our meal we will talk over our wine. My opinion is that officers of a regiment should be good comrades. The regiment benefits by it, and everything goes on more smoothly and comfortably. This is specially so in a newly raised regiment, where the officers either are altogether new to military matters, or join from other regiments, and have no previous knowledge of each other. In the same way the men are all new to each other, and to their officers. Unless there is perfect harmony among the officers, there cannot be perfect harmony in the regiment.

"If one officer looks after the comfort of his company, and treats them as he should do, while another company is neglected and left solely to the care of the sergeants, there will necessarily be envy and ill feeling. The regiment will cease to be a unit. I may say, gentlemen, that this is the dictum not of myself, but of Marshal Turenne, who was my instructor in the art of war, and who followed out the better system from the time that he was a boy of fourteen until now. The result is that his regiment is the finest in the service. It will be my aim and ambition to raise the Poitou regiment as nearly as possible to the same condition, and I shall rely upon your assistance and co-operation to bring this about.

"Supper will be served at six. I have only just returned from the country, and have heard no news. I suppose that no intimation has been received as to what is our destination and whither we shall march?"

"None whatever, colonel," de Thiou, the senior captain, said.

"All the better. I hope that they will give us a couple of months to get into shape. There is but little time for drill and discipline when we are once in the field."

So saying he saluted the officers and returned to the hotel.

"Who would have thought of seeing a mere lad placed at the head of the regiment as colonel," one of the captains said. "I cannot imagine how such a thing can have come about, for certainly he can have no family influence. A newly-raised regiment like ours wants a bright man, one that all can look up to and respect."

"I fancy that you will find that this young gentleman will be respected," de Thiou said. "He is young and pleasant-looking, and whatever he is I should say that he is levelheaded, and that he has an infinite fund of firmness and resolution. I should certainly advise nobody to take advantage of his youth. I have seen more service than any of you, and had my family possessed any influence at court, I should have been a colonel by this time. Unless I am greatly mistaken we shall find that we have a man, a good man, and a strong one. Do you think that he could have won his way to a regiment at the age of twenty unless there had been something quite unusual? I was talking the other day with one of Gassion's staff, who has come back until the wound that he got at Rocroi is healed. He told me that Gassion—and France has no better soldier—said publicly after the battle that the victory was largely due to this young friend of ours, and that had it not been for him things might have gone altogether differently; and he said that Enghien, proud and ambitious as he is, frankly admitted the same thing. Of course I can only go upon what I have seen of him, but from what he said, and the manner in which he said it, I am convinced that we could not get a better chief than this young colonel. I believe that he will make it a comfortable regiment to be in, but I also believe that those who oppose him will find that they make a grievous mistake."

The next day Hector took up in earnest the work of organizing the regiment. In the first place he insisted that the officers should learn their drill; then, that instead of handing over the practical command of their companies to their sergeants, they should themselves command them on the drill ground, look after the discipline and comfort of the men in barracks, and become personally acquainted with the character of every man under their command. Many of the sergeants were inefficient; these were speedily deprived of their rank, and men of good conduct and zeal appointed to their places. The regard of the men was won by his insisting that the contractors for their food should send in meat and bread and wine of the quality that they had guaranteed to supply.

Three officers were told off every day to examine the quality of all food sent in; any reported as being bad was examined by Hector, and if the complaint was well founded, was at once condemned. Great attention was paid to the cooking, to the cleanliness of the barrack-rooms, and to many other details that had until then been entirely neglected. There were at first some grumblers, not only among the men, but among the officers as well; but the extraordinary and rapid improvement in the efficiency of the regiment, its appearance and condition, was such that these were not long in recognizing, that although the work was hard, no unnecessary labour was imposed upon them, while, as their knowledge of drill increased the work became easier and less irksome. All recognized that by far the hardest worker in the regiment was the colonel himself. Every morning for the first month he himself drilled the officers in a court-yard that was not overlooked, and when they all knew their work, sent them to take charge of their companies. Until he considered the officers competent, he drilled the companies by turn, and when drill was over, made a tour of every room in the barracks, visited the kitchen, and conversed freely with the men, listening to any complaints.

At first the number of men brought up for drunkenness was large. The first offence he always condoned, giving the offender a lecture on the folly of his conduct and of the discredit that it brought upon the regiment. For the second offence a man was confined to barracks, and forced to wear his coat inside out even at drill. The ridicule that the men had to suffer was worse than any punishment inflicted upon them, and no case occurred of a third offence. By turns the three officers of each company dined with him, and, chatting with them as a friend, he not only gained their liking but made himself acquainted with their individual characters. Turenne came to Paris a short time after Hector assumed the command of his regiment, and as soon as he heard of his arrival, the latter called upon him.

"I heard from the cardinal of your good fortune," the viscount said, "and congratulate you heartily upon it. Mazarin was good enough to say that the discovery of the

Spaniards' ambush was the result of my teaching, and indeed I feel somewhat proud of my pupil. I am going to the Rhine, as perhaps you may have heard."

"I hope to have the honour of serving under you with my regiment, sir."

"I shall be glad to have you, but I fear there is little chance of it. I am to take the command of the Weimar troops. The death of the duke has been a heavy blow to us, and it is thought that unless I go down there—I say it because I have served there and am known by the Weimar troops—that force will break up altogether. From what I hear, I hardly think there is much chance of having any French regiments with me, and those now being raised are likely to be sent to fight under Enghien in Flanders. My position is, as you know, a painful one, owing to Bouillon having gone to Italy to take the command of the Pope's troops. I believe that is the reason why Mazarin has withdrawn me from the command of our army in Savoy. However, as a soldier I accept the work he has given me, not allowing family matters to interfere in any way with it, though it is my opinion that Bouillon has been very hardly treated by the breaking of the engagements that were given him when he surrendered Sedan to France."

A week later Hector presented himself at the levée of Cardinal Mazarin.

"I was expecting to see you, baron. I received your note saying that you had taken the command of your regiment, and would do yourself the honour of presenting yourself as soon as you had put matters in trim. Are you satisfied with your men and your officers?"

"With both, your eminence, and trust that in two or three months' time you will do us the honour of inspecting us."

"And how did you find your barony?"

"I was delighted with it. The castle is a strong one, and I am taking steps to add to its strength; and I believe when it is finished that it will be almost impregnable save by an army, and that well commanded."

"Then you think," the cardinal said with a smile, but with a certain air of seriousness, "that you could offer me a safe asylum if I needed one."

"I trust that such an event may never occur, your eminence, but if it should, my castle is at your disposal, and I will guarantee that it will resist for three months, whoever might attack it."

"One can never say," the cardinal said mournfully. "Oh, these nobles! They are, as they have ever been, the curse of France. Each man thinks only of himself and of increasing his domains. What France may suffer matters nothing to them so that they are enriched. Were one of them capable of ruling France I would gladly retire; but who is there? Orleans, vain, empty-headed, treacherous to his friends, a man whose word is not to be relied upon. Condé, who thinks only of enriching himself and adding to his possessions. Beaufort, a roistering trooper. None of these men could maintain his position for a moment. The whole country seethes with discontent at the heavy taxation necessitated by the war; Paris, as is always the case when there is trouble in the air, is restless and turbulent. I have good friends, but they are insufficient to sustain me against the intrigues of my enemies. The queen alone upholds me. Truly, the burden is too great for one man to bear.

"You will wonder why I am speaking thus to you, Colonel Campbell, but it is of the greatest necessity that her majesty should know upon whom she can rely absolutely in case of trouble. You, sir, being altogether unconnected with any of the great families of France, stand in a different position from that of the great majority of officers of your rank. Look where I will, I see our regiments officered by men connected by birth and family with one or other of the men who are at present intriguing against us, and were they ordered to take steps to arrest, for example, one of those persons connected with them, they might, without openly refusing, give such warning to them that they would be able to escape. Now, sir, I ask you to tell me frankly whether, under all contingencies, the queen can rely upon your services? I give you my word that whatever your reply is, it shall in no way count against you. There are cases in which it would doubtless be painful to you to carry out such an order. You are a protégé of Monsieur de Turenne. Monsieur de Turenne is brother of the Duc de Bouillon, and, as I know, you yourself were staying for some months in the castle of Sedan, where you went to be cured of your wounds. Now, monsieur, frankly, were you ordered to arrest the Duc de Bouillon, would you carry it out without fear or favour?"

"Certainly I would, your excellency; and should you give such an order to Marshal Turenne he would do so himself. He is a soldier of the queen before all things, and has taught me that my duty is towards the sovereign who represents France, regardless of all other considerations."

The cardinal while speaking had watched the young soldier's face scrutinizingly. Faithful as Turenne had always been to the crown, even when his brother was in arms against it, Mazarin had still in his heart some doubts as to his fidelity under all circumstances. He could not but be conscious that faith had been absolutely broken with Bouillon, and, accustomed to tortuous ways, he could scarce imagine that Turenne would hold himself altogether above family interest. He saw by the manner more than the words of Hector that he was speaking from a profound conviction. In asking him the question, he had been thinking more of Turenne's loyalty than of the young colonel's. Having been four years in the closest connection with the marshal, he could not but know his real sentiments, and he felt sure that had Turenne expressed any anger at the treatment his brother had received, he would have seen it in the young man's face. The answer was a reassuring one.

"Thank you, monsieur le baron; the musketeers and the Swiss guards we know we can absolutely rely upon, and I shall be glad to be able to inform the queen that she can place implicit faith in your regiment. I need not impress upon you the necessity for our conversation being regarded by you as absolutely confidential."

WON BY THE SWORD

Hector, thinking the matter over, had no great difficulty in the end in arriving at the truth, namely, that his own loyalty was a very secondary object of interest to the minister, and that his real motive in thus apparently opening his mind to him had been, not to gather his own sentiments, but to endeavour to ascertain those of Turenne. From the talk among his officers he had already learned that the general opinion was, that although the queen had always entertained a most favourable opinion of Turenne, and had herself nominated him as marshal and commander of the forces on the Rhine, Mazarin had assented to the arrangement because he feared that the army of Italy would probably follow its commander should the latter take up the quarrel of his brother, while, on the Rhine with but a few regiments, to all of whom he was a stranger, under his command, he would be practically powerless, whatever his sentiments might be with regard to Bouillon.

In the middle of August Hector received an order from Mazarin to take part with his "regiment in a review which the queen intended to hold at Versailles two days later. At this review the musketeers, the Swiss guards, the Scottish regiment, and two regiments of the line besides his own, the queen, the young king, Mazarin, and most of the members of the court were present. The Poitou regiment acquitted itself admirably, and its marching, and the steadiness with which it went through its manœuvres, were in such strong contrast to that of the other two infantry regiments, which had both been formed for some years, as to excite the surprise and admiration of the spectators. After it was over a mounted officer rode up to Hector and told him that the queen wished to speak to him. Riding up, he dismounted, and advanced to the queen's pavilion.

"Monsieur Campbell," the queen said graciously, "I wish to express to you how well satisfied we are with the efficiency of your regiment, and the admirable way in which it has gone through its manœuvres. Never have I seen these better performed; and this is the more surprising as it has been but four months raised, and but three months under your personal command. The cardinal has informed me that he learns that this is due entirely to your personal exertions, and the care that you have bestowed upon it. I wish that all my officers showed the same zeal and diligence. In order to mark my gratification at the conduct of the regiment, I have requested monsieur le cardinal to order that two companies of your regiment shall be quartered at the barracks now occupied by the Scottish regiment, which is to march east to-morrow. Hector bowed deeply; and, immensely gratified at the praise that his regiment had received, returned to his place at its head, and marched back to St. Denis. On their arrival there he informed his men of the gracious words the queen had been pleased to say about the regiment, and the great honour bestowed upon them by the quartering of two companies in Paris. The men broke into loud cheering as he concluded.

Hector then called the officers together. "Gentlemen," he said, "I have to thank you for the admirable way in which you have seconded my efforts, and by the aid of which the regiment has just gained the high commendation of Her Majesty, within so very short a time after it has been raised. I have been thinking the matter over as I rode back, and I have decided that where all did so well, it would be invidious to give to any the sole honour of being thus quartered near the Louvre and furnishing guards, and to yourselves the pleasure of being in Paris. Therefore, gentlemen, I shall send, in the first place, the first and tenth companies. At the end of two weeks the ninth company will take the place of the tenth; a fortnight later, the second will take the place of the first, and so in order, so that each company will in turn have its share in this honourable service."

There was a general murmur of satisfaction. The next morning a formal order was received that two companies of the Poitou regiment should march into Paris, and occupy a portion of the barracks which the Scotch regiment had just vacated.

Hector called up the two companies he had selected.

"Now, men," he said, "you see the advantage that you have gained by discipline and good conduct. I have no doubt that before granting us the honour of forming a part of the garrison of Paris, the minister has made inquiries respecting the conduct of the regiment here, and has doubtless heard that it has been eminently satisfactory, and that the authorities and inhabitants have no complaint, of drunkenness or misconduct, against us. Of misconduct there have been no cases, of drunkenness very few, and, indeed, for the past month there has not been a single case among you. I trust that you will remember that while in Paris the credit of the regiment is in your hands, and that no single case of drunkenness or brawling in the streets will take place. I feel confident that this will be so, and I need hardly say that should there be an exception, the punishment will be vastly more severe than any that has previously been awarded, and I am sure that any offender will find, in the contempt with which he will be regarded by his comrades, a still more severe punishment than any that I can inflict."

That evening Captain de Thiou and the other officers of the two companies that were to march into Paris the next day dined with Hector; and after dinner de Thiou rose and said: "Colonel, I have been requested to express to you, on behalf of the whole of the officers of the regiment, our deep gratitude for the honours that our regiment has obtained. These you were good enough yesterday to ascribe partly to us; but we feel that they are wholly due to yourself. Although some of us were at first a little inclined to think that the changes made by you in our work were unnecessary, all now recognize fully how great has been the benefit, not only to the regiment, but to ourselves. Duties which were at first considered irksome are now regarded as pleasant. We feel that, as you said would be the case, we have acquired the respect of the men, and that it is upon us that they rely, and not upon their sergeants.

"Our own time passes more pleasantly from being fully occupied, and from consciousness that we are doing our duty. As to the regiment in general, the benefit has been enormous.

THE POITOU REGIMENT

The men seem pleased with the interest shown in them, as much as with the comfort that they now enjoy, and they in turn endeavour to satisfy us, both by their attention to drill, by their bearing and manner, and by their avoidance of giving any cause for complaint. All this, monsieur, has been your work, and I am sure that we are all conscious of the difference of the display we made in the park, and that which we should have shown had it not been for the reforms which have been introduced by you. We all trust that the day may not be far distant when we shall be able to prove on the field of battle the same efficiency that has won us credit upon the parade ground."

"I thank you heartily, Captain de Thiou, for what you have been good enough to say on your own behalf and that of the officers of the regiment. I can only say that I have endeavoured to act up to the teaching of Monsieur de Turenne, and I felt sure that although my methods might at first seem irksome to some of you, their value would gradually become appreciated. I am scarcely less pleased at the decrease in drunkenness, and at the general improvement in the men, than by the increase of discipline and efficiency."

"Do you mean to come to Paris, colonel?" De Thiou asked presently.

"No; I shall remain here. I shall ride in every day, but my presence will be more necessary with the regiment than with only two companies. You as senior officer will be responsible for the general order of the detachment."

Hector rode in the next day with his men, and after seeing them comfortably lodged in barracks, returned to St. Denis. A week later reports reached St. Denis of a strange scene at the court. The haughty and insolent Duchess of Montbazon, who belonged to the party of the Importants, had the impertinence to insult the queen grossly in the gardens of the Tuileries. She had at once been disgraced and ordered to retire to Rochfield, and the Duke of Beaufort and his friends were furious at this exercise of Mazarin's authority. The next day Hector received a message asking him to call at the Hotel de Cleves, the cardinal's residence. On his presenting himself, he was at once shown into Mazarin's private apartments.

"Monsieur de Villar," Mazarin said, "I am sorely in need of friends. You have heard of what has happened, and from the threats that he has publicly uttered against myself I am convinced that Beaufort will hesitate at nothing to bring about my ruin. I hear that you are still with your regiment at St. Denis. I shall be glad if for a time you will take up your abode at Paris, and will hold yourself in readiness to be of service to me if there should be occasion. Beaufort is capable of even attempting my life; he is very unscrupulous, and will hesitate at nothing. I shall be glad if you will take up your lodging within a short distance of this, so that I can communicate with you instantly."

"Certainly, your excellency; I will keep half a company always under arms, so that at the shortest notice they will be in readiness to act as you may direct. But surely, your excellency, you have the queen's musketeers close at hand?"

"The queen's musketeers are a body of gallant soldiers, but they will take their orders only from the queen. They were strongly anti-cardinalist in the late reign, and I do not suppose that they are better affected towards myself than they were towards Richelieu. If they heard that my hotel was attacked they would not move a foot until they received orders from the queen to do so."

"At any rate, you shall have no reason to complain of delay on our part, your excellency, and I can assure you of my devotion."

Hector at once went to an auberge but a few hundred yards from the cardinal's residence. He thought it better to put up there than to take lodgings, as he could then have his four mounted men with him; and, riding to St. Denis, he returned the same night with them.

"A horse is always to be saddled," he said to them when they had dismounted and his orderlies had come up to his room, and one of you by turns will always remain here armed and ready to mount without an instant's delay. The others will put aside their scarves; and one of you will always be at the cabaret nearest to the Hotel de Vendôme, the residence of the Duke of Beaufort, who is a son of the Duc de Vendôme. At times two of you can be there so as to drink and play cards together, as the appearance of one sitting too long might attract attention. Your object is to find out from the conversation of the duke's guards and servants whether they have any idea that anything unusual is going to take place. I have reason to believe that there is a plot against the cardinal, and I am much concerned in defeating it."

When the four Scotch soldiers had retired, Hector said to Paolo:

"Now, Paolo, I place more reliance upon your finding out anything that is afloat than upon the soldiers. It is not likely that any plans Beaufort may form will be communicated to his people until the moment for action, and indeed it is probable that he will rely solely upon his personal friends. Now I want you to disguise yourself in any way you may think best, and watch Beaufort's hotel; see who comes in and out, and if a messenger goes out follow him, see the houses he calls at, and mark if those who dwell there repair at once to the Hotel de Vendôme. If you perceive that this is the case let me know at once. See if you can get hold of half a dozen street-gamins, and employ them to watch the houses of all these gentlemen, and especially that of Monsieur Léi, captain of Beaufort's guards, and of the two Messieurs de Campion and the Count de Beaupuis, who are, I know, among the duke's most intimate friends. There are scores of these street-boys who for a few sous a day would gladly undertake the work."

"I will do that, master. You can take my word that by to-morrow at noon the lodging of these four gentlemen will be strictly watched. This is a business after my own heart."

"In the first place, Paolo, take a note from me to the Hotel de Cleves and wait for an answer."

The note was a short one. It merely gave the name of the auberge at which he had taken up his quarters, and added:

WON BY THE SWORD

If your eminence will be good enough to send me every morning a list of any visits that you may intend to pay, or any journey that you may make during the day, it would enable me to regulate my movements accordingly in order to be always here and ready to carry out any orders that you may send me from your hotel.

The cardinal's reply was even more brief:

It is well thought of. I shall go nowhere but to the Louvre to-morrow, and shall probably be there the greater part of the day. Unless you hear from me to the contrary, you need only remain in between twelve and one.

The next morning Paolo appeared dressed in ragged clothes.

"What is that bundle of papers that you have got?"

"They are lampoons on the cardinal. Nothing so natural as that I should try and sell them in front of the Hotel de Vendôme."

"Nothing could be better, Paolo."

"I have already picked up a dozen gamins, master, sharp little beggars, who jumped at the idea of being set to watch people. Between them everyone who goes in or comes out from the hotel will be followed, and they will, in the first place, find out his name and bring it to me, after that they will follow him wherever he goes, and from time to time let me know what he is doing."

Several days passed. The four gentlemen specially named, together with several others, were frequently at the hotel. There was in this, however, nothing suspicious, as Hector easily learned that they were all vassals or close friends of the house of Vendôme. On the third day, however, he heard that at least a dozen of these gentlemen met in twos or threes at various cabarets near the Duke of Beaufort's, and spent the greater portion of their time there. Hector at once procured dresses suitable for gentlemen of the middle class for the troopers, and gave them instructions to spend the greater portion of their time at the cabarets at which these gentlemen stopped. Their reports were that they talked of indifferent subjects, but that they were evidently waiting for someone, as they invariably turned a glance at the door whenever a fresh-comer entered.

The next day Hector received a note from the cardinal:

I am just starting with the Duke of Orleans for Maisons, where I shall dine with him.

Two hours later the three troopers who had been out returned almost at the same minute with the news that the persons they were watching had all got up suddenly and gone out after a messenger wearing the Beaufort cognizance had come in and spoken to them. And a few minutes later Paolo arrived and said that the Duke of Beaufort had gone with the Count of Beaupuis to the convent of the Capuchins, and that several horses had been taken there.

Hector thought the matter over. "Certainly," he said to himself, "as the cardinal's note is dated at nine o'clock, he is now some distance on his way. As soon as the duke received notice of his having gone, he notified his friends. It can only be on his way home that they will venture to attack him; but even if they have that intention they will scarcely do so if the Duke of Orleans returns with him, unless, indeed, the duke is himself in the plot, and as none of Paolo's scouts have brought news of any communications between Beaufort and Orleans, it is hardly likely that it is so.

"Paolo, do you go down and watch the convent of the Capuchins. If the Duke of Beaufort remains there with his friend—and he may doubtless be joined by others—let me know if he rides away. If he does so the attack may take place anywhere along the road; if he remains, he will doubtless attack the cardinal as his carriage passes. Should there be more than one entrance to the convent, put boys to watch them, and bring you news should the party sally out. I shall be at the barracks. It is there that you must bring or send me word."

The troopers were ordered to put on their military clothes and saddle their horses, and a quarter of an hour later Hector rode to the barracks, followed by them.

"De Thiou," he said, "I want you and the other five officers to have your horses ready at a moment's notice. I have some sort of idea that there is a plot on foot against the cardinal, and I want to take a hand in the matter. I fancy that with you and my five troopers we shall be strong enough to disconcert the plotters."

Two hours later he received a message from Paolo, saying that the Duke of Beaufort and three other gentlemen were still at the convent, but that most of the others had gone to the residence of Henri de Campion in the Rue St. Honoré.

"They mean to attack him just at the end of the journey," Hector said to himself, "and close to the Hotel de Vendôme. Now it only depends upon whether the Duke of Orleans stays at Maisons or returns with the cardinal."

He ordered the officers and troopers to mount, and with them took his post on the road by which the cardinal would return. In half an hour they saw his carriage approaching. They then moved forward. As the carriage passed them Hector saluted, and saw to his satisfaction that the Duke of Orleans was with the cardinal. After the carriage had gone fifty yards Hector turned, and with his party followed the carriage at that distance. When within a quarter of a mile of the Rue St. Honoré a horseman came along. He met the carriage, and immediately it passed him turned and galloped back along the road. Hector felt no doubt that he was placed there to warn the conspirators to be in readiness if the Duke of Orleans was not in the carriage, and that there would now be no attempt. However, he closed up to within thirty yards. As they entered the Rue St. Honoré all was quiet there, and nothing happened until the cardinal alighted at the Hotel de Cleves. As he did so he looked round, and beckoned to Hector to follow him.

CHAPTER XIII
THE BATTLES OF FREIBURG

THE cardinal did not address Hector until he had entered his private room, when he turned and said sharply, "What means this, colonel? When I saw you and your officers on the road I felt sure that you were not there for nothing, and still more sure when on alighting I found you so closely following me."

"I was convinced, cardinal, that there was a plot against your life, and I believe that it was only because the Duke of Orleans returned with you that it was not carried into effect."

"And possibly because they saw your troop behind the carriage. Now tell me your reason for supposing that I was in danger."

Hector related the various steps that he had taken.

"Your spies worked better for you than mine did for me," the cardinal said. "That a dozen or so of Beaufort's friends were for some reason or other spending their time at the Angel Inn and other cabarets I was aware, but I have had no word of their proceedings to-day. You have been better served, doubtless, because your plans were better laid. I hardly think that they would have attacked me when Orleans was with me, but there is no saying; for if Beaufort has daring and insolence enough to attempt to slay the queen's minister within a quarter of a mile of the Louvre, he would not trouble greatly whether princes of the blood were in the carriage or not, especially if he had some reason for believing that Orleans would not regard the deed with very great disapproval.

"However, whatever his intentions might be, it is clear that the appearance of your party of twelve armed men decided the question. We may regard it as certain that the news that had such an escort was carried to them by the man who galloped on ahead. I thank you, sir, I thank you very heartily, not only for my sake, but for that of France. I will ask you to go across to the Louvre; I will take half a dozen armed servants with me, but there is little fear that the attempt will be renewed to-day. They must be too much disconcerted by the failure of their plot to make fresh arrangements so speedily. I shall go first to the Louvre and inform her majesty of what has taken place. You will remain here for half an hour, and will then leave by the gate at the back of the house and make a circuit, and enter the palace by the river gate. The musketeers on guard will stop you, but I will give you a pass." And he wrote a few lines on paper. "The queen's confidential servant, Laporte, will be at the door to meet you, and will have instructions to escort you by corridors where you will be unobserved, and so to her majesty's private closet. Were you to accompany me, Beaufort would soon hear of it, and would be shrewd enough to perceive that your meeting with me was by no means a matter of chance."

Hector followed out his instructions, and on presenting himself at the palace was at once taken up to the queen's closet. Laporte went in, and returning immediately requested him to enter. The queen was walking up and down the room, her face flushed with indignation.

"Her majesty would fain hear from your own lips, monsieur le baron, the statement that you have made to me." The queen sat down and listened intently while Hector repeated the story.

"There can be no doubt about it, cardinal; this keeping of a number of armed men within call for days, the summons to them to gather in the Rue St. Honoré, while he himself with others took up his post at the convent of the Capuchins hard by, the moment his spies had discovered that you had left for Maisons, could but have been for one purpose. But they shall learn that although a woman, Anne of Austria, Queen of France, is not to be deprived of her minister and faithful friend without striking back in return. Monsieur de Villar, you have rendered me a great service. Is there any boon that you would ask of me? it is granted beforehand."

"I thank your majesty most humbly," Hector said. "Already I have received honours far beyond anything I deserve. I had the honour when thanking your majesty, to hope some day to be able to give proof that they were not unworthily bestowed, and still hope to do so."

"You have already shown yourself worthy," the queen said, "by the manner in which you have in so short a time rendered the regiment to which we appointed you so efficient. However, if there is at present no boon that we can bestow, then remember that the Queen of France holds herself your debtor, and that you have my royal word that any boon that you may hereafter ask for, that is in my power to grant, will be given you. Take this as a pledge of my promise." And she took off a gold chain exquisitely worked, and gave it him. He received it kneeling. "Now, sir, we will keep you here no longer. I have much to say to his excellency. I trust that you will present yourself at the levée this evening."

"One thing more, colonel," Mazarin added; "I doubt not that some of Beaufort's people will endeavour to find out how it was that you came to be behind my carriage. If they do so you might carelessly mention that you and your officers had ridden out in a party at St. Germain, and that on your way back you chanced to fall in with my carriage."

At the barracks Hector called the officers together. "Gentlemen," he said, "I have no doubt that your little ride to-day has somewhat puzzled you. I am not at liberty to tell you the reason why I requested you to ride with me; but it is very probable that you may be asked the question, and I beg you all to remember that we have been on a little party of pleasure to St. Germain, and having dined there were on our way back when we overtook the carriage of the cardinal; and seeing that he had the Duke of Orleans with him, we reined back and followed him, deeming that it would not appear respectful were we to gallop past the carriage. Please bear this story in mind. Recall also that we dined at the Lion d'Or there, that our dinner was a good one and that it was a sort of celebration on my part of our two companies having the honour to be chosen for duty in Paris. This is a matter upon which much depends; it is, in fact, a matter of state; and you may well imagine that I should not be recalling these events to your mind were it not that a good deal depends upon it, and that I have received strict orders that this little comedy shall be carried out. I know that I can rely implicitly upon your discretion, and I have indeed answered for you all. The story will be true in every respect. Instead of the excursion having come off to-day it shall come off on the first day I can arrange that we can be all off duty."

That evening at the palace Hector was, as the cardinal predicted, accosted by one of Beaufort's officers, to whom he had been previously introduced. After talking on other subjects for a few minutes, he said:

"I saw you to-day, monsieur, riding with a party of your officers along the Rue St. Honoré. You did not notice me?"

"I assure you that I did not, sir, or I should not have been so rude as to pass without saluting you." Then he added with a laugh, "We were riding slowly, too, for the cardinal's coach was in front of us, and it would not have been good manners to have galloped past him, especially as he had the Duke of Orleans with him."

"Had you been far?" the other asked carelessly.

"No great distance; a little party of pleasure with my officers to eat a dinner together, to celebrate the honour we had received in being brought into Paris. My officers have worked very hard, and the matter served as a good excuse for giving them a little dinner."

For the next day or two everything passed off quietly, but four of the officers reported that when dining at a cabaret two or three of the duke's officers had come in and entered into conversation with them, and had brought up the subject of their riding in after the cardinal.

THE BATTLES OF FREIBURG

"You almost looked as if you were serving as a body-guard to him," one of them laughed.

"I daresay we did," was the answer. "It was rather a nuisance; but it would not have been courteous to have ridden past the carriage." And he then repeated the story as had been arranged.

Although the Duke of Beaufort had been told by some of his friends that there were rumours abroad of a plot against Mazarin's life, and that it would be best for him to leave Paris for a time, he refused to do so, saying that even if it was discovered the cardinal would not dare to lay hands on him. Moreover, the replies which had been obtained from Hector and his officers convinced him that their riding behind Mazarin's carriage was an accident.

On the 2nd of September the duke presented himself at the Louvre as usual. After speaking with him for a few minutes, the queen left the room with Mazarin, and Guibaut, captain of the Guards, at once came forward and arrested him. He was kept at the Louvre that night, and next day was taken to the castle of Vincennes. Two companies of Swiss guards marched first, followed by a royal carriage containing the duke and Guibaut. The carriage was surrounded by the royal musketeers. A body of light cavalry followed, and the two companies of the Poitou regiment brought up the rear. Thus the people of Paris were shown that the queen had both the will and the power to punish, and the fickle population, who would the day before have shouted in honour of Beaufort, were delighted at seeing that the royal authority was once again paramount in Paris. The other members of the party of Importants either fled or were arrested. The Campions, Beaupuis, and others, succeeded in making their escape from France. The Marquis of Chateauneuf, governor of Touraine, was ordered back to his province. La Chatres, colonel-general, was dismissed from his post; the Duc de Vendôme was forced to leave France; and the ambitious Bishop of Beauvais and several other prelates were commanded to return to their dioceses. All the members of the Vendôme family were exiled to the château of Annette. Madame de Chevreuse, de Hautefort, and a large number of other members of the party were ordered to leave Paris. Thus the party of the Importants ceased to exist.

The people of Paris seemed greatly pleased at what appeared to them the end of the troubles, and they exclaimed that Richelieu was not dead, but that he had simply changed his appearance, and had become twenty years younger. Mazarin chose a number of soldiers belonging to his own regiment, and several officers who belonged to Richelieu's own guard. These were at all times to follow him wherever he went. He selected a number of noblemen, all of distinguished merit and influence, and created five of them dukes, and thus secured to himself a party that would to some extent balance the power of his adversaries.

He also made an effort to bring about a union between the Duke of Orleans and the Condés, but failed, owing to the enormous demands that each put forward. Condé demanded the government of Languedoc for himself, of Burgundy for Enghien, and Normandy for the Duc de Longueville, and the entire domains of his late brother-in-law, Henry of Montmorency. Orleans on his part demanded the province of Champagne, the three bishoprics of Metz, Toul, and Verdun, and the town and castle of Sedan. As these demands, if granted, would have rendered the two families all-powerful, Mazarin gave up the attempt, and decided that the best plan to prevent troubles was to let these dangerous families continue to be hostile to each other.

As soon as he had finished his work of crushing the Importants, Mazarin sent for Hector.

"Now, Monsieur Campbell," he said, "I have breathing time. The conspiracy among the nobles is for the time crushed, and now that they see that the queen is determined to protect me, and that I am not afraid of using the power committed to me, I hope that it will be some time before they venture to conspire again. I have further strengthened my position by granting honours to many distinguished gentlemen who were well inclined towards me, and on whose support in the future I shall be able to rely. Now it is time that I should turn to the man who has probably saved my life, and to whose evidence given before the queen I in no small degree owe it that she resolved to suppress these insolent nobles. I have not hurried in this matter, since, by your answer to the queen, it was evident that you desired no change in your position, and that the matter could wait.

"Still, monsieur, her offer was to grant honours for services rendered to the state. The matter of the service that you have rendered to Cardinal Mazarin is still untouched. It is something so new to me that anyone in France should be so perfectly contented with his lot as to refuse such an offer as that made to you by the queen, that I feel somewhat at a loss what to do. I can understand that, young and ardent, increased rank would have no charm for you. Were it otherwise I could bestow the highest rank upon you. I am aware that your habits are simple, for I have made inquiries, and that money in itself goes for little in your eyes; still, sir, one who has the honour of being first minister of France, and who is also a very rich man, cannot remain with a debt of gratitude wholly uncancelled. I hear from my agent in Poitou that you have voluntarily remitted the fine that your vassals would pay on the occasion of a new lord taking possession, on account of the heavy taxation that presses so sorely upon them.

"I honour you, sir, for such a step, and have even mentioned it to the queen as a proof of the goodness of your disposition, and I feel sure that there is nothing that would please you better than that I should grant the tenants of your estate an immunity from all taxation; but this I cannot do. All private interests must give way to the necessities of the state. I deplore the sufferings of the cultivators of France, sufferings that have of late driven many to take up arms. It is my duty to repress such risings; but I have ordered the utmost leniency to be shown to these unfortunate men, that the troops should not be quartered upon their inhabitants, and that the officers shall see that there is no destruction of houses and no damage to property; that would increase still further their difficulty in paying the imposts, which I regret to say press so sorely and unduly upon them. Tell me frankly what is the greatest object of your ambition?"

"I thank your excellency most heartily for your kind intentions towards me, but any ambition that I may have had is already much more than gratified. I have never for a moment thought of, or even wished that I might some day become lord of a fair estate and a noble of France. I had not ventured to hope that I might become colonel of a regiment for another fifteen years. Both these things have, thanks to the kind appreciation of her majesty and yourself for a very simple act of duty, fallen to me. If I might ask a boon, it would be that my regiment may be sent to join the force of Marshal Turenne. So long as there was danger here I should not have wished to be removed from a position where I might be of some assistance, however slight, to the queen and yourself, but now that all danger is at an end I should be glad to return to active duty. I have endeavoured humbly to make Marshal Turenne my model. He has but one thought and one desire—namely, to do his duty and to make the soldiers under his command contented and happy, but I have no hope of ever emulating his great merits as a commander."

"That request is easily granted," Mazarin said, and drawing a sheet of paper towards him, he wrote:

The regiment of Poitou will at once proceed to the Rhine, where it will place itself under the orders of Marshal Turenne.

He added his signature, and handed the paper to Hector.

"That counts for nothing," he said. "You must remember that life is short and, especially in the case of a minister of France, uncertain. In your own case you might be disabled in the field and unable to serve further. The advent of a party hostile to me in power would doubtless be signalized by acts of vengeance against those who have been my friends, and estates change hands so frequently in France that la Villar might well be confiscated. No man is above the chances of fortune. I have agents in England, and have this morning given an order to my intendant to place in the hands of Monsieur Wilson, a well-known citizen of London, a goldsmith, the sum of fifty thousand crowns to stand in your name, and to be payable to your order. Here is his address. It is but a small sum for the saving of my life, but it will place you above the risk of the contingencies of fortune in this country. I wish for no thanks," he said, with a wave of his hand as Hector was about to speak. "I have given more for the most trifling favours. I now bid you adieu, and doubt not that I shall hear that you and your regiment have greatly distinguished yourselves in the east, where hostilities will in all probability shortly be commenced. You had better present yourself at the levée this evening to make your adieus to the queen."

This Hector did, and early the next morning rode with his two companies to St. Denis, where the news that the regiment was to march towards the Rhine was received with great satisfaction. It was now the middle of October, and when, after ten days' march, the regiment reached Epernay, they heard that Turenne had withdrawn is troops from the Rhine, where the Imperialists had already gone into winter quarters, and had stationed them in the various towns of Lorraine. His head-quarters were at Nancy. Turenne greeted him warmly upon his arrival.

"Matters have been going on slowly since I saw you in Paris. I have been too weak to fight the Bavarians, who fortunately were too undecided to attack me. Could they but have made up their minds to throw in their fortune with Austria, they might have overrun all Lorraine, for aught I could have done to withstand them. The troopers were without horses, the infantry almost without clothes, and as the court was unable to send me any remittances I have been forced to borrow money upon my own estates for the public service, and have mounted five thousand horse and enrolled three thousand foot and am still sustaining them. However, I hear from Mazarin that he will in a week send off a large convoy of treasure, which will be welcome indeed, for I am nearly at the end of my resources. Some of my troops are quartered in the town, but the most part are among the mountains, where they trouble the inhabitants less and have small temptations towards rioting and excesses. Which would you rather?"

"I would much rather go into the country, marshal; my regiment is in good condition now, but to stay in quarters in a town is bad for discipline."

"So be it. You might make your head-quarters at the village of Samline; there are no other troops within thirty miles of it. On arriving there you will make inquiries as to the supplies to be obtained within a circle of fifteen miles round. Fortunately I have a good supply of tents, and any men for whom you cannot find quarters in the villages can be placed under canvas. You can draw as much wine as you require for three months' rations from the stores here, and two months' rations of flour. I will direct the intendants to take up carts for the transport of the supplies you take from here. You will doubtless be able to buy meat up there, and I hope that you will be able to obtain sufficient flour and wine to last you till the end of the winter, for transport will be very difficult when the snow is on the ground. Firewood your soldiers will, of course, cut for themselves in the forests."

The winter passed quietly. Hector managed to obtain quarters for all his troops—a village being allotted to each company. Before they marched off to their various quarters, Hector urged the officers to impress upon their men the advantage of behaving well to the villagers.

"Of course the presence of so many men will be of serious inconvenience to them, but they will doubtless make the best of it if they find that they are treated civilly and that their lodgers endeavour to give as little trouble as possible. See that everything down to the smallest article is paid for, and investigate every complaint, and I will punish any offenders severely. I have inquired into the average prices that sheep, fowls, pigs, goats, and other articles fetch, and have made out a list for each company; the peasants will be gainers by it, for they will be saved the journey down to the towns. Let this be stuck up in a conspicuous place in each village.

THE BATTLES OF FREIBURG

"The intendant will go round and make contracts for the supply of meat, and will see whether it will be more advantageous to erect ovens for the baking of bread in each village or to arrange to buy it ready baked there, we supplying the flour; for the troops, after being accustomed to good bread at St. Denis, will not be content with the black bread upon which these poor people exist. I shall pay a visit to each company in regular order, see that all is going on well, try men who have misbehaved themselves, and listen gladly to any suggestions that the respective captains may make to me."

The first company was quartered at Samline, and although the cold was severe and the life rough the troops were well contented, and Hector was glad to find that his instructions were carried out and that excellent relations were maintained between the troops and their hosts.

Early in the spring Turenne collected a force of three regiments of cavalry and two of infantry, and, passing the Rhine at Breisach, fell suddenly upon a force of Imperialists in the Black Forest, defeated them, and took three or four hundred prisoners, among whom were many officers, the rest of them escaping to the army commanded by Count Merci. In May the Bavarian army, numbering eight thousand foot and seven thousand horse, marched to besiege Freiburg, five leagues from Breisach, and Turenne followed with all his force, which now numbered ten thousand men. He found, however, that the Imperialists had occupied all the strong positions in the neighbourhood of the town, and not caring to run the risk either of defeat or great loss, and receiving information that the town had already opened negotiations for surrender, he fell back some five miles from the town, sending news to the court that his force was insufficient to attack the Imperialists. Mazarin thereupon sent orders to Enghien to set out at once for Germany. As soon as he reached the Rhine and his army prepared to cross, Enghien, who had been appointed generalissimo, rode forward with Marshal de Gramont, who was in command of the army under him, to the camp of Turenne. The meeting between

Enghien and Turenne was most cordial. Enghien had always felt the warmest admiration for the talents of the older marshal, had been most intimate with him whenever he was at court, and regarded him as his master in the art of war. Turenne was free from the vice of jealousy; and as the armies of France were almost always placed under the supreme if sometimes nominal command of princes of the blood, it seemed nothing but natural to him that Enghien should receive supreme authority.

The characters of the two men were in complete contrast with each other—the one was ardent, passionate, prompt in action and swift in execution; the other, though equally brave, was prudent and careful, anxious above all things to accomplish his object with the smallest possible loss of men, while Enghien risked the lives of his soldiers as recklessly as his own. They always acted together in the most perfect harmony, and their friendship remained unimpaired even when in subsequent days they stood in arms against each other. At the council Turenne was in favour of making a circuit and taking up their post in the valley of St. Pierre, by which they would intercept the Bavarians' communications and force them by famine to issue out from their strong lines and fight in the open, and urged that to attack a position so strongly fortified would entail terrible loss, even if successful.

Marshal de Gramont, and d'Erlac, governor of Breisach, were of the same opinion. The Duc d'Enghien, however, was for attacking the enemy in their intrenchments; the idea of starving out an enemy was altogether repugnant to one of his impetuous disposition, and as generalissimo he overruled the opinions of the others. He himself, led by Turenne, reconnoitred the position of the enemy, and decided that the one army, which was called the army of France, consisting of six thousand foot and four thousand horse, commanded by Marshal de Gramont, should attack the enemy's position in front and on their right flank, and the other, called the army of Weimar, of five thousand foot and as many horse, under Turenne, should move round by a narrow pass and attack the enemy on the left flank. Merci's army occupied an almost inaccessible hill whose summit was strongly fortified, and it was against this that de Gramont's army was to hurl itself. The entrance to the valley by which Turenne was to fall upon their left flank was closed at its mouth by very strong intrenchments, and it was behind this that the main body of horse was posted.

To gain his point of attack Turenne had to make a very wide circuit, and started at break of day on the 3rd of August. It was arranged that Enghien, who remained with de Gramont, should not attack until three hours before sunset, in order to give Turenne time to attack at the same hour. At the time agreed upon, Enghien sent forward two battalions to begin the attack. The regiments of Condé and Mazarin were to follow, while the duke held two others in reserve. In order to get at the enemy the assailants were forced to climb a very steep ascent, and cross a vineyard intersected by many walls four feet high facing the terrace on which the vines grew. These were occupied by the Bavarians, but the French attacked with such vigour that the enemy were driven back. When, however, the latter reached the great cheval-de-frise, formed by felled trees, in front of the intrenchments, they could make no further progress, so heavy was the fire maintained by the enemy.

Enghien, seeing this, dismounted, placed himself at the head of the regiment of Condé, and led them forward, while Marshal Gramont and the officers did the same. Encouraged by this example, the troops were filled with enthusiasm, and, following their leaders unfalteringly, made their way through the cheval-de-frise, and, pressing forward without a pause, obtained possession of the intrenchments, driving the Bavarians into the woods behind. The battle had lasted three hours, and had cost the Bavarians three thousand men, while the French suffered at least equally.

Turenne's force had been as hotly engaged. Merci, the best general in the Austrian army, had foreseen that an attempt might be made through the defile, and had posted strong bodies of infantry among the trees on either side.

WON BY THE SWORD

As soon as Turenne entered the defile he was encountered by a heavy fire from his unseen foes, who, falling back through the trees as he advanced, continued to gain strength. Turenne had to fight every foot of his way in order to dislodge the enemy, and it was not until Enghien had brought the battle to a conclusion on his side, that Turenne arrived and, forcing the intrenchments guarding the mouth of the defile, found himself in contact with Merci, who was now able to concentrate his whole force against him. The combat was a furious one. The troops were engaged at but forty paces apart, and sometimes had hand-to-hand encounters. Merci brought the whole of his cavalry into play, but Turenne was unable to use his, as they were behind his infantry and could not make their way out through the mouth of the defile.

For seven hours the battle raged in the darkness. After losing three thousand men here, General Merci decided that his army would be totally destroyed if Enghien should bring his troops down from the hill at daybreak. Accordingly, leaving a body of musketeers to hide the movement by their fire, he withdrew the rest of his army and took up another strong position, partly on a height known as the Black Mountain, covering the entrance of the valley of St. Pierre and partly in the valley itself, thus covering his line of retreat. Had the French been able to attack early the next morning before the Bavarians had time to intrench themselves they might have won an easy victory; but for the past twenty-four hours the rain had been falling incessantly, Turenne's army had been marching on the previous day, and had been fighting for seven hours, and was incapable of further exertions, while that of Enghien was in little better plight, having passed the night in the rain on the ground it had won.

After such hard fighting both commanders agreed that a twenty-four hours' halt was absolutely necessary. The day could not be termed one of rest, for there were thousands of wounded to be collected and cared for, arms to be cleaned, for they had been rendered useless by the rain, and provisions

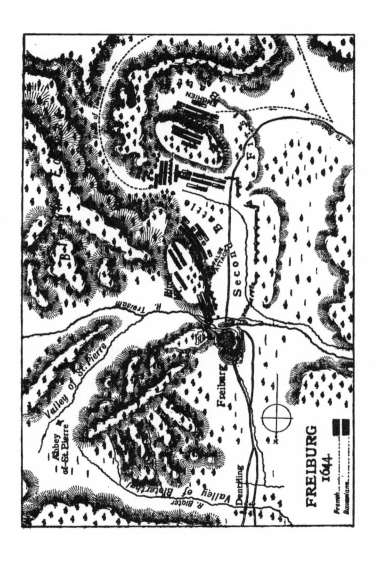

FREIBURG
1644.

French
Bavarian

to be brought up from the rear. Merci made the most of the time thus given him. The bottom of the mountain towards the plain was fortified by several rows of felled trees, and a portion of his infantry was posted between this point and the town of Freiburg, which was but half a mile away. The intrenchments that had been formed during the siege of the town were occupied by them; and as their front was covered by the fire of the guns from the fortress, as well as by that of the infantry on the hill, he considered the position to be impregnable, and therefore placed the main body of his army at the edge of the flat top of the hill, a strong body behind a wood about half-way up the slope, and his cavalry extended from that point to the walls of the city.

After reconnoitring the position, Enghien determined to make two attacks, one on the trenches between the foot of the hill and the town, and the other on the rows of felled trees at the foot of the mountain. A false attack was to be made between the two points. Turenne's force advanced nearly to the foot of the hill, the prince's army followed him, and also took up its position. But just as the attack was about to be made a great tumult was heard on the hill, and Enghien and Turenne rode to a neighbouing height in order to ascertain what was going on, leaving strict orders that no movement was to be made until their return. Count d'Espenan, who commanded the two advanced regiments of Enghien's army, however, ordered a detachment to attack a redoubt which stood within the line of attack, and Merci sent supports to its defenders.

D'Espenan sent more troops on his side and the engagement became serious. Suddenly the Imperialist artillery opened fire along the whole of their line, and Enghien's troops, apparently taking this for the signal of the beginning of the battle, moved forward for the assault without order or leader. As they were broken and confused by endeavouring to pass through the abattis of felled trees, the Bavarians rushed out and drove them back with great slaughter. Enghien and Turenne, galloping up in all haste, in vain attempted to rally them. Officers and men alike were panic-stricken. The two generals then rode to Turenne's army and advanced against the defence of trees. For a long time the battle raged without any marked success on either side. Several times the French made their way in to the intrenchments and were as often repulsed. Merci ordered his cavalry to dismount, and led them into the fray, but, darkness falling suddenly, the assailants ceased to attack, and occupied for the night the ground on which the struggle had taken place.

The fight that day had cost them two thousand troops, and the Bavarians twelve hundred, but as the latter had lost half their infantry in the first day's fighting the French were still superior in numbers. During the night Turenne had all the wounded of both nationalities carried to Breisach. After giving the army four days' rest, Enghien determined to resort to the tactics that Turenne had from the first recommended, and, marching along the plain, ascended the valley of Bloterthal and made for St. Pierre, where he would cut the Bavarian line of retreat. As soon as Merci saw the movement he gave orders for his army to fall back with all haste, and although Turenne pressed hard on his rear he succeeded in drawing his troops off, though, in order to do so, he was obliged to abandon his baggage and cannon. Altogether he lost between eight and nine thousand men, with their artillery and most of their horses. The French loss was equally great, and though the battle was claimed as a victory by them owing to the Bavarians having finally fallen back, it was really a drawn one.

CHAPTER XIV
JUST IN TIME

THE regiment of Poitou had suffered heavily in the battles of Freiburg. In the first advance Turenne had placed it in the rear of his infantry.

"I must have, Hector," he said, "a reserve upon which I can implicitly rely; brought up at the right moment it might decide the fate of a battle, if we are beaten it can allow the disorganized regiments to pass, check the pursuit of the enemy, and retire in good order, contesting every foot of the ground until the rest of the force have emerged from the mouth of the defile and been enabled to form up in sufficient order to withstand the effect of the enemy's cavalry."

The regiment, therefore, took no part in the work of clearing the defile of the enemy's infantry, and for the first four hours of the battle remained in the rear. Then Turenne ordered it to the front, to take the place of the regiments which had already lost half their strength, and were no longer capable of resisting the continued assaults of the Imperialists. Turenne himself rode with Hector at the head of the regiment. They pushed their way through the hardly-pressed troops in front, and when they faced the enemy deployed and poured a terrible volley into their assailants, and for the remaining three hours bore the whole brunt of the battle. Standing four deep, their flanks resting upon the rising ground on either side of the mouth of the pass, the two front lines alone maintained their fire so long as infantry only pressed them, the two lines behind being ordered by Hector not to fire a shot. When, however, the Bavarian infantry drew aside and the cavalry thundered down, the front lines fell back through those behind them, and the latter received the cavalry with such terrible volleys of musketry that they each time broke and fled.

Turenne, after seeing the Poitou regiment take up its post, occupied himself in re-forming the remains of the other regiments, and raising their spirits by warm words of commendation at the manner in which they had fought, until assured that they in turn could, if necessary, join the first line if it were forced to give way. When he had done this he rejoined Hector, who had dismounted and moved backwards and forwards among the men, seeing that the gaps caused by the enemy's fire were constantly filled up, and encouraging the soldiers with praise and exhortations. Turenne sat upon his horse some paces behind the rear line. When he saw the Bavarian infantry draw aside, and heard the roar of the cavalry charge, his lips tightened, and he half-turned his horse as if to call up the regiments behind. When, however, he saw the lines that had hitherto been in rear take up their place in front and stand there quiet and immovable, the look of irresolution passed from his face, and, after the Bavarian horse had fallen back, shattered by their volleys, he pressed a pace or two forward and shouted, "Regiment of Poitou, I thank you in the name of France; never saw I a regiment fight more bravely or steadily!"

The men responded with a loud cheer to this praise from one whom all respected and loved. Turenne then rode up to Hector.

"Splendidly done, Colonel Campbell! I had rather wondered why you kept half your men idle in such a fight; I now understand why you did so. Had all been firing, three-quarters of their muskets would have been empty, and you would possibly have been overthrown. It was a stroke of genius. I may have taught you many lessons in war, but to-night you have given me one."

Turenne remained with the regiment till the end of the fight, and marked with approval the way in which each line fought by turns, while the other remained behind them ready to receive the charges of the cavalry. As soon as the Bavarians drew off he saw that all the wounded were carried to the rear, where the surgeons rendered what aid was possible, while the rest of the troops threw themselves down to snatch a few hours' sleep. When, three hours later, Enghien's troops came down from the hill they had won, Turenne's force marched out from the defile. Turenne mounted his horse, and, calling upon Hector to follow him, rode forward with his principal officers to meet Enghien.

"It has been a terrible battle, prince, and if your loss equals mine the victory has indeed been won at a terrible cost."

"Mine has been heavy too," Enghien said, "but we have gained our object."

"Not wholly," Turenne replied, "for Merci has taken up a position as strong as that from which we have driven him."

"I wish that I could have lent you a hand in the fight," Enghien said, "but the Bavarians had fallen back into the woods, and we knew not whether they still held their ground there. In the rain and darkness it would have been dangerous to have crossed the broken ground with its woods and ravines, and the troops, after their exertions and heavy marches, were incapable of such an effort. Indeed, I had lost fully half my infantry, and the cavalry would be useless for such work. You must indeed have been sorely pressed, having Merci's whole force to contend with. Still, I had no doubt even if you could not issue from the defile you would be able to check the enemy." Then the generals in turn repeated the details of the battles in which they had been engaged and the losses they had suffered.

Turenne then introduced his principal officers to Enghien, and when he had done so called up Hector.

"I need not introduce this officer to you, prince," he said.

"No, indeed," Enghien replied, holding out his hand; "I have good reason to recollect you, Colonel Campbell. You have heard, marshal, what a good service he rendered me at Rocroi?"

"He has rendered me one no less this night," Turenne said. "I never saw a regiment stand more steadily than the one which he commands, and which he has trained to what seems to me perfection. For the last three hours that regiment alone bore the brunt of the battle, although assailed alternately by infantry and cavalry, and thus afforded time to re-form the regiments that fought earlier in the afternoon and to give me hope that even were the enemy to overcome the resistance of his men, I could still be able to check their further advance."

He then told Enghien the manner in which Hector had arranged and fought his troops.

"A good device indeed," Enghien said warmly, "and methinks it worthy of adoption whenever infantry have to meet other infantry and cavalry, for the muskets take so long to reload that there might not be half a dozen men ready to give fire when the cavalry charge. Is that one of the many lessons that he tells me you have given him?"

"No, indeed; it has not, so far as I am aware, ever been tried before. Parts of regiments are often held in reserve to reinforce their comrades if necessary, but this method, whereby half the regiment are able at a moment's notice to meet cavalry with their muskets loaded, is methinks, entirely new, and in such cases as the present very valuable."

In the second day's fighting Turenne's army had taken but small share, for during the retreat of the Bavarians the cavalry alone had come into play.

The Bavarians having retreated into Würtemberg, a council of war was held to decide in what manner the greatest advantage could be gained during their absence. Most of the chief officers were in favour of retaking Freiburg. Turenne was of a different opinion. He represented that the siege would occupy a considerable time, and that if successful they would, at the end of a campaign, have simply retaken a town that was theirs when it began. They could therefore point to no advantage gained by their efforts or by the loss of so many men. He advised, therefore, that as the Bavarian army was now sixty miles away, and could not very well return, as it would need large reinforcements, fresh cannon, and baggage wagons, they should take the opportunity of making themselves masters of the whole course of the Rhine and even of the Palatinate.

The Duc d'Enghien declared for this plan. Turenne went at once to Breisach, and arranged for the transport, by boat down the Rhine, of all the necessaries for the siege of Philippsburg. The army started on the 16th of August, a part of Turenne's army being detached to capture small towns and castles. On the 23rd of August Philippsburg was invested by Turenne, Enghien's force arriving on the following day. Philippsburg stood on the Rhine, which at this point formed a sharp elbow, and the land being low, many morasses surrounded the town, and the approach therefore was exceedingly difficult. Eight hundred paces from the town stood a square fort, which commanded the river, and was connected with the town by a causeway. The town itself had seven bastions, round these ran a very thick hedge, and the moat was wide and full of water. The garrison was a weak one, not exceeding a thousand men, but they had a hundred pieces of cannon and a large store of ammunition.

Feeling that he could not hold a fort so far from the town, the commander withdrew the garrison from it, and Turenne seized it, and placed a strong force there. Enghien then threw up strong lines in a semicircle round the town to protect the army in case any large force of the enemy should endeavour to relieve it. This occupied four days, and in the meantime the boats had arrived with cannon, ammunition, and provisions. A bridge was thrown across the river in twenty-four hours, and a force was sent over; this attacked and captured Germersheim, and then marched to Spires, which at once opened its gates on the 29th of August. In the meantime the siege of Philippsburg was begun in earnest. The approaches could only be carried on in one place, where the ground was sandy, and continued so up to two of the bastions of the town.

Turenne commanded the attack against the right bastion, de Gramont that on the left. They first diverted a brook running through the plain, and were enabled to use its channel as an approach, thus advancing fifteen hundred paces nearer to the town. They then formed an intrenchment that could be used by both columns, and from this on the 1st of September they began to open their trenches against their respective bastions. De Gramont's works were attacked on the following day by a sortie; this, however, was driven back. On the fifth night both columns made a lodgment on the counterscarp, and their batteries opened fire. After some days' work they filled up the ditch, and seeing that his force was too weak to oppose so strong an attack, the commander surrendered on the 12th of September.

Although Merci was advancing with an army, Enghien continued the project that had been formed, and, remaining with his own troops to protect Philippsburg, sent Turenne with all his horse and five hundred foot to Worms, which threw open its gates. Oppenheim surrendered without resistance, and he arrived in front of Mayence. The garrison was very small, and upon the threat of Turenne that he would attack it on all sides the citizens sent a deputation offering to capitulate. Turenne sent word of this to Enghien, who rode there at once, and received the surrender of the town. Bingen capitulated; Landor, Mannheim, Neustadt, and several other places were taken; and thus from Strasburg to a point near Coblenz, the whole course of the Rhine, the Palatine, and all the country between the Rhine and the Moselle fell into the hands of the French. Enghien returned to pass the winter in Paris. The greater part of the army was recalled, and Turenne was left with but a few regiments to hold the newly-acquired territory.

"Do you wish for leave, Campbell?" Turenne asked Hector. "You had but a few days in your new lordship, and have a right to spend at least a portion of the winter there."

"I thank you, marshal, but I have no idea of leaving you. You have been good enough to say that you will fill up the gaps in my regiment by embodying in it the remains of the regiment of Ardennes, which will bring it up to nearly its former strength. I certainly should not like to be away while the work of fusion is being carried out. The new men must be divided equally among the companies, and the officers so arranged that one of those now appointed shall be attached to each company with two of my own. Then I must see that all so work together as to arrive at the same standard as before. I should have wished that if possible the captains of the Ardennes regiment should be appointed to the new regiment that you are about to form, and that the places of those who fell in action should be filled from my list of lieutenants."

"Certainly. You lost five captains, did you not?"

"Yes, sir."

"If you send me the names of the five senior lieutenants, I will promote them at once."

"Thank you, marshal; that will make all my lieutenants captains. I lost five of them and three second lieutenants."

"Then you will require thirteen more officers." He looked at a list. "There are eight belonging to the Ardennes, the rest I will draw from other regiments. There is little fear of their objecting to the exchange, for your corps won such a reputation that all will be glad to join it; I will send you back to Nancy. There are barracks there, and no other troops; and as we are not likely to be disturbed until the spring, you will have plenty of time to bring the regiment up to its former mark."

The winter, indeed, passed quietly. The officers were all greatly pleased when they heard the arrangements Hector had made, by which most of them obtained a step in rank instead of being, as they had feared, passed over by officers belonging to the Ardennes regiment. The battle of Freiburg had shown them the great advantage that had been gained by the steadiness and discipline of their men. They took up the work of drilling again with even more zeal than before, and it was not long before the regiment was restored to its former state of efficiency. The reason why he had sent the regiment back from the Rhine was explained by Turenne to Hector before he started.

"The orders from court were," he said, "that I was to retain only the Weimar regiments, and I should have been obliged to send you back with those of Enghien had I not represented to him that it might be of the greatest importance to me to have even one good French regiment within call. We talked it over at some length, and he finally agreed to take upon himself the responsibility of ordering that your regiment should not go beyond Nancy, upon the ground that there were very few troops in Lorraine; and that peasant risings had taken place there, as in other departments, owing to the terrible distress caused by heavy taxation. He has handed to me a paper authorizing you to take such steps as you may think fit, as soon as you receive news of such risings, to aid the civil authorities, if they should take place at any point within reasonable reach. The regiments stationed at Metz will naturally maintain order north of Pont-à-Mousson, while you will send detachments to points south and east of Nancy. You will understand that you are not to move troops on the strength of mere rumours, but only when requests for aid are sent by local authorities."

Indeed, during the winter of 1644-45, as in that preceding it, troubles broke out in many parts of France, and in some the risings of "the barefooted ones," as they were called, became for a time very formidable. The rage of the unhappy peasantry was principally directed, as during the jacquerie, against the nobles, and many chateaux were sacked and burned, all within killed, and terrible excesses committed.

In February serious outbreaks took place. A messenger arrived at Nancy with an urgent appeal for help, and Hector took four companies and marched with all speed to the disturbed district. As soon as he reached it he broke up his force, despatching each company in a different direction, his instructions being that any body of armed peasants they might meet were to be dispersed, but, once beaten, were not to be pursued and cut up, and that life was not to be unnecessarily sacrificed. He himself, with one company, marched towards Poissons. He was within a mile of the town when a mounted man, bleeding from several wounds, rode up.

"The château of Blenfoix has been attacked by two hundred peasants," he said. "My lady and a dozen retainers are holding a tower, but they cannot long resist; even now the place may have been captured. I broke my way through, and, hearing that there were troops in this direction, I have galloped at full speed to implore your aid."

"How far is it?"

"About ten miles."

"You hear, de Mieville; bring the men on with all speed. I will gallop forward with my troopers and do what I can. Do I go straight along the road?"

"Yes, sir, nine miles hence you will see the château on an eminence a mile away to the right."

Followed by his troopers and Paolo, Hector dashed off at full speed. In three quarters of an hour, at a turn of the road, they caught sight of the château. Flames were pouring through most of the windows.

"Now, lads," he said to the men, "we have got long odds to face, but there is a lady to be rescued, and if any men can accomplish it we will."

The château was partly castellated, the new portion having been built against what had formerly been a small castle. On its summit a flag was still flying. Riding on at the top of their speed they soon saw a number of men swarming round a gate which opened into the older portion of the building.

"Put your pistols in your belts, lads. Don't use them if you can help it, but trust to your swords. Cut your way through that crowd. Ride in at the gate, and dismount at the door leading up to the turret. Then do you, Macpherson and Hunter, cover our rear while we fight our way up the steps. Follow us as we go, and if you want aid, shout and we will come down to you."

JUST IN TIME

On hearing the sound of the galloping hoofs the peasants for a moment made a movement of retreat, but when they saw that the six horsemen were alone, they began to gather courage, and again waved their arms, which were mostly axes or poles, to which scythes or bill-hooks were attached. Riding three abreast, the horsemen burst in among them, hewing and hacking with their swords; and the crowd, unable to resist the impetus of the charge, opened a way for them, and in a moment they had passed through the gate. A group of men round an open door that marked the position of the turret stairs, scattered with cries of alarm as they galloped up. In a moment they sprang from their horses and entered the doorway. The stairs were narrow, and but one man could mount and use his weapons at a time. They were, however, densely packed with men.

Hector sprang up, closely followed by the others. The resistance was feeble, for the height above the winding steps was but six feet, and insufficient for the use of either axes or longer weapons. Many of the peasants, astounded at seeing the armed men mounting from below them, and wholly ignorant of their numbers, threw down their weapons and cried for mercy. Hector contented himself with pushing past them, and running his sword through any who showed signs of resistance. One or two men armed with rough pikes made a stand; these he shot, and pressed upwards until within some twenty feet of the top, when the peasants, half-maddened at finding themselves caught, rushed down in a body.

"Close up!" he shouted to his followers. These pressed close up to him, but the weight was too much for them, and they were borne by the rush backwards down the stairs, when the peasants darted out through the door. Hector had received several knife-cuts on the shoulder and arms, and would have suffered still more severely had not Paolo and Nicholl, who were next to him, thrust their pistols over his shoulder and shot his assailants, whose bodies, borne along by the pressure from behind, protected him from the blows of those above them.

"Are you hurt badly, master?" Paolo exclaimed as they stood breathless for a moment at the bottom of the stairs.

"No, I think not; my gorget saved my neck; I have four or five cuts on the shoulders, but they are mere flesh wounds. Now let us mount the stairs; the men must have made a stout defence indeed to have held out so long."

The upper part of the stairs was indeed almost blocked with dead bodies. At the top of the stairs stood two men with axes, which they lowered as soon as they saw Hector.

"You have made a brave stand," he said, "in defence of your mistress."

"You have arrived but just in time, monsieur, for we are the last two left, and though we might have accounted for a few more, another five minutes would have finished it."

Stepping out on the platform at the top of the tower, Hector saw a lady leaning against the battlements; she was deadly pale, but her face still bore a look of calm determination. In her hands she held a dagger; clinging to her was a girl of some fifteen years of age.

"Thank God, madam, that we have arrived in time!" Hector exclaimed.

"Just in time, monsieur; we had given up all hope, when, as if sent by God, we saw your little band appear riding towards us. Even then I hardly ventured to hope; it seemed well-nigh impossible that six men should be able to clear a way through so many. Only two of my faithful retainers still held the stairs, and it was but too evident that these could not resist much longer; when one more had fallen I had resolved to plunge this dagger into my daughter's heart and then into my own. Death would have been a thousand times preferable to falling into the hands of these wretches."

"How long have you been beleaguered, madam?"

"My men have been fighting for four hours. For upwards of three hours they did well, for the peasants, being unable to use their weapons, frequently drew back. Then they hit upon the device of fastening a hook to the end of a pole, and, catching this round the leg of one of the defenders, dragged him down, and then despatched him with their

"Hector saw a lady leaning against the battlements."

knives. One by one four of my men were killed. For the last half-hour the two who remained stood back, one at each side of the doorway, so that they could not be so entrapped, and slew those who, mounting the stairs, tried to rush past them. Both were sorely spent, and the end must have come soon had you not appeared. Whom have I to thank for this unlooked-for deliverance?"

"I am Colonel Campbell, Baron de la Villar," Hector replied, and have the honour to command his majesty's regiment of Poitou."

"Your name is not French," the lady said.

"No, madam, I am a Scotchman."

"Then," the lady said, speaking in English, "I must claim you as a countryman, for I am Irish. My husband was an officer in the army of the Duke of Lorraine; he was killed in a skirmish four years ago, and a year later I married the Baron of Blenfoix, and was again widowed at the battle of Freiburg, where my husband, who had followed the fortunes of the Duke of Lorraine, his feudal lord, fell fighting by the side of General Merci. This is my daughter Norah. But I see that you are wounded," she went on as Hector bowed to the young lady.

"Not seriously, madam; but I feel somewhat faint from loss of blood, and will remove my helmet. As it turned out," he went on somewhat faintly, "it was unfortunate that I did not put on my body armour; but I had not anticipated hard fighting, and preferred to ride without it. Thanks for your offer, lady, but my men will see to me, they are all of them pretty well accustomed to the bandaging of wounds."

He was now, indeed, almost too faint to stand, and Paolo and Nicholl seated him against a battlement, and then proceeded to take off his upper garments and examine his wounds. They were all at the back of the shoulder, as his assailants, pressed closely against him, were unable to strike him in front. The lady tore off some strips off her garment and assisted in bandaging the wound, being, as she said, well accustomed to such matters.

"Is all quiet on the stairs?" Hector inquired of the two men whom he had placed on guard there.

"Save for the sound of some groans all is still, colonel," Hunter replied. "Methinks that after being withstood for four hours by six retainers they are not likely to make a fresh attempt against six well-armed men."

"What are they doing, Macpherson?"

"They are gathered in front of the château, sir. A large number of things were dragged out before the flames reached them, and at present they seem to be quarrelling over the division of them. They have got some barrels of wine out of the cellars and are making free with them."

"So much the better," Hector said. "The company will be up in half an hour at latest, and will give them a lesson unless they move away before that; and now that they have taken to drinking they are not likely to do so."

The bandaging of his wounds being now completed, Hector was assisted to his feet.

"I grieve, madam," he said, "that I did not arrive in time to prevent the château being burned."

"The loss is not mine; my husband's estates were confiscated when he crossed into Germany with the duke, and were some ten months ago granted to a Monsieur de Thours, a relative of the Prince of Condé; but he sent me a courteous letter to say that as he was serving with the Duc d'Enghien, I was welcome to continue to occupy the château until the war was over, receiving the rents as his châtelaine, paying the retainers, and keeping up the establishment, and sending the surplus to his agents at Nancy. This I was glad to do, for, indeed, had it not been for his kind offer my daughter and I would scarcely have known whither to go, as my husband expended his last crown in equipping a force for the service of the duke."

At this moment Macpherson exclaimed:

"I see the head of a company mounting the slope, colonel."

"Yes, and there is Captain Mieville. Ah! he has halted the men, and is riding forward alone to take in the situation. I hope that the peasants won't catch sight of him."

When Mieville reached a point where he could obtain a view of the front of the château he checked his horse, and after surveying the scene for a minute rode back to the company. A movement was at once visible.

"He is extending them on each side," Hector said. "That is good. He is going to inclose the peasants, and as from the slope in the ground they cannot see the troops until they are within a hundred yards, he will catch them in a trap."

The company moved round, in fact, until they had formed almost a semicircle, then they advanced, closing in as they neared the house. When they reached the spot where they could be seen by the peasants a trumpet sounded and they ran in. The peasants, bewildered at seeing the line of soldiers closing in around them, hesitated. Some were already too drunk to rise from the ground on which they had thrown themselves, the others caught up their arms and ran together. Retreat was impossible, for behind them was the burning house. Suddenly a stream of fire burst from the semicircle of troops. Some thirty of the insurgents fell, the others threw down their arms and fell upon their knees crying for mercy. The troops were rushing forward to finish their work, when Hector shouted "Halt!"

"De Mieville," he said, as the officer rode up towards the tower, "do not shed more blood. Thirty at least have fallen in their attack on this turret, besides those who have been killed by your fire. Take the rest, disarm them all, let the men cut some stout switches and give every man twenty blows well laid on the back, and then let them go. Before you do so, send a dozen of them to clear the staircase and to draw some buckets of water from the well and sluice the steps down. Paolo, do you run down and find a vessel of some sort and a goblet or horn, and bring up some wine from one of those barrels. The ladies sorely need something after what they have gone through, and I myself shall be all the better for it, for the loss of blood has given me a raging thirst."

Paolo had no difficulty in carrying out the order. The rioters had brought out several pails for holding the wine, a score of silver cups and other vessels lay where they had been dropped when the soldiers appeared, and the officer had placed two men on guard over them. Paolo thoughtfully brought up a pail of water as well as of wine. The ladies drank a little wine and water, while Hector took long draught, and made the two retainers who had fought so stoutly, and his own men, do the same. In half an hour the staircase was cleared and washed down, and the party then descended. The baroness had told Hector that for the present at any rate she would go to Nancy, and would report to the new lord's agents there what had happened, and doubtless he would send a man to take charge of the place.

"These cups," she said, "were all the personal property of my husband, and I am therefore free to take them. Many of them have been in his family for a very long time. Their sale will enable me to live until I can form some plans for the future."

The several silver vessels were collected and wrapped up ready for transport in some of the hangings that the rioters had torn down. An out-house adjoining the keep was cleared out and thickly spread with rushes for the accommodation of the baroness and her daughter. The troops had already had a very long march, and it was out of the question that they could return to Nancy that night. Fires were lighted in front of the house, and the soldiers prepared to bivouac there. Three of the troopers were sent off with orders to the captains of the other three companies to concentrate the next morning at a village on the line that would be taken on their return march. Some men were sent down to the little town of Blenfoix to purchase bread and meat, together with torches and other necessaries. At nightfall Hector posted sentinels, as he considered it quite possible that the peasants would raise the country for some distance round and try to take vengeance for the loss they had suffered. When Paolo took some supper round to the two ladies, he returned with a message that they hoped Colonel Campbell would join them in their meal.

"See that the sentries are on the alert, Mieville," he said as he got up from the fire round which he and the three officers were sitting; "you must remember that these poor fellows are desperate. Of course you and I know that they can do themselves no good by attacking castles and burning châteaux, but were we in their place—famished, despairing, and ignorant—we should doubtless do the same. And although, with men as well disciplined as ours, there would be little chance of the peasants overpowering us, they may trust in their numbers, and would believe that if they could destroy us, the whole country might well rise and join them. Should there be any sign of trouble, call me instantly."

Two sentries had been placed at the door of the out-house, and as he entered Hector said, "Keep good watch, men, and if you hear any noise that might betoken the approach of a body of men, warn me at once."

"I heard what you said to the sentries, Colonel Campbell; do you think that there is any danger?"

"No danger, I trust, madam, for I am convinced that we could beat off any number. Still, I do think that there is a possibility of our being attacked. The peasants know that we are but a company. They may send to all the villages round and call on them to come and revenge those who have been slain. The people of the hills are strong fellows—wood-cutters, charcoal-burners, and shepherds—and there can be no doubt that they suffer terribly from the enormous taxation. I have seen it on my own estate in Poitou, and can make every allowance for them. In many cases the amounts they are adjudged to pay are absolutely greater than their whole income. They are forced to live upon bread made of bran and sawdust, to eat acorns and beech-nuts; they are gaunt with hunger; they see their children dying before their eyes. They know not how their sufferings arise, they only know that they suffer, and in their despair they turn like hungry wolves against all who are better off than themselves."

"And your people are they suffering as much as these, monsieur?"

"Not quite so much, perhaps, but they are suffering. I have spent but a fortnight on my estates, of which I have only been master for a year."

"And could you do nothing for them, monsieur?" the girl asked.

"I did what I could, mademoiselle. I remitted half their rents, which was in fact but a small thing, seeing that I knew positively they could not have paid them. Still it was no doubt some alleviation to know that the arrears were not being piled up against them. As to the other half, I told my intendant not to press any who he thought could not pay, and that if he drew enough to pay his own salary and the wages of the retainers I should be content—for my pay as colonel is ample for my own wants."

"You are very young to be a colonel, Monsieur Campbell," the baroness said.

"Very young; but I have had singularly good fortune, and have been happy enough to please both Marshal Turenne and the Duc d'Enghien."

"And you have served under them both?" she said in surprise.

"I have had that good fortune. I was with Turenne for nearly four years in Italy, and fought under Enghien at Rocroi, and I may say under both of them at Freiburg."

"What is the name of your regiment, monsieur?"

"The Poitou regiment."

"Indeed!" she exclaimed. "Of course, we have heard all the particulars of the battle; and it was said that General Merci would have beaten Monsieur Turenne back had it not been for the Poitou regiment, commanded by a Scottish colonel, and said to be the finest under the command of the French generals. They say it stood for three hours against the attacks of the whole Bavarian army."

"We were in a strong position," Hector said quietly, "at the mouth of a defile, so that no more than our own numbers could attack us at once. However, I am proud of the conduct of my men; none could have fought more steadily than they did."

"My husband was killed in the battle against Enghien's army on the hill. I am glad that it was not by your regiment monsieur."

"I am glad too, madam."

"These wars are terrible, and we of Lorraine—lying between France and Germany—suffer whichever wins. Fortunately we lie at a distance from the roads that the armies follow, and therefore have escaped the devastation caused all along the line of march. Nevertheless we have the sadness of knowing that in the field neighbours must fight against neighbours, and kinsmen against kinsmen, for since the duke fled many of our nobles, seeing that the country has now become part of France, have joined her, while others, like my husband, followed the duke into Germany. However, as an Irishwoman it matters little to me now which is the victor."

"Do you think of returning home, madam?"

"As to that, I have not yet made up my mind. The land there is as distracted as is France by civil war. It is sixteen years since I left Ireland with my husband, a few months after our marriage. I was an orphan, and have no near relations to whom I can go, therefore it matters little to me whether I live in France or Ireland, so that I can see some way of earning my own living and that of my daughter. With economy, the sale of the silver would suffice to keep us for three or four years, and long before that I hope that I shall be able in some way to earn my living."

Hector sat silent for two or three minutes. "It seems to me, madam," he said at last, "that it would be better that you should not spend the proceeds of your silver before looking for a post. I can offer you one at once, if you will accept it."

"You, monsieur!" she exclaimed in surprise.

JUST IN TIME

"Yes, madam. It is bad for the vassals and tenants of a noble—even though a newly made one, and on an estate of moderate dimensions—when their lord is absent, and there is none to look after them save an intendant, whose duty it is to collect as much rent as he is able. Such is the position of my tenants. I am a soldier, and must perforce be absent. What I need greatly is someone who will fill my place in this respect. I have an old friend who is captain of the garrison, and sees to all things in the household; I have an intendant, I believe a worthy young man, who collects my rents and looks to the feeding and needs of the servants and garrison; but I need someone who would interest herself actively in the condition of my tenants, who would be a friend to them in sickness, would give aid from my purse to those who really need it, would send food to the starving, and aid my intendant by advising him as to who are worthy of relief and who are suffering from their own idleness or thriftlessness— who will, in short, act as I would have my wife act had I one.

"Now, madame la baronne if you will honour me by making my home yours so long as I am away at the wars, which may last, for aught I know, for years yet, you will be conferring a great favour upon me. You will have your own suite of apartments, where your meals will be served to you. You will have horses to ride. You will relieve my intendant of the necessity of seeing that the servants perform their duties, and give him more time to devote himself to the business of the estate, and will in fact act as châtelaine, save only in matters connected with the garrison in the defence of the castle."

"Your offer is kind in the extreme, Colonel Campbell, but I could not accept it," she said. "You are only inventing such an office in order to give a home to me and Norah."

"I can assure you, madam, that the thought is not a new one to me—I have often wished that there was a lady in the castle. One who would see after the wives and families of the vassals; and I should feel myself under a real obligation to you if you would fill the place. You see, madam, it would cost me nothing, for food and drink there is in abundance.

I have two splendid horses, given me by the Duc d'Enghien, standing idle in their stalls. I shall be happy in knowing that my tenants would be well looked after, and shall be glad indeed that you and your daughter, my countrywomen, should, for the present at any rate, have a home."

The tears were streaming down the lady's face.

"Accept, mother," the girl said, putting her hand on her shoulder. "Surely God sent this gentleman to our rescue when we were very near death. Why should we not accept this fresh kindness at his hands?"

Her mother looked up. "My daughter has chosen for me, Colonel Campbell. I accept your offer with the deepest thankfulness. Were I to refuse now, the time might come when I should be reduced to such straits that for my daughter's sake I should bitterly regret that I had refused your generous offer; therefore I accept it, and thank you from the bottom of my heart."

"I do not wish you to see it in that light," he said with a smile. "At best it is but an arrangement for our mutual advantage, and I, on my part, thank you and mademoiselle most heartily for falling in with my wishes."

CHAPTER XV
THE BATTLE OF MARIENTHAL

THE decision had scarcely been made when one of the lieutenants ran in. Captain Mieville requests me to state that sounds have been heard in the forest, and that he believes there is a large body of men approaching."

"Then, ladies, I must beg you to mount the stairs to the turret at once. I will place six men on guard there. The main body I must keep in front of the château, as that affords a protection to our rear. Do not be alarmed. I do not think the place is likely to be attacked; but should it be, the six men could hold it for any time. As soon as I have beaten the main body I will at once attack those who may be assailing the turret, though I hardly think that they will do so, for they know that there is nothing to be obtained that would in any way repay them for the loss that they would suffer. They are marching here for the purpose of attacking us."

He called to the two sentries.

"See the ladies up the stairs to the turret, and take up your post on the lower stairs. Four more men shall join you at once."

He found that Mieville had already got all the men under arms, and had ranged them between the bivouac fires and the still-glowing château.

"Move your men along farther Mieville. Let your left flank rest on the angle of the old castle, then we shall not be made anxious by another attack on the turret. Let the right flank rest upon the château where the old castle joins it. We shall then be in darkness, while the assailants, if they come from that side, will have to cross the ground lit up by the glow from the ruins. Let the centre of the line be some ten yards in front of the building; let the line be two deep."

As soon as this disposition was made he called down the six men, as they were no longer required to defend the staircase.

"Now, men," he said when all were formed up, "I need not admonish soldiers who were so firm under the attack of the whole of the Bavarian army of the necessity for steadiness. I have no doubt that if we are attacked it will be in considerable force; but it will be by half-armed peasants, and there probably will not be a gun among them. But even peasants, when worked up into a state of excitement are not to be despised. My orders are: The front rank shall continue firing until they are close at hand, and shall then fix bayonets. Until this is done the second line are not to fire a shot; but as soon as the front rank are ready to repel the enemy with fixed bayonets, you will begin. Don't throw a shot away, but continue loading and firing, as quickly as you can; and unless very closely pressed, let no man empty his musket until his comrade on the right has reloaded, so that there will always be some shots in reserve. Should they rush on in spite of the fire, I shall give the order, 'Empty your muskets and fix bayonets,' and we will then charge them. Hunter, you and your three comrades and Paolo will keep close to me, and if we find the men wavering at any point we will go to their assistance. If, however, we charge, remember that you six men I told off to guard the turret are at once to pass through the gates and take up your post on the steps, for some of them may slip in behind us and endeavour to rush up."

The horses, that had been turned loose when Hector and the troopers mounted the steps, had been seized by the peasants, and tied up to some trees close by when the latter began to feast. They had been recovered when the insurgents were scattered by Mieville's company and had then been placed in the court-yard of the castle. As soon as the alarm was given, Hector, the four troopers, and Paolo had mounted. The three officers were also on horseback.

"In case the company charges, Mieville," he said, "we nine mounted men can cover the rear and charge any of the insurgents who try to rush in and take them in the rear. I hope that we shall keep them off with our musketry fire; but I don't disguise from myself that if they fall upon us at close quarters we shall have to fight hard. Ah, here they come!"

Suddenly in the darkness from the other side of the château a great crowd of men poured out, shouting and yelling furiously, and brandishing their rough weapons, which shone blood-red in the glow of the fire in the ruins. Someone had evidently been placed on the watch, and had told them where the troops had taken up their post, for they came on without hesitation, bearing outwards until they faced the centre of the line, at a distance of fifty yards; then one of the men, who appeared to be the leader, shouted an order, and they rushed impetuously forward. The front line at once opened fire. Many of the peasants dropped, while the others hesitated a little, and so gave the men who had first fired time to reload; but, urged on by the shouts of their leaders, the peasants again rushed forward.

"Fire a volley, and then fix bayonets!" Hector shouted.

The fifty muskets flashed out, and as the peasants were but fifteen yards away every shot told, and their front rank was completely swept away.

"Every other man in the second line fire!" Hector ordered, and twenty-five shots added to the confusion among the peasants. The slaughter, however, only had the effect of maddening the great crowd, who numbered upwards of two thousand, and with a howl of fury they rushed forward again. Hector waited until they almost touched the row of bayonets, and then gave the order for the remaining men to fire and all to fix bayonets. The instant this was done he shouted "Charge!" for he saw that while standing quiet his men were no match for the peasants, whose long poles with the scythes at the end gave them great advantage over the shorter weapons of the soldiers. With a cheer the latter threw themselves upon their opponents, their close formation and more handy weapons depriving their enemies of this advantage. Thrusting and overthrowing all in front of them, the line burst its way through the mob, the little party of cavalry charging furiously whenever the peasants endeavoured to fall upon their rear, and the latter, boldly as they fought against the infantry, shrank back before the flashing swords and the weight of horses and riders.

As soon as they had passed through the crowd Hector gave the order for his troops to face about, and they again burst their way through the mob that had closed in behind them. Four times was the manœuvre repeated, the resistance growing fainter each time, as the peasants found themselves unable to withstand the charge of the disciplined troops. When for the fifth time they reached the gate of the castle the crowd no longer pressed upon their rear, but stood hesitatingly some fifty yards away. Hector took advantage of the pause, and ordered his men, who were, panting from their exertions, to load again. He formed them in single line now.

"Don't fire a shot until I give the word," he said; "then pour in your volley, fix bayonets instantly, and charge."

Standing in the shade as they did, the movement of loading was unobserved by the peasants, who, as they saw the line again advancing, prepared to meet them, but gave a yell of surprise when a terrible volley was poured into them at a distance of twenty yards. Then, before they had recovered from their surprise, the long line was upon them with levelled bayonets. Only a few stood their ground. These were instantly overthrown. The rest, throwing away their weapons, fled in all directions.

"Thank God that is over!" Hector said, as he told the troops to halt and reload. "If they had all been as courageous as their leader they would have annihilated us, but each time we charged I observed that a considerable number fell away on either flank, so that it was not a solid mass through which we had to make our way. What is our loss, Mieville?"

"I rode along the line and counted the numbers. There are but seventy-five on foot," he said, "and most of these have got more or less severe wounds with their ugly weapons."

"Let the ground over which we have passed be carefully searched," he said, "and any of our men who show signs of life be carried in front of the château.

Twelve men were found to be living; their wounds were at once attended to and bandaged.

"I think most of them will do," Captain Mieville said. "They are ugly-looking gashes, but it is not like a bullet in the body."

The men who had been killed were found in most cases to have been slain outright from the blows of hatchets, which had in several cases completely severed their heads. While the wounds of the soldiers were being attended to, Hector went to the gate at which the baroness and her daughter were now standing.

"You are unhurt, I hope," the lady said as Hector approached.

"I have two or three more wounds," he said, but, like those I had before, they are of little account."

"It was a terrible fight," she said. "We watched it from the top of the turret, and it seemed to us that you were lost each time you plunged into the crowd, you were so few among such numbers. Have you lost many men?"

"We have only had thirteen killed outright," he said.

"Twelve more are very seriously wounded, but I think most of them will recover. As to the rest of the company, I fancy that most of them will require some bandaging. And now I shall recommend you and your daughter to return to your shelter. I have no fear whatever of their coming back again."

"That we cannot do," she said firmly. "It is our duty to do what we can to aid those who have fought so bravely."

"The men are now attending to each other's wounds," Hector said. "Every man in my regiment carries, by my orders, a couple of bandages. We found them most useful at Freiburg, and many a life was saved that would have been lost but for their use; but if you insist upon doing anything,

I would ask you to carry wine and water round. The troopers will draw the water for you from the well in the court-yard here."

"That we will do willingly," she said.

For the next two hours the ladies were busy at work, moving among the men and supplying them with refreshments. Not until all their wants were amply supplied did they retire.

In the morning Hector said:

"Now, Madame de Blenfoix, I have been thinking the matter over, and consider that it would be a wholly unnecessary journey and a loss of four days were you to travel to Nancy with us. You are only ten days' journey from Poitou, and I should advise you to start at once. My man, Paolo, and two of the troopers will accompany you as an escort. Your road will lead through Orleans, which will be almost half-way, and you will also pass through Tours. At both these towns you can, if you will, stay for a day to rest. I will ride down with you into Blenfoix, where I shall be able to get paper and pens, and will write letters to Captain MacIntosh and to my intendant explaining exactly the position that you will occupy. One of the troopers will ride forward with these from your last halting-place before you arrive there, in order that you may find everything prepared and be received properly on your arrival. Do you both ride, or would you rather have a pillion's place behind the troopers?"

"We both ride," she said; "but I should prefer, on a journey like this, that my daughter should ride behind me on a pillion. You are altogether too good, Colonel Campbell. You are heaping kindnesses upon us."

"Not at all, madam. And now you will doubtless be glad to hear that in searching round the place this morning, we have discovered that two of your horses that had doubtless been turned loose by the peasants have found their way back. No difficulty will therefore arise on that score. The saddles are hanging from the beams in the stable, so that everything is in readiness for your departure."

THE BATTLE OF MARIENTHAL

A quarter of an hour later the whole party left the ruined château, the troops taking their way to the point at which they had left the road, while Hector with his four troopers and Paolo rode down into Blenfoix with the ladies. Here the baroness purchased a few necessaries for the journey while Hector was writing his letters. Hunter and Macpherson were to form their escort, and were by turns to lead the spare horse, which on alternate days was to carry the double burden. Paolo carried the purse, which contained a sum ample for the expenses of the journey. When all was ready the adieus were said, and the baroness repeated the heartfelt thanks of her daughter and herself for the kindness shown them. Paolo took his place beside the ladies, the two troopers fell in behind, and they started west, while Hector with the other two troopers galloped off to overtake his company.

At Joinville they found that de Thiou's company had just marched in, but it was not until the next day that the other two returned. All had met with scattered bodies of peasants, but these had dispersed as soon as the troops were seen, and there had been no actual fighting except with the parties Hector had met. The bodies of the soldiers that had fallen were buried near the château. Those of the peasants were left where they lay, and would doubtless be carried off by their friends as soon as the latter knew that the troops had left. The lesson had been a severe one indeed, upwards of two hundred and eighty being killed in the two encounters. The insurgents were completely disheartened by their loss, and during the rest of the winter the aid of the troops was not again called for.

As soon as spring set in, the Poitou regiment marched to join the marshal. The Bavarian army had been weakened by the withdrawal of four thousand men to aid the Imperialists, who had been defeated by the Swedes in Bohemia. Turenne, on hearing the news, at once prepared to take advantage of it, crossed the Rhine on a bridge of boats at Spires, and passed the Neckar, General Merci retiring before him. Stuttgart opened its gates, and Turenne established himself at Marienthal on the river Tauber. Merci, as he fell back, had caused a rumour to be spread that he was making for the Danube.

There was a great scarcity of forage in the country round Marienthal, and the officers of the cavalry strongly urged upon Turenne that they should divide and take up stations at various points where they could obtain food for their animals, which were much exhausted by their long and heavy marches. Turenne for some time resisted their entreaties, but at last, seeing that the cavalry would speedily be ruined unless they could obtain food, permitted this course to be taken. Before allowing them to leave, however, he sent parties of horse forward in various directions to discover what the enemy were doing. These returned with the news that the Bavarian army had broken up, and was fortifying itself in the towns among which it had been divided. Turenne, however, was still apprehensive. He kept his cannon and the greater part of the infantry with him, and also General Rosen with a portion of his horse, and refused to let the rest of the cavalry go farther than three leagues from the army. He himself rode out with a regiment of cavalry some ten miles beyond Marienthal, along the road by which the Imperialists would advance were they to assemble to attack him.

At two o'clock the next morning a party he had sent to watch the Bavarians brought in the news that Merci was advancing with all his force. Rosen was ordered to hurry forward to the spot where the advanced division was lying. Messengers were sent off in all directions to recall the scattered cavalry, and having seen that everything had been done to place affairs in a better position, Turenne rode off with what troops he could gather to aid Rosen. The latter had made a serious blunder. In front of the position held by the advanced division was a large wood, through which the Bavarians must pass. Instead of taking possession of this and holding it until reinforcements came up, he fell back, drew up his troops on the plain, and allowed the Bavarians to occupy the wood without resistance. With the troops which arrived with him, the marshal had now under him some three thousand infantry and seven regiments of horse. He placed his infantry on his right with two squadrons to support them; with the rest of his cavalry, he formed his left wing.

He himself took the command here. Rosen commanded on the right. Merci, after passing through the wood, drew up his army in order of battle and opened fire on the French. The artillery, however, in no way shook their firmness, and seeing more troops in the distance advancing to reinforce them, Merci began the battle by an attack on a little wood on which the French right rested; while at the same time Turenne charged the Bavarian right wing with his cavalry, broke it up, and captured the cannon and twelve standards. But while on this side the victory was almost won, on the other side disaster had befallen the French. Their infantry, perceiving that the Bavarians, who were advancing to attack them, were much superior in force, were seized with a panic and scattered in all directions. The left wing of the Bavarians advanced rapidly, and, throwing themselves behind Turenne's wing, prepared to fall upon him in the rear.

Turenne ordered his cavalry to retire, and passing through the wood found beyond it three regiments that had just arrived. These with the fifteen hundred horse that had been with him in the battle placed him in a position to make a vigorous defence, but the Bavarians did not venture to attack him. He now sent an officer to rally the scattered infantry, and gave orders that they should at once retreat without a stop to Philippsburg, a distance of seventy miles. He himself with his cavalry started for Hesse, whose landgravine was in alliance with France. With two regiments he covered the retreat, and so enabled the rest of the cavalry as they came up from their distant quarters to cross the Tauber. This was a bold and successful movement, for had he fallen back with his infantry to Philippsburg the enemy would have possessed themselves of all the towns he had captured, whereas they could not now advance without exposing their line of communication to his attack.

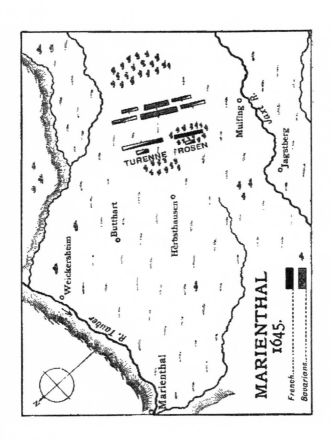

MARIENTHAL
1645.

French.......
Bavarians.......

THE BATTLE OF MARIENTHAL

The Poitou regiment had, when Turenne advanced to Marienthal, been left at a town some four leagues away.

A messenger reached Hector from Turenne with a note scribbled in pencil:—

We have been beaten. The infantry behaved shamefully, and are hastening, a crowd of stragglers, towards Philippsburg. I shall retire along the Tauber with the cavalry and make for Hesse, do you march with all speed for that river. If, as you approach the river, you hear that we have already passed, do you direct your march to Hesse. I leave the choice of route to you, and you must be guided by circumstances. At any rate you are unlikely to be attacked except by cavalry, and these, if not in too great numbers, you may be trusted to beat off.

Ten minutes after the receipt of this order the regiment was on the march. They arrived on the Tauber just in time, for a quarter of an hour after they had piled arms, after a tremendous march, the cavalry came along. They were in scattered parties, for the roads were terribly bad, and they were obliged to break up and make their way as best they could by mere tracks across the rocky and hilly country. Turenne himself, when he arrived, had but twenty horsemen with him.

"I hardly expected to be up in time, Campbell," he said, as he dismounted. "Your men must have marched well indeed. As you see, though unbeaten, for we on our side defeated the enemy's horse, we are as much dispersed as if we had suffered a disaster. I am trying to cover the retreat with two regiments of cavalry that were not engaged in the battle. Half an hour since we charged and drove back in confusion a party of Bavarian horse, but they formed up again. The main body is ahead, but is as scattered as we are, for besides the difficulty of keeping together on these horrible roads, it is necessary that we should occupy every track by which the enemy's horse could move, or they might get in front of us and play havoc with us.

WON BY THE SWORD

"You will have to march all night, and I should advise you to break up your command into half companies, with orders to each to attach themselves far as possible to such parties of my two regiments of cavalry as they may come across. We shall not proceed at any great pace, as we must give time for the troops ahead of us to get clear. The horses are utterly worn out being half-starved and fatigued with their march. So far we know not whether the whole of the Bavarian cavalry is behind us, but it is probable that one of their two divisions is pursuing the infantry. I wish you had been there with them. In the first place your example would have prevented their breaking, and in the second you could have covered their retreat. As it is, I fear that but few of the three thousand who were with me will reach Philippsburg. I shall be glad if you yourself will remain near me. If your regiment were going to keep together I would not take you from them, but being broken up into fragments, you could exercise no supervision over them in the darkness."

Hector at once called the officers together, and gave them the necessary orders. "You understand," he said, "that your main object is not so much to save yourselves, though that is most important, but to enable the cavalry to beat back the Bavarian horse."

It was a terrible march; both horse and foot made their way along with difficulty through the darkness. Men and horses were alike fatigued, and the cavalry for the most part dismounted and led their animals along. There were several sharp fights with bodies of the enemy, who, ignorant of the line by which the French were retreating, feared to press the rear-guard too close, lest they should find them in very superior numbers. Once, when they passed a lane running down to the river Turenne—who had taken every opportunity of making his way across the line of retreat and seeing how all was going on—said to Hector, "Will you ride up here, Campbell, and cheer up any parties you may come across. Tell them that all is going on well, and that by morning we shall find that the enemy have given up the pursuit, and shall be able to halt and take a few hours' rest, and give battle

260

should the enemy come up in force. Their horses must be as fatigued as ours, for they must have been marching for eight or ten hours since the morning."

Hector had only Paolo now with him, having appointed the four troopers to go with different parties of the infantry, and to act as orderlies to their captains. He rode rapidly up the lane, and presently heard the cavalry passing across it.

"There is one party, Paolo," he said, urging his horse into a gallop. In two or three minutes he came up with the column of horse.

"Where is your officer?" he asked, drawing rein as he reached them.

"Seize him!" a voice cried in German, and before he and Paolo could turn their horses half a dozen troopers were upon them.

"I surrender," he cried in German, seeing that resistance was impossible.

"Who are you, monsieur?" an officer demanded.

"I am colonel of the Poitou regiment of infantry," he said. "This man is my lackey."

"Where are your cavalry, sir?"

"That I cannot tell you exactly, seeing that no one knows. I thought that you formed part of our rear-guard."

"How comes it that you, an infantry officer, were there?"

"We heard that there were no infantry with them."

"We joined them just before nightfall, and were at once divided up among the various regiments of horse."

"I must inform our colonel of that. Come along with me," and they pushed past the troopers until they arrived at the head of the column, when the officer reported to the colonel.

"Donner Blitzen!" the latter exclaimed, "it is well that we learned this news, for we should have fared very ill if we had come upon horse and foot together. The Poitou regiment! That is the one that we heard beat back our charges so often at Freiburg, and they say the best regiment in the French service. It is no use our going farther; we might well fall into an ambush, and in these lanes they could

" 'Seize him!' a voice cried."

shoot us down helplessly. We will move on quietly until we get to a place where there is space enough for us to dismount and bivouac. We could not have gone many more miles, for if we did we should be a regiment without horses to-morrow morning."

They proceeded very slowly and cautiously until, when they came upon an open tract of ground, the colonel ordered them to dismount and sound the trumpets. His regiment, like those of Turenne, had been broken up, and he had but half a squadron with him. In an hour the whole regiment was assembled; a few fires were lighted, but most of the men threw themselves down by their horses and at once went off to sleep. The colonel and his officers sat down at one of the fires, where Hector was requested to join them.

"I suppose that your regiment took no part in the battle?"

"No, sir; we were some way from Marienthal, and I received orders only after the day was lost, to join Marshal Turenne and his cavalry on the Tauber. We arrived on the river just at sunset, having marched ten leagues in eight hours. I regret bitterly that my regiment was not on the field, for assuredly they would not have given way. Had they stood, the rest of the infantry would have stood."

"And in that case you would now be the pursuers," the colonel broke in, "for Turenne completely shattered our right wing. Well, sir, it is the fortune of war, and we at least have the honour of having given your marshal a defeat. He is a grand general, but we caught him napping to-day."

"It was not his fault, sir."

"General Rosen and his officers insisted so strongly that unless they were allowed to move off in search of forage, the whole army would be disabled by the loss of their horses by hunger, that he was almost forced to comply with their request."

WON BY THE SWORD

"But, even so, he made a mistake," the colonel said. If instead of marching to meet us in front of Marienthal he had fallen back directly he had the news of our coming, he could have been joined by all his detached troops before we came up with him."

"He said as much to me to-night," Hector replied; "but even the greatest generals are liable to make a mistake sometimes. And, indeed, had General Rosen with the advanced division held the wood in front of them, instead of retiring on to the plain, they should have been able to keep you at bay until all our troops came up."

"Undoubtedly that was a terrible blunder on his part," the colonel said, "and he rather than Turenne is to blame. And now, sir, may I ask how is it that you, who cannot be more than twenty, come to be a colonel, and in command of a regiment?"

"I have been five years an officer, and was fortunate on two occasions to obtain the approval, once of Monsieur de Turenne, and once of the Duc d'Enghien."

"I congratulate you, sir. It is seldom indeed that so young an officer has opportunities of distinguishing himself. I myself had seen well-nigh thirty years service before I came to command a regiment. And now, sir, will you give me your parole not to attempt to escape?"

"Certainly, sir," Hector replied promptly. He knew that should he refuse four or five troopers would be set to watch him, and even if he evaded these, which was well-nigh impossible, he might be recaptured on the following morning, as detachments of the Bavarian horse would be sure to be pressing hard upon Turenne's troops. The pursuit was indeed taken up again during the night, but Turenne succeeded in keeping his pursuers at bay, and reaching the frontiers of Hesse. There he found the infantry and cavalry who had not been engaged already assembled, for they had received orders to march instantly to that spot. He had now with him some four thousand horse and two thousand foot, and was joined by six thousand troops from Hesse and four thousand Swedes. He was thus soon in a position to advance with a much stronger force than that which he commanded before the battle of Marienthal.

The Bavarian cavalry that had followed him rejoined General Merci at Kirchheim. Hector was with Paolo taken to that place, and upon his refusal to continue his parole, was confined in a prison there, Paolo, being allowed at his request to remain with him. He had had an interview with General Merci, who had treated him with much courtesy; for there were Scotch and Irish officers serving in the Imperial army as well as in that of France, and they were held in high esteem for their courage and daring.

The battle of Marienthal was fought on the 2nd of May, and it was late in July before any fresh movements took place. Turenne would willingly have advanced with his army, but his movements were arrested by a peremptory order from Paris, sent on receipt of the news of the defeat, that he was not to take the offensive until joined by Enghien, who had with him a force of eight thousand men. He therefore marched to join the reinforcements, and the two armies met at Spires on the 2nd of July. As before, Enghien was in supreme command, with de Gramont as his lieutenant-general. Long conferences took place between these generals, Turenne, General Geis, who commanded the Hessians, and Königsmark, who commanded the Swedes. The Bavarians were known to be very strongly posted, and to have been reinforced by four thousand Imperialists under the command of General Geis.

There was much difference of opinion between them as to the best course to be pursued, but Enghien, who was always in favour of great battles, finally determined so to place the army that the enemy would be forced to come out and fight. He therefore marched to Venecher, captured Wimpfen, and threw a bridge across the river, whereupon General Merci fell back twenty leagues into Franconia. As soon as they had passed the river an occurrence took place that threatened to overthrow all the plans of the campaign. Some hasty words spoken by Enghien so angered the

Generals Geis and Königsmark that they determined to retire at once with the Swedes and Hessians. Turenne was requested by Enghien to endeavour to arrange matters, and by his kind and gentle manner succeeded in conciliating Geis, who consented to remain with the Hessians. Königsmark, however, as hot-tempered as Enghien himself, refused to do so, and with his whole force retired to Bremen, in Lower Saxony.

The French and Hessians marched towards the Tauber, captured Rothenburg and other towns, and thereby obtained a large quantity of provisions and stores; and hearing that the Bavarians were advancing to Nördlingen, marched in all haste to give them battle there.

CHAPTER XVI
AN ESCAPE

AFTER being confined for a week in the prison at Kirchheim Hector was sent with a number of other prisoners to Ingolstadt. Here he was confined in the castle, a separate room being allotted to him in recognition of his rank, and Paolo was, at his request, allowed to remain with him.

"I cannot but think, master, that we should have done better if you had given your parole not to try to escape. In that case we might have had comfortable quarters in the town instead of this somewhat bare chamber. If there had been a chance of escape it would have been different, but seeing the strength of the castle, methinks there is no prospect whatever of our being able to get out."

"That remains to be seen, Paolo. I fancy there is always a chance of escape if one does but hit upon the right way. At present we know nothing of the castle or the vigilance of the guard, and no doubt it will take us some little time to find these matters out. The first thing we require is patience. No doubt they will allow me out to take exercise, and like enough, if I give my word that you will return every day at a certain hour, they will allow you to go in to the town, seeing that you can scarcely be called a prisoner, having no military rank or position, but being in their eyes only a lackey. If they will do that it will be a great step gained, for you will be able to bring in anything that we may require. However, I will not ask that you should be permitted to go in and out for some little time.

WON BY THE SWORD

"Lose no opportunity of making yourself friendly with some of the soldiers, and if the chance should occur, be useful to any of the officers. The commandant is evidently disposed to be civil, and says that he will grant me any indulgence in his power short of passing the gates of the castle. I have no doubt that when the campaign is over and the army has gone into winter quarters Turenne will offer to exchange some prisoners of the same rank for me. But I have no wish to be cooped up here when perhaps a great battle may be fought. As far as I can see, the difficulty will not be so much in getting out of the castle, but out of the town itself, for this is one of the most strongly fortified places in the empire. One reason why I want you to go into the town is that you may be able to obtain shelter there for us should we find, as I expect we shall, that it is impossible for us to escape from the citadel and town at the same attempt."

The place was indeed so strong that but a careless watch was kept over the prisoners in the castle. The soldiers were confined to their quarters save that they were allowed for an hour a day to take exercise in the court-yard, a company of troops being kept under arms while they were out; but the officers were free at all times to wander about. Hector was soon on friendly terms with many of the officers of the garrison, as in his case there was none of the hostile feeling with which the French officers were regarded. His youth, and the singularity of his having so soon attained the rank of colonel, also predisposed them in his favour. It was evident that this young soldier of fortune, unsupported by powerful family interest, must have distinguished himself in an altogether exceptional manner to have obtained the command of one of the best regiments of France.

Paolo was as popular among the sergeants and men as his master was with the officers. As an Italian, and as Hector's lackey, he was not regarded as a prisoner of war; and by his unfailing good-humour, his readiness to enter into any fun that might be going on, or to lend a hand in cleaning accoutrements or completing a job that a soldier had left unfinished when his turn came for duty, he became quite a popular character. The colonel who commanded frequently walked with Hector in the court-yard, sent him dishes from his own table, and more than once invited him to dine with him. As he was very curious to learn how his young prisoner had so early attained his rank, Hector one evening gave him a sketch of his career, from the time when Turenne gave him his commission to that at which he was taken prisoner, omitting only the incident of the attempt to assassinate Mazarin.

"You have certainly been fortunate," he said, "but it is equally certain that you have deserved it. The fact that, in addition to your military duties, you have learned Italian and German, besides transforming a newly-raised regiment into one of the best in the French service, shows how assiduous you have been in your work. I trust that when the campaign is over you may be exchanged, and I think it is foolish of you not to give me your parole, for you must know well that you have no chance of escape from here."

"They say everything comes to those who wait, colonel," Hector laughed, "and if I see a chance I shall certainly avail myself of it. Even if no such chance comes I shall still be a gainer by not giving my parole. I am exceedingly comfortable as it is, and can wish for nothing better. The one drawback is that I have nothing to do, except perhaps to improve my German, and it would be just the same if I were living in the town. But if I were on my parole I should lose the amusement of planning methods for escape, which I do unceasingly; but up till now, I may tell you in confidence, I am as far from having hit upon a plan as I was when I entered. By the way, colonel, although it is clear that I cannot be allowed to go outside the castle gate, I should be glad if my lackey could be given leave to do so. He is not a soldier, neither is he a Frenchman, and can scarce be counted as a prisoner of war. He is a willing and cheerful fellow, and would enjoy a run in the city much more than I should. Besides, occasionally I may want a book or some other little thing which I cannot get here."

"Such as a file, a rope, or a disguise, Colonel Campbell," the commandant laughed.

"I am not thinking of that at present," Hector said smiling. "Besides, you can give orders that he can always be strictly searched when he comes in."

The colonel shook his head.

"I will tell you what I will do," he said; "I will let him have a pass to go in and out at will, if you will give me a promise, on your honour as a soldier, that he shall not bring in anything that can be used by you for facilitating your escape. I would much rather trust to your word than to any search the soldiers might make as your man comes in."

"Thank you, colonel," Hector said cheerfully, though at heart he felt considerably disappointed. "I give you my word of honour that he shall bring in nothing that may aid me in making my escape, and I am much obliged to you for letting him have the run of the town."

The colonel at once wrote a pass authorizing Paolo Monti, lackey to Colonel Campbell, to enter and leave the castle at all times when the gates were open.

Paolo laughed when Hector told him the conditions on which the pass was granted.

"The commandant is a shrewd fellow, master, but he is not quite shrewd enough; he forgot that though I may bring in nothing myself I may be able to arrange with someone else to bring something in."

"That flashed through my mind at once, Paolo; but at present neither file, rope, nor disguise would be of any use. However, they may be so later. The first thing for you to do when you get this pass will be to make yourself master of the plan of the town and the fortifications, and see if there is any place where you think an escape is possible. But even when you find one, and you think that it might be managed, you must afterwards find a place where I can be hidden for a time, at any rate for a few hours. You see, were I to go out in disguise I must do so in broad daylight, for my supper is served almost directly after the gates are closed; and were I missing there would be a search for me at once, the sentries on the wall would all be warned, and it would be impossible to get past them. If I could get out two or three hours before the gates are closed at nine o'clock I might, as soon as it became dark, attempt to get over the walls before the alarm was given, or I might possibly go out in the same disguise that I left here in, through the city gate and across the bridge."

"I see that, sir, and it seems to me that this would be easier than trying to find a hiding-place for you in the town. However, I will set my wits to work. I have been able to think of nothing in here; but one's eyes always help one's wits, and if I were in the town I might see something that would give me an idea how the matter might be set about."

Day after day Paolo went into the town, always returning discouraged.

"I must be growing a downright numskull," he said one evening in disgust; "I have been three weeks at it and no single idea has come to me."

"You need not be discouraged at that, Paolo; it's not such a simple thing to plan an escape from a fortress like this as it was to get into the citadel at Turin, where we also had the advantage of starting with disguises. I can no more think of a disguise in which I can pass the gates than you can. I am a good deal too tall to pass as a woman. My face is perfectly well known to every soldier in the castle, and even if we hit upon a disguise it would be very difficult to get it brought in. It struck me to-day that if I am to get out it must be in some vehicle that has come in with supplies."

"That is a great idea, master; if I had not been a thick headed fool I should have thought of that before. But at the same time it will not be easy to manage."

"I quite see that, Paolo; even if the driver were bought over it would be difficult indeed to manage to get into the cart with so many soldiers standing about."

Paolo shook his head.

"Yes, I don't see that that could be managed at all, master."

He stood thinking a minute.

WON BY THE SWORD

"I have it!" he exclaimed joyfully. "You know, sir, sometimes a train of waggons containing faggots, or flour, or other things, comes in late. Those that are unloaded before the gate is closed go out at once; the others are unloaded that evening, but the empty carts have to remain in the castle till morning, as the great gates are never opened between sunset and sunrise, though officers come in by the postern. Now, if you could manage during the night to slip into one of the waggons, say one that has brought in flour, you might be so covered over by the empty sacks they take out, that no one would dream anyone was hidden there."

"Capital, Paolo ! it is evident that your head is not so thick as you thought it was just now. Yes, I have noticed that as a rule if eight or ten waggons came in together, the full sacks are carried in, and the same number of empty ones are placed in one of the carts, being counted as they are put in. Certainly I could hide myself easily enough if you were there to assist in arranging the sacks as regularly as before over me. As I do not generally get up until eight o'clock, and my first meal is not brought to me till nine, I might be on my way two hours before it was discovered that I was missing. How would you manage?"

"I would get a countryman's suit, master, would go out soon after the gates were open, find some quiet spot where I should have hidden the clothes the day before, and slip them on over my own. Then I would join the carts as they came along. They don't generally begin to harness the horses up till the gates are open, so that I should get a quarter of an hour's start of them, and I should go out with them without question, as it would be thought that I belonged to the party. I should pay for some beer at the first cabaret we come to, and make signs that I wanted a lift in a waggon. I must, of course, pretend to be deaf and dumb, as, although I have picked up a little German since we came into these parts, I could not possibly pass as a countryman."

"It would be better still, Paolo, for you to put a blister on to your cheek, then before you join them put a great lump of tow into your mouth, so as to swell your cheek out

272

almost to bursting point, and then tie a bandage round your face; you could then by pointing to it make out that you had so terrible a swelling that you were unable to talk."

"That would be better certainly, master, indeed, it would be a capital plan. Of course I should get into the waggon in which you were, and gradually shift the sacks so that you could crawl out. When we smuggled you in we would try and put in with you a couple of brace of pistols, and if we were armed with them the carters would not venture to interfere with us. Of course, master, I should have to get a disguise for you. We could never be tramping across the country with you dressed as a French officer."

"Get something that I could put over the clothes I wear. A long frock, some loose breeches, and rough cloth to wrap round the legs below them, and of course a pair of countryman's shoes. The best plan would be for you to stand treat again at a cabaret a few miles out of the town, get them all in there, then I could slip out of the waggon and throw the sacks back into their place. Of course you would choose some spot where the cabaret either stands alone or is at the end of a village, so that there may be no one standing by, and I could, when I got down, walk quietly back along the road. You can make signs to them that you live hard by, and would leave them there; then if there should be any suspicion that I had escaped in the waggons, and a troop of cavalry were sent in pursuit, the men would be all able to declare that they had seen nothing of me, and so could give no clue whatever that would set them on our track.

"Well, it is quite settled that we will try that way, but it may be some time before the opportunity occurs. However, you may as well get the two disguises and the two brace of pistols, and stow them away somewhere where they are not likely to be found."

"There are plenty of places where one can do that, master; there is a row of old trees inside the fortifications, and I warrant that if I cannot find one with a hollow large enough to stow them away in, I can hide them in the branches with small chance of their ever being seen."

WON BY THE SWORD

Another month passed. Paolo made a point of occasionally going out soon after the gates were open, saying casually that his master had a fancy for a bottle of better wine with his breakfast, or that he was going to get some eggs to make an omelette for him. Hector was in no particular hurry, for the news had come that Turenne with his own troops and those of Hesse had, with the Swedes, marched away for the Rhine. It was rumoured that they would be joined by another army, for in no other way could the Imperialists account for Turenne having retired when he had a force at least equal to any that Merci could set in the field against him. Hector saw that at any rate there was no chance of a great battle being fought just then, and felt, therefore, no impatience to be off. Two or three times carts with faggots had been unloaded after the gates were closed, but as they took nothing out, it was impossible for him to conceal himself in them.

At last, to his satisfaction, a number of waggons of flour came in late one afternoon, and he determined to carry his plan into execution that night. The storehouses were not in the great court, but in a smaller one off it. Beyond two soldiers at the gate and a sentry at the commandant's door, no guards were kept in the court-yards, though a few sentries were placed upon the walls. Hector had his supper as usual, and Paolo brought in the news that eight of the waggons had not been unloaded in time to go out. A fatigue party of soldiers were now completing the work, which would be finished about nine o'clock. Taking off their boots a little after that hour they went quietly downstairs, then put them on again and boldly crossed the court-yard, for the night was so dark that there was no fear of their figures being perceived.

As they entered the inner yard they again took off their boots and walked up to the carts. In two of these the carters were fast asleep. They passed on quietly, feeling in each cart for the sacks, and were delighted to find that they were all placed in the one farthest up the yard, which would therefore be the last to go out. They were tidily piled in lines side by side at the forward end of the waggon. They cautiously removed the sacks of the middle lines; Hector lay down feet foremost, and Paolo laid the sacks regularly over him till they reached the level of the others. Half a dozen were doubled and packed neatly in at the end, so as to conceal his head and prevent its being noticed that any had been taken out. The rest were distributed evenly, so that the sacks were all as level as before, and no one would have suspected that they had been disturbed.

Paolo then returned to Hector's room. As the double sacks closing the orifice at his head had not been packed very tightly, enough air entered for Hector to breathe. He increased the opening somewhat by pressing one of the sacks a little aside, but left it so that he could readily pull it into its position in the morning. As soon as Paolo reached the room he applied a blistering plaster to his cheek and kept it on till he could no longer bear the pain, then he threw himself down on his pallet. But neither he nor his master slept much, Hector being kept awake by the heat and discomfort of his position, and Paolo by the smarting of his cheek. As soon as it was light the latter rose, and sat impatiently waiting for the time when the gates would open. Looking into the court-yard, he could see the troops coming out from their quarters and moving about, then the gates opened, and, tying a bandage over his cheek, he went down and crossed the yard.

"You are out early," the sergeant of the guard remarked.

He nodded. "I am nigh mad with pain," he said, pointing to his cheek, "and I am going to get some salve from an apothecary."

"You seem to be bad indeed," the sergeant said commiseratingly, " 'tis a terrible inflammation."

Paolo went down to the spot where he had hidden the bundles in the hollow of a tree. It was an unfrequented place, and slipping his disguise over his clothes, after putting the pistols in his belt, he took the second bundle and returned to a street through which waggons leaving the castle must pass. A few minutes later he saw them coming along. He had already stuffed his cheek full of tow, and several people, struck with the raw and swollen appearance of his face, had compassionately asked him what was the matter. He had simply shaken his head, opened his lips, and pointed to his clenched teeth, signifying that he could not speak. He fell in with the waggons as they came along and passed through the gate without question. When a short distance away from the town he made signs to the driver of the last waggon, that if he would give him a lift in the cart he would pay for some drink. The carter nodded and told him to climb up. After they had gone four miles from the town, they came to a wayside inn.

"Now is the time, master, they are all going in to get some drink. There is no one about."

The waggons all stopped there, for there had been no opportunity for the drivers to obtain refreshments as they passed through the town. All therefore sauntered into the inn, their salutations to the host showing that they were accustomed to stop there. Paolo followed them in, and putting down the money for a large jug of beer, handed it to the carter, and, shaking him by the hand, made a motion that he was going no farther. Then he went back to the end waggon. Hector had already pushed out the bags in front of him and had with great difficulty crawled out.

"It is all right, master, we have a good ten minutes; there is no one about, but you had better keep below the waggon rails until you have got your disguise on."

A couple of minutes sufficed for this, then Hector leapt to the ground, while Paolo replaced the sacks in their position; and then together they hurried across some twenty yards of broken ground and entered a wood.

"That was a capitally-managed business, Paolo. Now we have to find our way across country. We cannot keep by the river, for it turns away to the south, and would take us far from the point we want to reach. At any rate, for a day or two we must travel at night, after that I think we can venture boldly along—for it is not likely that the news that a prisoner has escaped will travel very far—although no doubt a strict search will be kept up for a day or two. I think that for to-day we had better make our way north, keeping in the woods as much as possible; they are less likely to search for us in that direction than to the west."

They found that the forest was fully two leagues across, and agreed that it was unlikely in the extreme that any attempt would be made to search so extensive an area, where two men could anywhere conceal themselves. Paolo had on the previous afternoon placed a couple of loaves and some cold meat in the bundles, and they now sat down by a little stream and ate a hearty meal, then, crawling into a thick growth of underwood, they lay down to sleep and did not awaken until the sun was setting.

"There must be some country tracks through this forest, Paolo. We cannot do better than keep along the edge of the stream until we come to one and then follow it. It is sure, sooner or later, to take us to some small hamlet, and I can go into a cabaret and get a couple of flasks of wine and buy enough bread to last us until to-morrow, and perhaps a sausage, they are not likely to have any other meat in a place of that sort. My German is good enough to pass muster, and even if it sounds strange to their ears, they will merely suppose that I have come from a different part of the country, for the dialects differ greatly from each other."

As soon as it became quite dark they found it impossible to follow the rough ground, and after one or two falls had to stop. Hector said, "This won't do, we shall twist an ankle or break a bone if we go on."

"Shall we light a fire, master? I have brought flint and steel with me, for I knew that we should want it."

"No, it is better to run no risks; there may be a road near for aught we know, and if anyone passing saw a fire among the trees, he might come to see who had made it."

"Not he, master; there are too many robbers about, deserters from their army, or men who have been ruined by the war. You may be sure that if any belated villager had the courage to go through this forest by night he would, on seeing a fire, hurry on as fast as his legs would carry him."

WON BY THE SWORD

"Well, no doubt you are right, Paolo; and though the night is warm enough the air is damp under this thick covering of leaves, and it will certainly be more cheerful. We will go a short distance among the trees before we light it."

Feeling their way—for it was pitch dark in the forest—they went on until Hector stumbled over a fallen trunk.

"This is the best place for a halt," he said, "for here is wood ready to hand. This tree has been lying here for years, I can feel that it is quite rotten."

Paolo set to work—took a handful or two of the crumbling wood, broke it up into dust, then struck a spark on to the tinder, touched it with a slow match and inserted this into the little pile of wood; a minute's blowing and the flames sprang up. He drew out the slow match and putting his foot upon it placed it in his wallet, then he broke off some more wood and soon had a blazing fire.

"We have enough food left for supper, master, and if I spit some of this cold meat on the ramrod of one of my pistols and hold it over the fire it will be all the more tasty. I wish we had those flasks of wine that you were speaking of. It seems to me that after sleeping for some ten hours we shall find it hard to go off again for some time, even though neither of us got any sleep last night. How furious the governor will be when he finds that you have escaped!"

"He is a good fellow," Hector said, "and save that he will be annoyed—because he will be blamed for my escape—I do not think he will be sorry that I have got off. I left a note for him on the table saying that I was about to make my escape, but that on my honour I had not obtained anything that would aid me, by your assistance, and that you had never brought anything into the castle save what you showed on entering to the guards. I should not like him to think for a moment that I had broken my promise and taken advantage of his kindness. How does your face feel?"

"It is mightily sore, but it does not smart as it did at first. I can tell you that I was very glad when I was able to slip that great lump of tow out of my mouth as soon as I entered the forest."

"I don't think in future that you need use so large a wad, Paolo; half that size will be ample; and of course you need only slip it into your mouth when we are going through a village, or meet a party likely to question us. As to your cheek, it will be days before that fiery mark disappears."

They talked until nearly midnight, and then lay down and slept till four, by which time day had broken, for it was now the first week in July. After walking for half an hour along the edge of the wood, they came to a track issuing out of it. This they followed, and in about two hours saw a village in front of them.

"I will go in and buy the things that we want, Paolo, and do you make a circuit round it. If the news has reached them of our escape they will have been told to look for two men; and the entry of a single countryman will excite no suspicion, for of course no one will know what disguise we have chosen.

"Do not be anxious if I do not come along for half an hour. It will be more natural that I should call for bread and cheese and beer and eat them there; then I can say carelessly that I may as well take some with me to eat later on."

"You are early!" the owner of the cabaret said as Hector entered.

"I ought to have been earlier," he replied in a grumbling voice; "but it was so late before I reached the other side of the forest, that instead of passing through it I thought it best to wait till daybreak, for it would be desperately dark under the trees, and sometimes there are pretty rough fellows to be met with there; so I slept in a shed until an hour before daybreak and then started, and I lost no time in getting through it, I can tell you. What can you give me now?"

"The usual thing," the man said, shrugging his shoulders. Bread and beer and black sausage."

"It might be worse," Hector said as he seated himself. The food was soon placed before him. He ate a hearty meal. "I have a long way to go," he said when he had finished, "and as I am blessed with a good appetite it will not be long before I am hungry again. I suppose there is no one in the village that sells bread and sausage, so if you will let me I will buy a whole one from you and a couple of loaves."

"I will sell them to you willingly enough; but you will come to another village three miles on."

"I sha'n't be hungry enough by that time," Hector laughed. Besides, I like to choose my own place and time and sit down by the wayside and eat my meal. One need never go very far without coming upon a stream; and though I like beer better than water, I can put up with it when there is nothing stronger to be had."

"Nothing but bread and sausage again, Paolo," Hector said as he joined his comrade a quarter of a mile beyond the village.

"And good enough too for a hungry man. I have often longed for such a meal in the days before you took me, in spite of all warning."

"And we have often done no better since, Paolo, when we have been on the march. Will you start on it now, or wait until we get to a stream?"

"I will hold on for a bit, master. This black bread is so hard that it needs a lot of washing down."

Making several detours to avoid villages, they walked all day, and towards evening came upon a main road running west.

"Unless I am mistaken in the line that I have taken, this must be the road through Eichstadt. I can see some towers ahead, and I have no doubt that they are those of the town. There is a bridge there across the Altmuhl. The river makes a loop at this point, and the road cuts across it to the northwest to Gunzenhausen, where there is another bridge. From there the road runs to Hall. Thence we can cross the Neckar, either at Heilbronn or Neckarsulm, and we are then in our own country, and but a short distance from either

Spires or Philippsburg, where we shall be likely enough to meet Turenne advancing again, or shall at any rate learn where he is. We will lie up now and not cross the bridge until it gets dusk."

"I wish we had swords, master."

"Yes, but they would not suit our disguises. But when we get into the town I will buy two woodmen's axes and a couple of the long knives that all the peasants here carry. I fancy from what I heard when we were at Hall with Turenne that the country between Eichstadt and there is for the most part a great forest, and there are rough hills to pass before we get to Hall. It will be just as well to have some weapons that we can use with effect if we should come upon any bands of robbers."

"Quite so, master. A good axe is as good as a sword in a rough sort of fight; but is there not some way we can travel so as to avoid this great forest that you speak of?"

"Not without making a great detour, and that through a country where there will be bodies of Merci's troops quartered everywhere."

"Very well, master. Then I think that the risk will be less with the robbers, especially as we have not apparently much worth stealing upon us."

"Not only apparently, but really, Paolo. Fortunately my purse was pretty well filled when we were taken prisoners; but we spent a good deal at Ingoldstadt, principally in buying articles we could have done without, but which we got in order to give an excuse for your going into the town, and in these disguises and pistols. However, we shall not, I hope, require much more outlay; and after getting axes and knives we shall have enough to pay for our food, such as it is, for some time. However, there is certainly nothing in our pockets to tempt robbers."

"No, master; but if they searched you they would notice your clothes. They would show at once that you are a person of quality; and although, as you left your scarf behind you, they might not know that you are an officer, they would see that there was a mystery about you."

"That is true, and I think that perhaps it would be as well if both of us were to take off our own clothes when we get beyond the town to-night, and go on only in those you got for us. When we rejoin our friends we can get money and replace them."

"I have money with me, master," Paolo said. "I have had no occasion to spend aught for a long time, and have changed my wages as you paid them into gold, and have forty pistoles sewn up in the waist-belt of my breeches. I heard you say that it was always a good thing to carry a certain amount about with one in case of being taken prisoner or laid up wounded."

"It was a wise precaution, Paolo; but just at the present moment I would rather that you did not have it about you. However, I do not suppose we shall be interfered with. You may as well continue to wear your breeches under those you have outside, but leave your doublet when I change. After all, if you were to be searched the pistoles would show that we are not what we seem, unless we could make up some plausible tale as to how we came possessed of them."

"Oh, we could manage that easily enough, master! There are other ways of getting pistoles than by earning them."

Thus chatting they had crossed the bridge and were now entering Eichstadt. Going to a quiet cabaret they ate a hearty meal, and Hector afterwards bought the axes and knives, and they left the town just before the gates were closed. They had walked some miles when a thunder-storm, which had for some time been threatening, broke over them.

"We must get some shelter if we can," Hector said. "I see a light on ahead. Let us push on and take refuge before we are wet to the skin."

On reaching the house they saw that it was a wayside inn.

"We are in luck, Paolo," Hector said as he lifted the latch.

The door, however, was fastened, and on his knocking a voice asked, "Who is there at this time of night?"

"Travellers," Hector replied. "Come, open the door quickly or we shall be wet to the skin!" and he emphasized his words by kicking at the door. It was, however, a minute or two before it was opened, and Hector, who was becoming furious at this delay, had just taken his axe from his belt and was about to break the door in when it opened, and a man with a torch in one hand and a sword in the other stood on the threshold.

CHAPTER XVII
A ROBBER'S DEN

W
HAT mean you by knocking thus furiously?" the landlord of the little inn asked angrily.

"What mean you by keeping your door shut in the face of travellers on such a night as this?" Hector replied, even more loudly. "Are honest men to be kept waiting in the rain while you are taking no steps to let them in?"

"How could I tell that you are honest men?" the landlord retorted.

"Because if we had not been honest men we should long before this have battered your door down, as indeed I was just going to do when you opened it."

"Well, come in," the landlord said with an evil smile. "Maybe you would have done better to have passed on."

He showed them into the tap-room, where two or three rough men were sitting.

"What did these fellows mean by knocking so loudly?" one of them asked angrily.

"It means," Hector replied, that travellers have a right to claim shelter of an inn; and indeed, inn or no inn, no one would refuse shelter to travellers on such a night as this is going to be." And his words were emphasized by a crash of thunder overhead.

"You crow pretty loud, young fellow," the man growled.

"I speak loud because I have right on my side. I desire to quarrel with no man; but one need indeed be a saint to keep one's temper when one is kept standing outside a door with the rain coming down in great drops, and threatening in another minute to come in bucketfuls. It is all the worse when, as you see, one has a sick comrade with one."

The man spoke in a low voice to the three others seated at the table with him. "May I ask whither you were journeying when thus caught in the storm?" he asked in a more civil tone than he had hitherto used.

"Certainly you may. We were in haste to get on to Gunzenhausen by morning, as a friend of ours has work ready for us there. We did not expect this storm when we left Eichstadt just before the gates closed, and as the nights are short we thought we would push straight through."

"You are woodmen, I see."

"Ay, woodmen and charcoal-burners."

"You are not from this part, at least, judging from your tongue."

"Nor, I fancy, are you," Hector replied.

"No," the other said. "In times like these every one is liable to be driven from home either because the troops of one army or another have plundered and destroyed everything, or perhaps because he has been forced into the ranks."

"That is just our case, and you will understand that in times like these, as you say, no one cares to answer questions on the part of strangers. But we have no particular cause of concealment. We have both been in the army, and, as you see, have left it, and have our reasons for wishing to travel at night, when there is no chance of falling in with troops whose officers might ask inconvenient questions. As, thanks to our host and you, we are nearly wet through, we will thank him to get ready as quick as may be two flagons of hot beer, and if he has got a couple of eggs to beat up in each of them, so much the better."

The landlord left the room, and a minute or two later the man who had spoken to Hector got up and went out.

"These men are up to no good," Hector whispered to Paolo as they sat down on a bench at a table some little distance from that at which the other men were seated. "I am sorry now that I asked for the liquor, it was necessary to order something. I should not be surprised if they drug it. Do you put yours to your lips, and then groan as if it hurt you too much to try to swallow, and leave it standing in front of you. I will pretend to drink mine, and will manage to pour it away on the floor. Presently do you lean forward on to the table and appear to fall asleep. As I am in the corner, I will lean back and seem to go off also. Unless I am greatly mistaken this is a regular thieves den. Keep one hand on the butt of a pistol. We will both keep awake for a time, and if nothing comes of it we will then watch by turns. It is clear that they suspect that we are not what we seem."

The men at the other table were talking together in low voices, and, listening intently, Hector could hear a murmur of voices in the room behind him.

"There were more than two voices there," he whispered presently to Paolo. The latter nodded, for he too had been listening. Presently the landlord returned with the two flagons of hot beer, which were set down on the table before them. The room was lighted only by a torch stuck in a cresset on the wall, and Hector had purposely seated himself as far from this as possible. Paolo took up his mug, raised it to his lips, and then set it down again with a sudden cry.

"I am afraid that you will not be able to take it," Hector said aloud.

"What is the matter with your comrade?" the landlord asked.

"He has a terrible abscess in his jaw, and is unable to speak or to swallow."

The landlord took the torch from its place and walked over and looked at Paolo's cheek. "There is no mistake about that," he said. "It is indeed a terrible swelling, and the cheek looks almost raw."

"He has put liniments on it," Hector said, "but they seem to have done him harm rather than good. However, he is not so bad as he was, and I hope that the abscess will break ere long."

The landlord fastened the torch up again, and said in a low tone to the other men: "There is no doubt about his face being bad." As he turned away from the table he stood between Hector and the other men, and the former seized the opportunity of pouring the contents of his mug against the wall by his knee, knowing that as the floor was of earth it would soak it up at once. From time to time he lifted the mug to his lips, until he apparently drained it. Then half closing his eyes he leant up against the corner. Paolo had already laid his head down on the table, and after a time both breathed heavily and regularly. Half an hour later one of the men rose noiselessly and left the room. Two or three minutes afterwards he returned with the host, the man who had gone out before, and two others.

"Seven against two," Hector thought to himself. However, we shall have the advantage of a surprise. He touched Paolo with his foot to assure himself that he had not really gone off to sleep, but the responsive movement showed that he also was on his guard. The man who had first left the room and one of the others drew their long knives and stepped quietly forward, while the others, also with bared weapons, prepared to support them if necessary. Hector waited until the two leaders were close, then he exclaimed sharply, "Now!" at the same moment throwing forward his hand with the pistol. Two reports rang out at the same moment, and the men pitched heavily forward. A yell of surprise and fury broke from the others, but ere they could step over their fallen comrades, Hector and his companion stood erect with their second pistols in their right hands and their axes ready for action in their left.

Hector's second shot took effect on the landlord, Paolo's apparently missed, for the other four rushed forward. Hector dashed the table aside, and he and Paolo, poising their heavy axes, rushed forward to meet their assailants.

"Mind the beams," Hector shouted, as with a sweeping side blow he clove in the head of one opponent. But the warning came too late. Paolo struck a downward blow, the axe caught the low beams of the ceiling, and it flew from his

The fight in the inn.

hand. His opponent sprang upon him. Paolo caught the man's right wrist as he struck at him with his knife, and drew his own from his girdle. His assailant threw his other arm round him, and, grappling, they fell on to the ground. Hector could do nothing to assist him, for the other two men were trying to circle round him, keeping beyond the swing of his axe but watching for an opportunity to spring upon him. Keeping his back against the wall he made feints against them. Presently one of the men passed between him and the two antagonists struggling on the ground. Suddenly they rolled over and over, coming in contact with him from behind and almost throwing him over. Before he could recover from the shock Hector's axe struck him below the ear.

The other man would have turned and made for the door, but Hector knew that it was important that he should not escape and carry the news to others of his party, who might be in the forest. He therefore sprang after him, and before the wretch could open the door struck him between the shoulders with his long knife. As he did so Paolo sprung up with a shout.

"Thank God that you are alive, Paolo! I was afraid that he might have killed you."

"No, no, master. I had him by the wrist too firmly for that, and my knife did its work almost directly. But with those two fellows hovering round I should have been at their mercy had I tried to get on my feet. So I kept on struggling until I saw my opportunity, and then as that fellow's back was turned I rolled over against him, and so gave you the chance that you were waiting for. Well, master, it has been a sharp business."

"It has indeed. Now the first thing is to see if there is anyone else in the house, and the next to look about for some clothes for you to put on for those you wear are covered with blood. Then we must be off, and put as many miles between us and this place before morning as we can."

WON BY THE SWORD

A brief search showed that the place was empty, save for the dead in the tap-room. An old doublet belonging to the landlord was found hanging up in the loft where he slept. Taking off his outer garments, Paolo put this on.

"It is lucky I kept my breeches on under the others," he said, "for I certainly could not have gone into a town with these stained things on. I suppose there is some money hidden somewhere, but we have not time to look. You may be sure that many a traveller has been murdered here."

"I quite agree with you, but we have certainly no time to spare to hunt for it. Let us be off at once."

Reloading their pistols and carefully wiping their axes they went out by a door at the back of the house, for neither cared to re-enter the scene of the slaughter. Before doing so, however, they took a long draught from the landlord's beer barrel, to make up for the drink of which they had deprived themselves. The storm had passed, and the stars were shining brightly. They met nobody on their way until within two or three miles of Gunzenhausen; it was found that the haft of Paolo's axe was deeply stained with blood; and he threw it away on issuing from the wood, as it did not accord well with his present attire, which was rather that of a discharged soldier or a worker in cities than of a countryman. Soon after eight o'clock they approached the town. They were now greatly fatigued, for they had done two long days' marches without any sleep between them, and turning off from the road they made their way to a little clump of trees, and there threw themselves down in the shade and slept until late in the afternoon.

"I think that after our experience of last night, Paolo," Hector said, as they walked towards the town, "we had better wait until we can join some party going to Hall before we leave this place. From what I hear, the road is a great deal more infested with bands of lawless men than that along which we have come."

"Then, master, I think we had certainly better wait, for I don't want anything worse than we had yesterday."

A ROBBER'S DEN

They went to a small inn, had supper, and then lay down on some straw in an outhouse and slept soundly until morning. Then they breakfasted, and as there was no one else in the room Paolo was able to eat freely. Presently the landlord came in, and Hector entered into conversation with him.

"We want to go on to Hall," he said. "We have friends there, and we are obliged to leave home because we should be taken for the army."

"Well, I don't think that you will find yourself better off at Hall than here. They are catching up every able-bodied young fellow and putting him into the ranks, and as you both look strong and active, except for your comrade's face, you are both likely to be seized as soon as you enter Hall, especially if you have no papers to show."

"We are not thinking of entering Hall, landlord. Our friends live a few miles away, and they will hide us till the army moves away from these parts."

"That will be before long, thank the saints! There is news that a great French army marched from Spires three days ago, and there is like to be a great fight before long; and if the French are beaten Merci will chase them back to the Rhine, recapture all the towns that they have taken, and perhaps enter Alsace."

"Which way do they say that the French are marching?"

"They took the road to Weisloch. Some think that they will come through Wimpfen, and then by Weinsberg here, unless Merci bars the way. Others again think that they will make their way down through Stuttgart. Five hundred men march from here to-morrow to Hall, whence they go on to Heilbronn to strengthen the garrison there. All the waggons in the town and country round have been fetched in to carry their stores and baggage and a convoy of ammunition. I should say that you could not do better than go on with the waggons. No one is likely to ask you any questions, for it will be thought that you are drivers."

WON BY THE SWORD

"Thank you very much," Hector said; "that would certainly be a capital plan. We were afraid of going through the forests alone."

"Yes, and you were right. They are full of marauders. A party of troopers arrived here from Eichstadt yesterday evening. They stopped to get a drink at a cabaret in the forest, and on entering found seven men lying dead, and no one living to say how they got there. That some, if not all, were robbers was evident from the fact that, on the bodies being searched, articles evidently plundered from travellers were found upon all of them. An examination was made of the house, and considerable quantities of plunder found hidden. Searching in the forest behind, several mounds of earth, evidently graves, were discovered. The landlord himself was among the killed, for one of the troopers, who had before stopped at the house, recognized him. It was supposed that the brigands were killed by some other party with whom they had quarrelled. Three of them were shot and two killed by tremendous blows from an axe, and as neither pistols nor axes were found in the room it is clear that those within had been killed by some other band."

The next morning, when the column started, Hector and Paolo fell in among the carts, and rendered good service on the road by helping to move them when the wheels of the waggons stuck fast at spots where the road crossed marshy valleys. So bad was the journey that it occupied two days. Then the waggons were parked outside the walls of Hall, a guard being placed round them to prevent desertion. The troops slept inside the town. At daybreak the next morning their march was arrested by an officer riding out from the town, saying that news had arrived on the previous evening that the French were marching upon Heilbronn, that General Merci was concentrating his army there to oppose the passage of the river, and that the troops were to push on with all speed, leaving their baggage-train at Hall. Hector at once decided that, with the Bavarian army gathering in front, it would be madness to endeavour to push on, and that indeed it would be far better to fall back until the direction of the

French march was fully determined, when they could make a detour and come down upon their flank without having to pass through the Bavarian army. He did not, however, care about remaining in Hall, which might be occupied by the Bavarians if they fell back, and they therefore, after entering the town with the waggons, purchased a store of provisions, and, going out again, established themselves in a small farmhouse, whose occupants had deserted it and fled into the town upon hearing that the French were but some thirty miles distant.

Every day Hector went into the place to gather news, and learned that Wimpfen had been captured by the French by a sudden assault, and that they had crossed the Neckar. On returning he at once started with Paolo, but on approaching the Neckar learned that the French had marched on to Rothenburg. They fell in, however, with a detachment which had been left on the Neckar. Hector found among them several officers to whom he was known, and, borrowing Paolo's money, fitted himself and follower out again, bought a couple of horses that had been captured from the Bavarians, who had, he learned, retired to Franconia, and set out to join the army. Rothenburg had been, he found out on his arrival, captured in a few hours, and the main body of the French had marched to Dinkelsbuhl, and there he came up with them. He had learned from the party on the Neckar of the defection of Königsmark and the Swedes, and that Condé and Turenne's united army did not exceed twenty thousand men, and, as he knew, that of Merci was at least equal to it in strength. His first question on entering the camp was as to the quarters of his own regiment, and he at once rode there. As soon as he was recognized the men ran to him, cheering wildly, and so great was the tumult that Turenne himself, whose head-quarters were but a short distance away, rode to the spot to enquire the cause of the tumult. When he saw Hector surrounded by his cheering soldiers he passed through the crowd, and, reaching him, shook him warmly by the hand.

I had hoped that we might have made an exchange for you during the winter, colonel, but I had not thought it possible that I should see you again before that time; for in the first place, we captured no prisoners in this campaign, but, on the contrary, have had many of our own officers taken; and in the second place, we have been too busy ever since Marienthal to enter into negotiations. You have, I suppose, given them the slip, you and that varlet of yours, for I see him over there."

"Yes, marshal; we had no very great difficulty in getting away. I have been very well treated, and until I heard that you were again taking the offensive, I had no reason to fret over my imprisonment."

"Well, you have joined us just in time, for at any moment we may fight a great battle. When you have leisure this evening come over to my tent. I shall be glad to hear how you managed to escape, and any news you have gained as to Merci's force and intentions."

As soon as the marshal had ridden off, his officers pressed round him, but before speaking to them individually Hector said a few words to the men, thanking them for the greeting they had given him, and saying that he was glad indeed to be back among them. Then he talked for a time to the officers, two or three of whom, after saying a few words apart to Captain de Thiou, had hurried away. Half an hour later de Thiou said:

"I have no doubt that you will be glad of supper, colonel. Ours is just prepared, and we hope that you will join us."

"I am hungry, de Thiou, now I come to think of it, for except a crust of bread this morning I have not touched anything to-day."

"It is fortunate that we are better off than usual," de Thiou said. "We had the luck to buy a pig from one of Weimar's troopers. The cavalry get the best of it, for though there are orders against pillaging, there is no doubt that a good deal of it goes on; and, marching as we have been, there is no one to see that orders are strictly carried out. However, we have benefited by it this afternoon."

Accompanying de Thiou, Hector was surprised to find that at a short distance in front of the spot where the regiment was bivouacked a large arbour had been erected.

"I did not notice this as I rode in," he said.

"It was not even thought of then, colonel; it was begun a few minutes after you rode up, and the men have worked right willingly, and fortunately there was a copse hard by. I may say that it was the men's own idea. I had given orders that a table should be made of any materials that came to hand, and one of the men started the idea of building an arbour over it, and as many hands make quick work it has, as you see, been constructed in little over half an hour."

As the evening was warm the front of the arbour had been left open. Inside, a rough table had been constructed of empty casks, planks taken from the bottom of the waggons, and a couple of doors from cottages near, while powder-barrels served as seats.

"Now, colonel, will you take the head of the table?" de Thiou said.

"Certainly not, de Thiou. I am your guest upon this occasion, so do you take that place, and I will sit upon your right hand."

"I only wish that we could have given you a dinner like those you so often gave us at St. Denis."

"I shall enjoy it as much as if it were a royal feast," Hector said, seating himself; "for indeed since I escaped from Ingoldstadt some ten days ago I have been living on black bread, sausage, and cheese."

The meal was a joyous one, for at the assault of Rothenburg on the previous day several barrels of wine had been captured by the soldiers of the regiment. These had been bought from them by the officers, who had feared that some of the men might drink to excess, and so damage the reputation which the regiment had obtained for sobriety and discipline. One of these had been broached, and this and the pork afforded an excellent supper even though the bread was of the worst possible quality. When the meal was over, de Thiou stood up and proposed the health of the colonel, and congratulated him most warmly upon his escape from the enemy, expressing the extreme satisfaction of all the men as well as officers at his return. The toast was drunk with enthusiasm, and Hector briefly returned thanks. Then, in accordance with the general request, he related the particulars of his escape from Ingoldstadt and of his journey. Paolo, who had been waiting behind his master's chair, came in for warm praise for the share he had taken in the matter.

"I certainly did not think when I first, against the advice of everyone, took Paolo as my lackey five years ago, that he would turn out so valuable a servant as he has done," Hector said as de Thiou handed a goblet of wine to the man. "He has been more than a servant, he has taken part in all my adventures, and truly I regard him as my friend. Indeed, gentlemen, had it not been for him I certainly should not be here to-night, for my own money gave out altogether at Hall, and I had to borrow from his store the means of buying clothes and horses."

"By the way, colonel," de Thiou said, "from the day that you were captured I have drawn your pay for you, knowing that if it fell into arrear you would have had hard work in getting it, so that I have now three months of your money in the regimental chest."

"Thank you, de Thiou, it will be very welcome; though Paolo would not have been a very hard creditor."

At eight o'clock the party broke up, and Hector walked across to Turenne's quarters. The latter had just returned from a consultation with the other generals.

"We shall open our trenches here to-night; the place is of some importance, as it is on the direct road to Nördlingen, and it is as well not to leave it behind us. This, however, we shall do, if news comes that Merci is marching to give us battle before that city, which we expect he will do. The Imperialists will like to fight there, for it was the scene of their great victory over the Duke of Weimar and the Swedes."

"We must hope that we shall reverse matters this time, marshal."

"We must hope so," the latter said gravely; "if we fight on a fair field I have no misgivings whatever. But Merci always takes up strong positions and entrenches himself, and Enghien is so anxious to fight that he will do so at a disadvantage rather than wait until we can meet them on even terms. You know what happened at Freiburg, where we lost some nine thousand men and gained no great advantage; while if we had moved round and threatened their line of retreat the enemy must have fallen back at once, we should have obtained our object without the loss of a man, and might possibly have fallen upon Merci in his retreat, and well-nigh annihilated his army. Do not think, Campbell, that I am for a moment underestimating Enghien's genius. It is extraordinary, and in the hour of battle he is superb, not only from his extreme personal bravery, but from the quickness with which he grasps every point, seizes upon the spot where a blow can be best delivered, and snatches victory, where another would see only defeat before him. But he is reckless of life so long as he carries his point, and rather than lose a day in turning the enemy's position and so forcing him to relinquish it, will sacrifice whole regiments by marching straight against the most formidable entrenchments. Had he but patience in addition to his own splendid qualities, I think he would be the greatest military genius the world has ever seen. And now let me hear what happened to you after you left my side that night after Marienthal."

Hector again related his adventures. Turenne laughed at the account of his escape, hidden under the flour bags.

"It was a good scheme," he said; "and it was well that you had that lackey of yours with you, for I do not think that you could ever have managed it unaided."

"I am sure I could not, marshal; it was entirely his suggestion, and he arranged all the details splendidly. He was equally valuable in another way afterwards;" and he described the fight in the cabaret.

WON BY THE SWORD

"That was more dangerous than taking part in a pitched battle; seven against two are heavy odds indeed, though you had the advantage of weapons. The fellow has a ready wit to think of rolling against the man who was waiting for a chance of running in and stabbing you; he would have made his fortune somehow even if he had not had the good luck to fall in with you. In some respects you resemble each other; you both have enterprise, quickness, and daring, but he lacks your studious habits, your determination to master everything connected with your profession, and your ability to turn your knowledge to account. He would have made a good soldier, an excellent leader of an irregular corps, but he would never have gained distinction. Well, I am very glad to have had a quiet talk with you; it takes one out of one's worries and anxieties. By the way, I had a letter from Mazarin; it reached me while I was at Spires. He said he was sorry to hear that you had been taken prisoner, and requested me to make an exchange for you as soon as possible, even if I had to give a general officer for you, for he was very deeply your debtor, and had the highest esteem for you. What have you been doing to make him your debtor? You never mentioned anything of the sort to me."

"The matter was to some degree a state one, marshal, or I should have told you of it; but as it took place nearly a year ago, and the circumstances are altogether changed, I can mention them to you in confidence—for even now, were it known, it might make me some powerful enemies." He then related how it was that he had thwarted the attempt on Mazarin's life.

"That was a piece of singular good fortune," Turenne said. "Mazarin is a stanch friend and a bitter enemy. I owe him no good-will, for he has behaved shamefully to de Bouillon, refusing to hand to him the estates for which he exchanged his principality of Sedan; but I do not permit myself to allow family interests to weigh with me against my duties to France. Truly, as you say, it were well to hide your share in a business that sent De Beaufort and a score of others to prison, and a dozen members of powerful families into

298

exile; it might well cause you serious trouble were it known. You did well to keep the matter to yourself, and you did specially well to refuse to accept any personal honour, for had you done so Mazarin's enemies would at once have connected that fact with the discovery of the plot."

On returning to his regiment, Hector found that an order had come just after he left, for four companies to march down under the guidance of an engineer officer to begin work on the trenches. De Thiou, knowing that he had gone to the marshal's, had gone down with the four leading companies. The other infantry regiments had furnished similar contingents, showing that the siege was to be pushed forward with all haste.

"Enghien does not allow the grass to grow under his feet," Captain Mieville said. "We stormed Wimpfen a few hours after our arrival before it; we carried Rothenburg in a single night, and I expect that by to-morrow evening we shall be masters of this place."

In the morning four more companies went down to relieve those who had been at work all night, and these had made great progress when, in the afternoon, the news came that Merci was marching with all his strength towards Nördlingen. Trumpets at once sounded to recall the troops from the trenches, a meal was hastily cooked, and at sunset the army marched for Nördlingen. All night they pushed on through the forest, and just as the leading squadrons emerged from it on to the plain, Merci's forces were seen issuing out from the forest facing them. Both armies at once formed in order of battle.

Enghien, anxious to attack, rode forward with Turenne, de Gramont, and Geis to reconnoitre the ground. It was found that between the armies there was a small river, with great pools and swamps on either side, and that the only approaches were by narrow and winding paths where two horsemen could scarcely ride abreast. Even Enghien felt that it would be madness to venture upon an attack. His artillery opened fire, that of the Bavarians replied, and the cannonade was continued till nightfall, inflicting a certain amount of loss on either side but in no way altering the position. Seeing that a battle could not be brought on here, Enghien marched two hours before daybreak for Nördlingen. At nine the army came down on to the great plain in front of that town, but he found that Merci had been beforehand with him, and had already taken up a strong position two leagues away, and between him and the city, and that his troops were already at work throwing up intrenchments.

The prince ordered all the baggage to be left behind, and at once marched against the enemy. At four o'clock they were facing each other. Merci had, as usual, chosen his position with great judgment. In the middle of the plain rose two little hills about a thousand yards apart. On the hill on his left stood the castle of Allersheim, and here Merci's left wing, under General John de Werth, was posted; while at Weinberg his right, commanded by General Gleen, took up its station. The main body of the army, under Merci himself, lay behind a village a couple of hundred yards beyond the hills, and at the head of the passage between them. He had his cavalry on his two wings, his infantry in the centre, and had thrown forward some regiments to hold the village. On the two hills he had planted his cannon, sheltered by intrenchments, and in a position to sweep the entrance to the valley.

His army consisted of between fourteen and fifteen thousand men, that of Enghien of seventeen thousand. After examining the position a council of war was held. Turenne was strongly against attacking the enemy in a position of such strength, but Enghien as usual overruled his opinion. Turenne then urged that the cavalry on the wings should not charge up the hills and attack the positions held there until the enemy's centre had been defeated, and his advice in this respect was taken. The generals then separated and rode to their respective commands. De Gramont commanded the right wing, consisting of all the French cavalry, and having as a second line a reserve consisting of four battalions of infantry and six squadrons of horse commanded by Chevalier de Chabot. Turenne commanded the left, which consisted of his own army, with twelve squadrons of Weimar's cavalry, with the Hessian army—six battalions and six squadrons—as a second line. The centre, consisting of ten battalions and five squadrons of horse, was commanded by Count de Marsin. Enghien took no special command, preferring to remain free to go where his presence was most needed.

CHAPTER XVIII
NÖRDLINGEN

IT was five o'clock in the afternoon when all the arrangements for the attack were completed. But as on the 3rd of August the evening is long, it was judged that there would be sufficient daylight to carry out the battle. The French began with a cannonade against the village, and this was replied to by the guns on the two hills. Not only did the position of the latter give them great superiority, but much time was lost by the French in being obliged to move forward their guns as the army advanced, a slow and tedious process in days when cannon were very heavy and cumbrous. Seeing that they were losing time and suffering more loss than they inflicted, Enghien gave the order to the infantry of the centre to advance.

They went forward with great speed and eagerness, for they were burning to retrieve their cowardly conduct at Marienthal. They carried the intrenchments Merci had thrown up at the mouth of the pass, and, heedless of the firing of the guns, rushed at the village. Here, however, they were received by so heavy a fire of musketry from the infantry posted there, who had loopholed all the walls and houses, that they came to a stop, and, being shot down in great numbers, turned and fled. The Count de Marsin was himself dangerously wounded. The Duc d'Enghien sent the Marquis de la Moussaie forward with a reinforcement of several regiments, but these, too, fell back before the Imperialists' fire. The Duc d'Enghien then rallied the infantry, added to them all those not yet engaged, and himself led them to the charge. Merci on his part brought forward his main body to the village.

The battle was now a desperate one. Enghien seemed to lead a charmed life. He was ever where the fight was hottest, encouraging the soldiers and setting them an example. His clothes were shot through in many places. Two horses were killed under him, and he received a contusion in the thigh. Merci on his part showed equal valour and intrepidity; but he was less fortunate, for he was struck by a musket-ball and killed. The news of his fall excited his soldiers to fury, and, hurling themselves on their assailants they cut the greater part of the infantry to pieces.

The French on the right had done no better, for the Bavarian cavalry charged them with such impetuosity that although they fought sturdily they were broken and routed. De Gramont did all that a leader could do to check their flight and lead them back to the battle; and when he saw that he was powerless to do this he put himself at the head of two regiments that had not yet been engaged, received the Bavarian horse with a heavy volley, and leading his troopers to the charge, broke into them, but advancing too far was surrounded and taken prisoner. John de Werth then fell on the reserve, broke them, penetrated the baggage, which was plundered, and then pursued the fugitives far away from the field of battle. Had he, instead of allowing his troops and himself to be carried away by their ardour, brought them round and attacked the French left in the rear, the Imperialist victory would have been complete.

Here for a time the conflict was doubtful. Turenne, in spite of the fire of the Imperialist artillery, led his troops in good order up the hill of Weinberg. His horse was shot under him and his cuirass was struck, but not pierced, by a musket-ball. On gaining the top of the hill a terrible fight took place between the Weimar and Hessian troops on one side, and the Austrians and Bavarians on the other. The former showed valour in strong contrast with the conduct of their French allies; and after repeated volleys had been exchanged

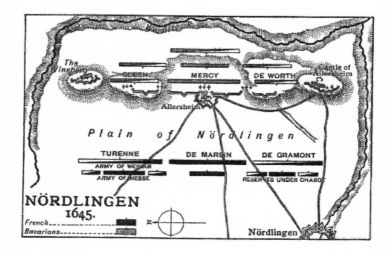

infantry and cavalry rushed upon each other and fought with bayonet and sword. At last the first line of Imperialists gave way, but General Gleen brought up the second line and threw Turenne's first line into disorder, although they still maintained their ground. At this moment Condé, seeing that his centre was destroyed and his right utterly dispersed, came up and joined Turenne, and placing himself at the head of the Hessians, who formed the second line, brought them forward. The enemy's squadrons were broken, and the infantry defeated. The guns were then turned upon the Imperialists on the slope of the hill leading down to the village, and when they were shaken by the fire Turenne's squadron charged down upon them and completed their defeat. General Gleen was taken prisoner, and Turenne's troops, descending the hill, took the village in flank.

Had the defenders here fought with the same courage that they had previously evinced, they would have given time to John de Werth to return, and the fate of the battle would have been doubtful, but they were seized with unreasoning panic, and at once surrendered. The night had long since closed in, and so far as the fighting had gone the battle might be considered a drawn one. The French right and centre were utterly routed, but their left had captured one of the keys of the position and the village behind it. Had John de Werth, when he returned from the pursuit, shown himself an able general, rallied the Imperialists and sent them to recapture the village, and with his victorious cavalry made a circuit of the Weinberg and fallen upon Turenne's rear, the Imperialist success would have been as complete and striking as that which they had won on nearly the same ground over the Swedes; but although an impetuous leader of cavalry, he had no military genius, and on returning after dark, and hearing that the Weinberg was lost and the village captured, he drew off from the field.

He was joined by the Imperialist infantry, and when the morning broke Turenne's division stood victors on the field. A number of officers, many standards, and all the cannon of the enemy fell into their hands. Of the French infantry not more than fifteen hundred were rallied after the battle, and of the allied army Turenne's German troops, although they had suffered severely, alone remained intact. John de Werth retreated with the remains of the Imperialist force to Donauwörth, and crossed to the other side of the Danube, although his force was still superior to that of Turenne, for the loss suffered by the French and Turenne's German troops was very much greater than that of the Imperialists. Enghien, in his despatch announcing the victory, acknowledged in his letter to the queen that it was due to the valour and honour of Turenne.

Nördlingen and Dinkelsbuhl opened their gates to the victors. Enghien fell ill and was forced to return to France, leaving Turenne in command. De Gramont was exchanged for Gleen, and he and Turenne took counsel as to the course that had best be pursued. John de Werth had already recrossed the Danube, and the French generals fell back to Hall, where they remained for twelve days to refresh the troops, provisions being plentiful in the neighbourhood.

But their position was daily becoming more untenable. The Duke of Bavaria, greatly alarmed by the result of the battle of Nördlingen, wrote to the emperor that unless Austria largely increased her force in the field he should retire from the contest, of which he had hitherto borne the brunt, and make terms with the French. The emperor, who had just brought a war with Hungary to a close, despatched the Archduke Leopold, his son, with a great body of horse, and he soon effected a junction with Gleen and John de Werth, and together they pushed forward at the utmost speed to surprise the French. As soon as Turenne received news of the movement he and de Gramont agreed that an instant retreat must be made, seeing that their force was less than half that which was advancing to attack them. The baggage was abandoned, and as there was no bridge available the army crossed the Neckar by swimming, each cavalryman taking one of the infantry behind him. They continued their retreat until they arrived at Philippsburg. Here Turenne with the whole of his army took up his position, covered by the guns of the fortress, while Gramont passed the river with the remains of Enghien's army and all the cavalry.

The Imperialists, after examining Turenne's position, came to the conclusion that it could not be attacked, and, marching away, besieged and captured all the towns taken by the French in their advance. Thus beyond the empty honour of a nominal victory at Nördlingen, the campaign under Enghien and Turenne ended, without any solid advantage whatever being gained by the French.

The Poitou regiment, which was the only French battalion in the army of Turenne, had been placed with the Hessians in the second line. It had fought with distinguished bravery on the crest of the Weinberg, and had publicly been thanked by Enghien, who had on the day of the battle ridden by the side of Hector at their head when they fell upon the Imperialists. They had suffered but a small number of casualties, for the enemy were already shaken before they charged, and had, after receiving a shattering volley, broken and fled as the regiment charged with fixed bayonets. Turenne was always anxious to impress upon Hector the lessons that were to be learned from each action, and while they were encamped round Hall he went over the events of the campaign with him on a map.

"You see," he said, "that what I said to you on the evening before we marched from Dinkelsbuhl has been completely justified. Instead of manœuvring so as to fight in the open, we dashed ourselves against this strong position, with the inevitable consequences, two-thirds of our army were routed, and the infantry of the centre and right all but annihilated; and although by hard fighting we on the left gained an advantage, it was only the impetuous folly of John de Werth that saved us from destruction. Now, you see, we are in no position to fight another battle. A victory won in one's own country is decisive for a considerable time, but a victory in an enemy's country, unless it involves his disastrous defeat and the utter break-up of his army, is practically without value. We can receive no reinforcements, for none can reach us from France in less than a couple of months; the enemy, on the other hand, have rapidly filled up their ranks, and have received, or are about to receive, large reinforcements, and as soon as they advance we must retreat in all haste, sacrifice all the advantages we have gained, and shall be lucky if we can maintain a footing on this side of the Rhine.

"Five or six thousand lives have been thrown away and nothing whatever gained. Now, you see, had we instead of knocking our heads against the enemy's position, manœuvred to place ourselves between him and the Danube, he must have retreated without fighting a battle, for he was inferior to us in numbers, and we should have been able to go into winter quarters in Nördlingen and possibly lay siege to Eichstadt. A genius may win a battle, Campbell, but genius, if accompanied by impetuosity and a thirst for great victories, will very seldom win a campaign. I love as well as admire Enghien; he is chivalrous and generous, he has great military genius; possibly with age his impetuosity may be tempered with discretion, but at present, although a brilliant leader, he is not the general that I would choose to serve under in a long campaign."

When Weimar's cavalry crossed the Rhine with de Gramont they broke into mutiny, declaring that they, were raised to fight in Germany and would not fight in France. Turenne crossed and endeavoured to get them to return to their duty, recalling to them how nobly they had fought under him, and appealing to them in the strongest way not to desert him now. A portion of them gave in to his entreaties, but the rest rode away to effect a junction with the Swedish army, and he was therefore deprived of a considerable portion of the force that had been the mainstay of his little army. Upon the other hand, the Archduke Leopold marched away to Bohemia to oppose the Swedes, who had gained several successes in that direction. Turenne, however, determined to carry out one more enterprise before the winter set in, and to reinstate the Elector of Treves, who had been deprived of his dominions for twelve years, in consequence of his having entered into an alliance with France. In order to effect this he marched in the first week in November with a small force of infantry and his cavalry to the Moselle, a distance of forty leagues.

He was joined by some of Enghien's troops from Metz, and on the 14th of November he invested Treves. The Imperialists were unable to gather a force of sufficient strength to relieve the town, which was, therefore, after a short resistance, forced to capitulate. The small garrisons from other towns in the elector's dominions were speedily driven out and the elector restored to his possessions, a result doubly gratifying, since his restoration produced a widespread effect among the German princes who had thrown in their lot with France, while the material advantage was no less, as it closed a door through which the Imperialists, when in sufficient force, could at any time pour their troops into France. This brought the campaign of 1645 to a close. Turenne was called to Paris, where he received the honours that were due to him for the skill and bravery by which, with altogether insufficient forces—raised, equipped and paid to a large extent from his private purse—he had for two years guarded the Rhine frontier from invasion by the united forces of Bavaria and Austria. Hector's regiment had been left at Philippsburg when Turenne marched away; but the marshal told him that there was no occasion whatever for him to remain with it during the winter. He thought indeed that it would be advantageous that he should pay a short visit to Paris, present himself to Mazarin, and then go down and see how matters fared with the estate, to which he had paid but a flying visit. He therefore set out without delay, Turenne entrusting him with some despatches to the cardinal.

"They are of no great importance," he said, "but it is always well for an officer returning to Paris to carry despatches with him. It shows that he has the hearty approval of his commander in leaving his post for a while, and that he has distinguished himself in a special degree to be thus selected. I have several times in my despatches had occasion to speak of the excellent service rendered by your regiment, and it will ensure you a good reception at court. Besides, Mazarin is evidently disposed to regard you with special favour, and an occasional visit keeps that feeling alive, whereas it naturally cools down after a prolonged absence. Therefore in every respect it is as well that you should show yourself in Paris for a short time before going down to Poitou, where I hear there have been some troublesome risings of the peasantry. The province, being broken and hilly for the most part, offers considerable advantages to irregular forces, who move unencumbered with baggage, and against whom cavalry cannot well act. I do not know that any of these troubles have occurred in the neighbourhood of your estate, but you would naturally wish to see for yourself how matters are going on."

"It seems more than two years since we left here, master," Paolo said, as they rode into Paris.

"It does indeed. It is more than six years now since I first rode away with Turenne, and a month later you entered my service. We have gone through a good deal together since those days, Paolo."

"Yes, indeed, sir. It was a fortunate day for me when my brother took me to your quarters."

"It has been quite as fortunate for me, Paolo. I doubt whether I should ever have proposed undertaking to carry Turenne's message into the citadel of Turin had I not felt that I could rely upon you as my companion in the business, and it was that which gave me my first step. Since then you have always been by my side, and have more than once saved my life."

On reaching Mazarin's hotel Hector found that he was at the Louvre, and immediately went there, and as bearer of despatches from the army was at once introduced to the minister's apartment.

"Come with me at once to the queen's closet," the cardinal said as he entered. "She has just sent for me, and her majesty, being at once a woman and a queen, does not like being kept waiting. She always wishes to receive the first news from the army, therefore I can venture to take you with me without asking her permission.

"I have brought Monsieur de Villar to your majesty," he said as he entered the queen's apartment. "He has just reached Paris with despatches from the Viscount Turenne. He has only this instant arrived, and I thought I might venture to bring him at once to you."

" 'Tis a long time since we have seen you, monsieur," the queen said graciously, "but we have heard of you from the marshal's despatches, and were glad to see that your regiment bore itself as well in the field of battle as in the park of Versailles. What news do you bring? Nothing of importance, I hope, for there can hardly be good news when the marshal has so scanty a force with which to guard the frontier."

"The Viscount de Turenne is too zealous in your service, madam, to remain idle, however small his force. He started suddenly the day I left with his cavalry and a small body of infantry to march to Treves, with two or three regiments he has persuaded the Duc d'Enghien to send him from Metz with some guns, and he hoped to capture the city and clear the electorate of the enemy before they can receive strong reinforcements, seeing that they are all scattered in their winter quarters."

"A bold stroke indeed, cardinal," the queen said, much gratified. "It has touched our honour that the elector should so long have suffered for his fidelity to France; and, moreover, its possession in his hands will relieve us of much anxiety and give us the Moselle as a barrier against the incursions of the enemy in that corner of our dominions. He is indefatigable, this good viscount, cardinal; and he is not one of those who look for great rewards for every service. He has indeed carried on the war largely on his own resources, which has been of no slight advantage to us, seeing that our exchequer is but too often strained to meet demands from other quarters. If he succeeds in this enterprise, you must write in our name and bid him come hither to receive our thanks in person, and to rest for a while from his labours in our service. You have changed somewhat, Monsieur de Villar, since we last saw you. The ladies of the court called you then the little colonel—not because of your size, for you already overtopped the greater portion of our courtiers, but from your age. Now you look all over a soldier, and a weather-beaten one."

Hector had indeed aged during the past two years. He was now nearly two-and-twenty, his moustache had grown, and, as was the custom of the time, he wore a small imperial. The habit of command had given to his face an expression of decision and resolution unusual at his age, and a life spent in the open air, and for the most part sleeping without cover, had bronzed his skin, and had counteracted the youthful appearance caused by his fair complexion.

" 'Tis but some three months since we heard of you as a prisoner, having been captured while with your regiment covering the retreat after the unfortunate battle of Marienthal. The cardinal told me that he had written to the field-marshal to try and arrange an exchange for you if possible. We had not heard that he had done so when the Duc d'Enghien's report of the battle of Nördlingen spoke of you as doing good service with your regiment there. I suppose Turenne in the press of business, omitted to say that you had been exchanged."

"I was not exchanged, madam. I succeeded in effecting my escape from the fortress of Ingoldstadt."

"You seem born to have adventures, monsieur," the queen said. "We heard before of your regiment performing prodigies of valour at Freiburg, and of withstanding Merci's whole army, foot and horse, for three hours. Last winter the governor of Lorraine reported that you and a company of your regiment from Nancy had defeated a great body of insurgent peasants, and had rescued Madame de Blenfoix and her daughter from massacre at their hands. There is no officer under the rank of general whose name has been so frequently brought under our notice. You intend to make some stay in Paris, I hope?"

"I shall do myself the honour later on, your majesty; but I hear that there are peasant troubles down in Poitou, and as I only paid a visit of a few days there, when your majesty had the goodness to present the fief to me, I am anxious to know how matters are going on, and to see that my castle is secure from attack by the insurgents."

"Your excuse is a good one. It would be well if more possessors of estates would spend their time in endeavouring to alleviate the condition of their people, instead of wasting their time and money in Paris."

"Monsieur de Villar took steps in that direction, your majesty, before leaving for the war; for my agents, who keep me informed of most things that take place, acquainted me with the fact that Monsieur de Villar entirely remitted the usual fines on taking possession, and reduced the annual payment of his tenants by one half until times should mend."

"A noble example!" the queen said warmly. "I would that we could afford to do the same through all the royal domains. It is a pleasure to us to know that one at least of our fiefs has been so worthily bestowed. Well, sir, I shall see you at the court this evening."

Hector bowed and withdrew. His first step was to go to the clothing establishment most frequented by men of good family. "I have to attend at the court this evening. I have just returned from the army, and have but the clothes that I stand up in. Have you any garments that will fit me suitable for such an occasion?"

"Of shoulder cloaks I have great store in silks, satins, and velvets of all shades and colours. There is no difficulty about doublets, for of these I always keep a large stock in hand; and although you are a bigger man than the majority of my customers, I think that I can suit you. Tight pantaloons are chiefly worn by those who affect the latest fashion, but it would be impossible for me to make these at such short notice. As you are a military man this matters little, for these chiefly affect loose breeches trimmed at the bottom with rich lace, stockings of silk, and shoes with rosettes. Such breeches I could promise you in three hours, for they require but little making. The stockings of all shades I have in stock, also shoes. These would need but rosettes of the colour to suit the dress, to be added to them."

"I put myself in your hands," Hector said. "I wish for a handsome dress, and yet one which shall in no way be foppish, but shall be suitable to my station. I am Baron de la Villar, colonel of the Poitou regiment of infantry."

"Do you incline to silk, velvet, or satin? I should say a velvet cloak and satin tunic and breeches would suit you best with your fair hair. I should choose for the cloak a crimson or violet, and for the doublet and breeches a yellow. If you would prefer a blue cloak I should say a white satin doublet and breeches would become you."

Hector shook his head. "No, I should prefer the first mixture. I care not whether the cloak is crimson or violet."

"I think violet, monsieur, and rosettes of the same colour on your shoes. It were best, I think, that the stockings should match the doublet. You will, of course, have a pointed lace collar for your cloak, and at the bottom of your breeches and at your wrists to match. I think, sir, that a large collar and gold embroidery would go best with the costume."

Hector nodded. "I leave it entirely to you, Master Poitrou, so that everything is ready in time for me to wear them. I also want a travelling suit of good fashion—I leave the matter of colour to you—and also a suit for wearing here in Paris."

The cloak and doublets were speedily chosen, as M. Poitrou had several of the colour and material in stock. Hector was then measured for the breeches, which were of the fashion now known as knickerbockers, but somewhat looser. He then chose a violet cap with a yellow feather to match the court dress, a court sword, high riding-boots, and loose turned-over boots used for walking, but left all other matters to the tailor.

"When your man brings the things to me at the auberge Pomme d'Or I will pay him at once," he said. He was indeed well supplied with funds, for as he passed through Nancy he had drawn the sums standing to his credit from an agent there, to whom he had, as occasion offered, transmitted the greater portion of his pay, and also the balance of the sum that had been paid him when he first took possession of his estate, after paying for the various expenses he had incurred in St. Denis and in Paris. Monsieur Poitrou was faithful to his promise, and although free from vanity, Hector could not but perceive, after he had donned his court suit, that he made a good figure. Such, indeed, was the opinion of not a few of the ladies of the court as he entered the great reception room.

He had now adopted the general fashion, and wore his hair in ringlets hanging down on to the collar. His fair complexion contrasted strongly with the much darker one of the majority of the courtiers, and this, as well as his height and erect soldierly bearing, rendered him a conspicuous object among them. The queen and cardinal both honoured him with marked attention; but what pleased him most during the evening was the hearty greeting that he received from Colonel MacIvor, of whom he had seen but little during the campaign, as the Scottish regiment formed part of Enghien's command, and was not present at the battle of Nördlingen, being left in garrison at Metz when the duke marched to join Turenne. Mazarin himself presented him to many of the ladies of the court, thereby showing that he wished him to be regarded as a particular friend of his; and Hector, having gained much in self-possession since he had last appeared there, was able to make himself more agreeable to them than before, to bandy compliments, and adapt himself to the general atmosphere of the court. The cardinal sent for him again the next morning.

"The news is bad from Poitou, Colonel Campbell, and I think that it would be well that you should proceed there at once. So we will release you from further attendance, and you can make up for it by giving us a longer time on your return."

Hector, however, tarried two days longer in Paris, by which time he had received all the clothes that he had ordered. Early on the morning of the third day he mounted and rode away with Paolo and three of his troopers. Hunter had been left behind at Philippsburg for the cure of a wound that he had received at Nördlingen. Hector was mounted on one of the horses that Enghien had given him; the other was in the hands of the Imperialists. They travelled fast, and met with no adventure until they arrived at Poitou, where Hector learned that in the western part of the province the peasants had almost everywhere risen, had defeated the royal troops who had marched against them from La Rochelle and Nantes, and had captured and burnt many châteaux, slaying all persons of the better class who fell into their hands.

As he neared his own estate, learning that the tenants there had so far not joined the rising, but that several bodies of insurgents were in the neighbourhood, he rode still more rapidly forward. Signs of the trouble were everywhere apparent. In the villages only women were to be seen; there was no sign of life or movement in the fields; and he passed two châteaux which were now but empty shells. As soon as he had crossed into his own estates he found the houses entirely deserted; no man, woman, nor child was to be seen; no animals grazed in the fields, and the little stacks of hay and straw had been carried away.

"It is evident," he said to Paolo, "that MacIntosh has called all the tenantry into the château; had they joined the insurgents the women and children would still be here."

As they ascended the steep hill on whose brow the château stood, he could make out that there were a number of men posted upon the walls.

He is evidently determined that he will not be caught napping, Paolo, and all the peasants of Poitou could not take the place unless they were well provided with cannon."

The château, indeed, still retained the characteristics of a castle. The site had evidently been selected with a sole eye to defence; the hill on which it stood fell abruptly away on three sides, and could hardly be attacked except in front. Here a plateau extended some three or four hundred yards long and upwards of a hundred yards across. A wall with flanking turrets had been a sufficient defence on the other three sides, but here there was a strong tower on each flank, and also on each side of the central gate. The walls inclosed a space of some two acres, in the centre of which stood the castle. This had been to some extent modernized—windows having taken the place of loopholes in the upper floors, while those looking into the inner court-yard extended to the ground. The point where the road reached the plateau was some three hundred yards from the gateway, and as Hector galloped towards the walls it was evident that he was recognized, for shouts were raised by the men on guard and the drawbridge over the fosse—cut in the solid rock along the foot of the wall—was lowered.

As he rode across it the gate swung open and MacIntosh ran out to meet him.

"Is all well, old friend?" Hector asked as he sprang from his horse and clasped the sergeant's hand.

"All is well so far, colonel; still, I am glad indeed that you have returned, for at any moment trouble may begin. We hear that the peasants mean to attack us. I hardly think they will venture to do so, but I have no doubt they will play havoc on the estate and burn every house, because the tenants, instead of joining them, have come up here to aid in the defence. It was a good day indeed when madam and her daughter came here, they have made themselves so loved by the tenants that they would do anything for them. Ah, if all the ladies of France had been as good to their people as they have been, we should not have these troubles on hand! Here they come to welcome you."

Hector hurried across the outer court, where two lines of palings had been erected, forming a passage from one gate to the other, and keeping back the animals that crowded the enclosure.

"Welcome back, welcome back, Colonel Campbell!" the baroness said as she came up with both hands extended, and her words were echoed by her daughter. In the year that had elapsed since they started under the charge of Paolo both had changed. The look of care and anxiety, which had been heightened by the terrible events of the two previous days, had passed from the elder lady's face, and had been succeeded by one of contentment and happiness.

Norah showed an even greater change; she had now attained her full height, her figure had filled out, and she stood on the threshold of womanhood and bid fair to attain a high degree of beauty of the type characteristic of her nationality. Her hair was dark, her eyes gray, her expression changing rapidly from grave to gay, the latter movement generally predominating.

"I need hardly ask, madam," Hector said as they entered the château, "whether you have been comfortable here, for your face shows that you have at least been contented with your lot as châtelaine."

"I have been more than contented, I have been very happy, Monsieur Campbell. It has been a pleasant task indeed to be your almoner, and to be able to carry comfort to those in distress, sympathy and aid to those in suffering. Within the castle, nothing could be more pleasant than our position. Captain MacIntosh has been unwearied in his efforts to make us comfortable, and your steward has in all cases been willing to aid me with money and counsel when I asked for them. The proof that your goodness has been appreciated by the tenants is that every one of them without exception has refused to join the insurgents, and has forsaken his home in order to come up and aid in the defence of the castle."

"That is indeed gratifying, madam; but methinks their action is due rather to the kindness of yourself and Mademoiselle Norah, than to the gifts they receive."

"I do not choose to be called Mademoiselle Norah," the girl said, tossing her head. "I am Irish on both sides, and have not a drop of French blood in my veins. To strangers I am Miss Norah O'More; to you, and to any I may love, I am plain Norah."

"I don't think that you can be that to anyone, Norah."

"Now I don't like that, Colonel Campbell. That may do at the court of Louis XIV., but not at the château of la Villar, and if you are going to pay compliments I shall be stiff and unpleasant, and shall insist upon being addressed as Miss Norah O'More."

"As I did not mean to compliment you, for I spoke but the truth, I shall not accept the penalty. Now," he went on, "unromantic as it may sound, I own that I am hungry, and I am sure that my four followers are also, for we have ridden far and fast, and have not stopped save to bait our horses and snatch a mouthful while they ate, since daybreak. In truth the news we received made me sorely anxious, though I felt sure that MacIntosh could hold the château against any attack that was likely to be made on it."

CHAPTER XIX
THE PEASANTS' REVOLT

A FTER eating a meal Hector had a talk aside with
MacIntosh.
"Do you really think that these varlets will venture
to attack us?"

"I do indeed," the old sergeant said. "They have taken
several places as strong as this by sudden assault. They are
desperate, and, as I hear, fight like demons, regardless as to
how many fall. As far as stout arms go we are well supplied,
for there are at least a hundred men capable of bearing arms,
and all have had more or less drill since I have been here.
Unfortunately, however, our wall-pieces are old and scarce
fit for service, several of them will, I feel sure, burst at the
first discharge."

"But they have no artillery at all, MacIntosh?"

"I am sorry to say that they have, sir, and a good amount
of it. They captured ten field-pieces when they defeated the
troops, and have obtained a score of others from the châteaux
that they have taken. They have only to plant them three or
four hundred yards away at the end of the plateau, and they
would easily batter down the gates, and might even in time
effect a breach in the walls."

"That is serious indeed, MacIntosh. Is there any other
way in which they can attack us save in front?"

"I think not. I was careful to examine the face of the
precipice when I first took command here, and wherever it
seemed to me that an active man could climb up I had
portions of the rock blown up, and have so scarped the face
that I do not think it is scalable by human foot. But there is

nothing to prevent their crossing the fosse on a dark night, and so stealing along and making an attack on all sides of the house."

"Then our first care must be to prevent this, MacIntosh, by building walls along by the fosse from the corner towers to the edge of the plateau. The distance is very short, not more than eight or ten yards at the outside. We have, I see, any number of horses and not a few carts. Let the tenants be set to work at once, and, going down the road into the ravine below, fill their carts with blocks of stone and haul them up here. Let active boys be sent out in all directions as scouts to bring in word when the insurgents are approaching; and at the same time let twenty well-armed men of the garrison go down with the carts, so as to give confidence to the tenants and cover their retreat up the road if the insurgents should suddenly make their appearance. Let some of the men take bill-hooks and axes down with them, and cut poles. These must be sharpened, and as the walls are built, fixed among the stones so as to make a cheval-de-frise. At the same time let half a dozen stout ladders be constructed, so that the defenders of these walls may, if unable to hold them, make their retreat up to the battlements. I wish now that I had ordered a strong bastion to be thrown up so as to cover the gate from an attack by artillery, but it did not seem likely that we should be besieged by any force having guns, and I let the matter remain until the tenants should be better off and we could spend our money on such work. However, it is too late now to think of that. I suppose there is a portcullis to the gate?"

"Yes, and I got it in good working order when I first came here; but the cannon would speedily shatter that, as well as the bridge drawn up in front of it and the gate behind it."

"Then as I have no doubt that there are plenty of flour sacks, we must fill these with earth and pack them between the bridge and the portcullis, and fasten the bridge in its place with any chains that may be available, so that it will keep erect. The earth packing, however much it may be battered, will protect the portcullis of the gate for some time against their fire."

"It is a good idea if we have time to carry it out, colonel. We have still four or five hours' daylight, and as I think that this is of even greater importance than the side walls, we will set the tenants to work at once, and it will save time if they take down the sacks, of which, as you say, we have an abundance."

A few minutes later a dozen active boys left the castle, and scattered to various points on the hills around, so as to command a view over a considerable extent of country. Soon after, some thirty carts went down the road accompanied by a number of men with shovels, and twenty of the garrison commanded by one of the old soldiers. All returned loaded with sacks of earth; these were taken into the castle, when the portcullis was lowered and the drawbridge across the fosse raised. An opening was left on the top to allow the sacks to be lowered into the space between the bridge and the portcullis. A score of men with ropes went on to the wall above and lowered them behind the drawbridge, where five or six men stowed them away. As soon as it became dark torches were lighted, and by ten o'clock a solid mass of sacks filled with earth were packed in the space between the portcullis and the drawbridge.

The night passed off quietly, the horses and carts remaining beyond the fosse. Planks had been placed across one end of this, and the horses and carts taken over. The horses were picketed round the castle, a supply of forage being placed there for their use, while the carts were packed closely by the fosse, so as to form an obstacle to any of the assailants who might try to pass. At daybreak they were again run across the planks, the horses brought round and harnessed, the scouts being sent out as on the day before. All day the work went on, and by nightfall two walls twenty feet long and eight feet high, bristling with pointed staves, were erected. They stood some twenty feet back from the edge of the fosse, and extended from the wall to the verge of the precipice. The carts and horses had, before the walls were built, been taken round to the back of the castle, where the plateau extended some fifty yards beyond the defences. Evening was just coming on when the boys came in, two of them bringing a report that a great crowd of men could be seen approaching from the west.

MacIntosh, with thirty men, were at once lowered down from the battlements, and took up their places in an intrenchment which had been during the day thrown up at the point where the road came up to the plateau, while a score of the tenants assembled at the edge of the cliff, where great piles of blocks of stone had been collected in readiness to throw down. Lighted torches were placed at intervals along the road, and three or four great cressets, holding balls of tow soaked in turpentine and oil, were set up on the edge of the plateau; these were to be lighted when the peasants attempted to mount the hill.

An hour passed, and then a flame sprang up from a house and outbuildings in the valley, lighting up the ground around and showing that a great crowd was gathered on the road there.

"How many should you say there were, MacIntosh?"

"I should put them at four or five thousand."

"Yes, they are certainly not short of four thousand. What wild-looking figures ! they are just the same in appearance as those who attacked Madame de Blenfoix's château. See, they are lighting torches, and I expect they mean to make an attack at once. Their guns are with that group in the rear of the others; at any rate they will not be of any use in assisting them to make their way up this road. They are evidently working themselves up to a state of madness. There are half a dozen fellows addressing them from various points."

The men who had been brought down to guard the intrenchments at the head of the road were all armed with muskets, and carried in addition long pikes. Presently a roar of shouts and yells was heard, and then there was a rush on the part of the crowd towards the foot of the long ascent.

Hector moved to the place where the tenants were posted.

"Do not hurl a single stone down until I give you the word, nor light the cressets; the torches they carry will be quite sufficient for us to make them out, and the attack will be all the more successful if it comes as a surprise."

Then he returned to the breast-work. The men here had been posted by MacIntosh eight abreast. When the head of the column of insurgents were half-way up the hill they opened a scattered fire; they had armed themselves with the muskets they had taken from the troops.

"Their guns will be of little use to them, for few of them can ever have had firearms in their hands before; do not fire a shot, MacIntosh, until I give the order. It is clear that someone must have told them that we have thrown up this intrenchment to-day, or they would not have wasted their ammunition."

Not a shot was fired until the leaders of the peasants were within forty yards. Up to this time no torches had been shown in the intrenchments, but now these were suddenly brought forward, and Hector, in his helmet and body-armour, mounted on to the breast-work. The head of the column paused on seeing a row of levelled muskets and three rows of pikes forming a hedge of steel.

"My men," Hector shouted in a loud clear voice, "halt, I beseech you, before harm comes to you! I know that you have sore grievances, I know that you and your wives and families are well-nigh famishing, but how do you think that you will better your condition by assaulting castles and burning down châteaux? You are but preparing labour for yourselves and heaping up fresh imposts on your own heads, for it is you who will have to rebuild them, it is you who will have to pay for the damage that you have done. At any rate, none can say that you have cause for enmity against me and mine, for I have done all in my power to mitigate the sufferings of my people, and the proof is that not one of them has joined you. The taxes that press so heavily upon you are not the work of your feudal lords, they are caused by the necessity for defending France against the assaults of foreign enemies, and were every noble in the land slain it would still be necessary that these taxes should be collected, unless France is to be overrun by the Spaniards and Austrians. I would fain abstain from spilling one drop of your blood, but I must defend myself if you attack me, and I warn you that, numerous as you are, you will not succeed in capturing my castle. I am a soldier of France, and as I have shed my blood in defending her against her enemies, so if you persist I shall not hesitate in shedding yours in my own defence. I implore you to disperse to your homes; even if you gain successes for a time, it would but draw down vengeance upon you."

The assailants had paused when he commenced to speak, and those in front had listened to his words, but those behind, not knowing what was going on, continued to shout and to press up the hill. As he finished speaking there was a yell of defiance, and the column rushed forward.

"Aim low," Hector shouted as he leapt down among his men, "fire!" Eight muskets flashed out. "Second line, fire! Now handle your pikes, the rear lines will reserve their fire."

Although ten or twelve of the leading rank of the insurgents had fallen, there was no pause among the others, and they rushed forward to the hedge of pikes.

"Take charge here, MacIntosh; I will run and get the stones at work." In half a minute he stood by the side of the tenants.

"Heave them down!" he said. He had chosen a spot where the rock rose perpendicularly above the road. "Drop them over," he said, "so that they may fall straight. The biggest you must roll over with your levers, but work them to the edge and let them topple over; don't thrust them out or they will bound over the road. Now!"

Twenty rocks were dropped down together. Even above the din of shouting the crash as they fell below was heard, followed instantly by yells and cries.

"Twenty rocks were dropped down together."

THE PEASANTS' REVOLT

"Move farther on and give them another shower," Hectors said; and again the rocks fell on the crowded causeway. The first volley had caused a pause—numbers had been crushed, many of the stones as they rolled down the road had carried confusion to those below; the second volley completed their discomfiture. Appalled by a discharge against which they had no shelter and which was wholly unexpected, those near whom the stones had fallen turned, and in their panic swept those below them on the road down into the valley, many being overthrown and trampled to death. Ignorant of what was going on behind them, the crowd above the spot where the stones had fallen were still pressing upward, those in front hewing with their scythes and axes at the pike-heads.

Hector ran back there. "The two rear ranks will now fire!" he said.

The men dropped their pikes, and two volleys of musketry were poured into the insurgents. Those of the front line were swept away by the fire, and for a moment the whole recoiled.

"Now, men," Hector shouted, "cross the breast-work and sweep them away with your pikes!"

With a cheer the men leapt over the embankment. There was room for ten abreast, and in a treble line with levelled spears they bore down upon the rebels. The charge was irresistible. A few of the leaders of the peasants threw themselves on to the spears and died there, the others strove, but in vain, to fly. Their comrades behind, ignorant of what was going on, still pressed up, and it was not until the screams and shouts of those in front, and the pressure downwards, brought the column to a stand and then bore it backward, that they learned that the defenders had taken the offensive, and were sweeping all before them. Then a panic arose, and the peasants rushed down the road, the tenants above saluting them as they passed with another volley of rocks.

Half-way down the hill Hector halted his men, and led them up to the intrenchment again over a road encumbered with dead bodies.

"I think that will do," he said. "After the tale those who have got down safely will have tell, we may be sure they will do nothing until morning, and it may well be that they may think it advisable to be off to attack some other place not so strongly defended. However, we will presently beat them up, and if possible capture their cannon, and without them they could not hope to take any fortified house well defended."

For a time there was a prodigious din in the valley, sounds of men shouting and quarrelling, of others trying in vain to make their voices heard, and to address the excited peasants. In an hour it quieted down, and by midnight all was still. Hector had been busy with his preparations.

"How many horses have we?" he asked.

"Well-nigh a hundred, colonel."

"That is more than enough. Now, MacIntosh, do you and the men here go down the road and pitch the bodies over; we should never get the horses over them."

Then he went to where the tenants were still waiting. "Now, my lads," he said, "I want a big gap made in one of these walls we built to-day, wide enough for a horse to pass through it, and strong planks laid across the fosse." Then he ascended the ladder up to the battlements. He found the baroness and her daughter standing over the gateway.

"Is all over?" they asked, as he came up to them.

"Yes, for the present. We have beaten them handsomely, and without the loss of a single man."

"Will they attack again in the morning, do you think?"

"I feel sure that they will not do so. You see, they relied upon their cannon for taking the château, and they find they are useless. I am going to make a sortie before daybreak, for I want to capture those cannon. So long as they hold them they will continue their work, and they may not always meet with so stout a resistance. The loss of their cannon will dishearten them, as well as lessen their power for evil. I shall take every man who can carry arms, and leave ten at the breast-work to defend it; but there is no chance whatever of their attempting to come up here while we are attacking them, so you need have no fear."

"We shall not be afraid, Colonel Campbell, our confidence in you is absolute; but do you not think that you are running a great risk in attacking a force some forty times as large as your own?"

"One cannot call it a force, it is simply a mob, and a mob that has suffered a terrible repulse, and the loss of three or four hundred men to-night. We shall take them by surprise. I am going to mount all the tenants. MacIntosh tells me that they have all been drilled as cavalry as well as infantry. He, with the twenty men of the regular garrison on foot and ten of the tenants, will make straight for the guns. I shall be with the horsemen, and as soon as we have scattered the mob, we will harness the horses to the guns and bring them up here, so that I shall strengthen the castle as well as weaken the peasants."

The tenants were all informed of what was going to be done.

"It will be to your benefit as well as ours," he said, "for you may be sure that in the morning, if they give up the idea of again attacking us, they will scatter all over the estates and sack and burn every house, whereas if we succeed in dispersing them, no small portion of them will at once scatter to their homes, and the rest will take care not to come near this neighbourhood again."

At twelve o'clock MacIntosh sent a man to say that the road down was clear, and that three hundred and twenty dead bodies had been thrown over. At three o'clock in the morning the horses, round whose hoofs pieces of sacking had been tied, were led across the fosse. One of MacIntosh's sergeants was put in charge of the ten men who were to remain at the intrenchment, the castle being left entirely in the hands of the women and boys. The mounted tenants were eighty in number, all carrying long spears and swords. The torches had long since burnt out, and each man leading his horse went noiselessly down the road, MacIntosh with the footmen leading the way. They halted at the bottom of the road. There was no sound from the spot where the insurgents were lying a couple of hundred yards down the valley, fatigued by a very long march on the previous day, and the exertion of dragging the cannon, for only a few of these were horsed. Presently the day began to break, but not until it became light enough to see perfectly, did Hector give the order to mount, and leaping into the saddle prepared to lead them.

The mounted men had been divided into four bands of twenty each. Paolo and the three troopers each took the command of a party. Hector's orders were: "Keep together until the peasants are in full flight, then separate in pursuit. The movement must be put down or the whole province will be ruined, therefore give no quarter, and pursue until your horses are tired, then return here. Now, MacIntosh, do you advance straight upon the guns; it is probable that they are all loaded, therefore carry them with a rush. The moment we see you engaged we will charge."

The horsemen were in single line, extending from side to side of the valley. Hector kept his eye upon MacIntosh's party. They were close to the guns before any of the sleepers awoke. Then there was a sudden shout, and numbers of the men rushed to the cannon. MacIntosh was there as soon as they were, and pouring in a volley rushed upon the guns. At the same moment Hector gave the word to charge, and with levelled spears the horsemen rode down into the midst of the crowd. Appalled by this sudden attack, which was wholly unexpected, the resistance was but slight. Many of the peasants at once threw away their arms and fled. Those who resisted were speared or overthrown by the horses. As the valley widened the four troops separated a little, each cutting a way for itself through the peasants. It was no longer a fight; and a wild panic seized upon the whole of the insurgents. Some rushed straight down the valley, others ran up the opposite hillside; but the slope here was gradual, and the horsemen were able to pursue.

THE PEASANTS' REVOLT

"Paolo, take your troop up the hill. Let the others keep straight down the valley." And, heading these, Hector galloped on, shouting to MacIntosh to harness what teams there were to some of the guns and take them up to the top of the road, and then bring the horses back for some more.

For two hours the pursuit continued. Occasionally a group of peasants gathered together and tried to stem the tide, but these were speedily overcome, the long spears bearing them down without their being able to strike a blow at the riders, and at the end of that time the insurgents were scattered over a wide extent of country, all flying for their lives. Hector now ordered trumpets to sound; he was soon joined by the other troops, and at a leisurely pace they rode back to their starting-point. Not more than half the guns had as yet been taken up, for MacIntosh had found it necessary to put double teams to them in order to drag them up the steep road. The mounted men had all brought ropes with them, and, dismounting, eight yoked their horses to each gun, and in an hour the whole were brought up to the plateau, the drawbridge was lowered, the sacks of earth cleared away, and the portcullis raised, the gates thrown open, and the garrison filed into the court-yard, greeted by cries of welcome from the women.

"I think that we have crushed the insurrection in this part of Poitou," Hector said to Madame de Blenfoix. "We have certainly killed six or seven hundred of them, and I am sure that the remainder will never rally. We will rest to-day, and to-morrow morning we will set to work to complete the defences of the château, so that it may be held by a comparatively small number of men."

The joy of the women was extreme when they found that not a single man had fallen, though a few had received gashes more or less severe. The next morning the whole of the men and boys set to work under Hector's directions. The intrenchment at the top of the road was greatly strengthened, an opening through which a cart could pass being left in the middle.

A gun was placed on each side of this, and twenty sacks of earth laid down by the side of the opening, so that this in the course of a few minutes could be closed, and a gun placed close by run into position between the other two. The greater part of the men, however, were employed in raising a mound of stones and earth in front of the gateway, so as to cover this from the fire of any guns which, after the outward intrenchment had been stormed, might be brought up on to the plateau. The women, and even the children, assisted in the work by carrying earth, while men, with the horses and carts brought stones up from the valley.

It took a fortnight's hard work before the outwork was completed. It was twenty feet high, triangular in form, and solid in construction. Many of the tenants were accustomed to stone-work; and while the rest of the bastion was constructed of rough stones mixed with earth, a parapet four feet thick, of roughly-dressed stones, was carried along on the crest of the two outward sides. Four guns were mounted here; the rest of the cannon were placed on the outer wall instead of the honey-combed guns before in position, and the castle was thus prepared to stand a regular siege.

Hector remained for a week after the work was completed, paid the tenants liberally for the services they had rendered, and dismissed them to their homes, for the terrible blow that had been inflicted upon them had so cowed the peasants that order had been completely restored in that part of Poitou. Then, after taking an affectionate adieu of Madame de Blenfoix and her daughter, he rode back to Paris, where he remained for two months.

At the end of that time, being heartily tired of the frivolity and intrigues, and disgusted at the immorality of the court, he obtained leave from Mazarin to rejoin his regiment, as the campaign might be expected to open shortly again. The cardinal had warmly congratulated him upon the suppression of the insurrection in Poitou, of which he had received full details from his agents long before Hector reached Paris.

"I have always exhorted the officers and the troops engaged in putting down these risings to spill no more blood than is absolutely necessary. But it needed a great lesson, such as you have given them. Otherwise, as soon as the troops were withdrawn the peasants would rise again."

Turenne had also been in Paris, and had strongly represented to Mazarin the necessity for the armies of France and Sweden in Germany acting together, since while they were acting separately, and at great distances apart, the Austrians and Bavarians could unite and crush the one, while the other could offer it no assistance. It was owing to this that the conquests made by the troop of France and Weimar had been repeatedly wrested from them. The cardinal listened to his advice, and determined to bring about a union between the two armies of the confederation. In the meantime a conference was going on at Münster between the representatives of the various conflicting powers, but each put forward such exorbitant demands that no progress was made.

The Duke of Bavaria, indignant at the small support that Austria had given him, was paying off France against the latter power. Mazarin was persuaded that he was only waiting for an opportunity to desert the Imperialist cause, and therefore ordered Turenne not to cross the Rhine, as the duke had promised that he would remain neutral unless the French advanced into Germany, when the feelings of his subjects might force him to take the field again on the side of Austria.

Turenne was therefore ordered to besiege Luxembourg. The marshal, however, had no belief in the Bavarian promises, and on arriving on the Rhine early in April, and seeing that were he to march with his army away to Luxembourg the cause of France and Germany would be lost, he continued to make various excuses for not moving, until the Duke of Bavaria, having obtained many concessions from Austria, threw off the mask, and marching with his army joined that of the emperor in Franconia. Thus the whole Imperial forces were posted between the French and the Swedes.

Turenne saw that his only hope of success would be to effect a juncture with the Swedes, and wrote to the cardinal to that effect; then, without waiting for an answer, he set his army in motion. A tremendous circuit had to be made. He forded the Moselle six leagues above Coblenz, the bridges over the Rhine being all in possession of the enemy, marched up into Holland, and obtained permission from the king to cross at Wesel, which he reached after fourteen days' march. Crossing the Rhine on the 15th of July he marched through the country of La Mark, and through Westphalia, and on the 10th of August joined the Swedes under General Wrangel, who had received news of his coming, and had intrenched himself so strongly that the enemy, who had arrived before him, did not venture to attack him. The enemy now fell back at once and encamped near Freiburg. Their army was superior in force to that of the allies, they having fourteen thousand horse and ten thousand foot, while the allies had but ten thousand horse and seven thousand foot. The allies had, however, sixty pieces of cannon against fifty of the Imperialists. The allies advanced to Freiburg and offered battle, but the Archduke Leopold, who commanded the Imperialists, declined to come out of the great intrenchments he had thrown up round his camp.

Turenne then marched towards the Maine, and, halting ten leagues from Mayence, sent for the infantry, of which he had left a portion there, to join him. The whole force of the allies was now united, and took many towns. As, however, they were still inferior in force to the Imperialists, Turenne refused to weaken himself by placing garrisons in these places, contenting himself with blowing up the fortifications of some and carrying off the principal inhabitants of others as hostages. The Imperialist army still remained inactive, and Turenne was able therefore to turn his attention to Bavaria. Crossing the Rhine at Donauwörth he besieged Augsburg and Rain. The latter place was captured, but the former, being reinforced by fifteen hundred men, held out stoutly, and it was necessary to open trenches and proceed in regular form against it.

The Duke of Bavaria, greatly alarmed at this invasion of his dominions, sent off message after message to the emperor, complaining of the manner in which the Imperial army remained inactive, leaving the allies to employ their whole force against him. He threatened that unless the army advanced at once to his assistance he would make terms with France. Imperative orders were thereupon sent to the archduke to move against the French. The allies fell back, as his force was greatly superior to theirs, and the archduke took up a strong position, intending to force the allies to retire into Franconia as soon as the country round them was exhausted.

Turenne and Wrangel divined his purpose, and although it was now the beginning of November and snow was on the ground, they marched against him. On arriving near his camp they found that it was strongly fortified, and could be attacked only by passing behind great marshes and defiles. Changing their intentions, they left two thousand horse in front of his camp, making believe that they intended to attack him then marched with all haste to the Lech and advanced against Landsberg, which they took by assault. In the city were the principal magazines of the Imperialist army, and the allies, finding sufficient provisions there to last for six months encamped round the city and decided to winter there unless attacked, in the meantime sending out bodies of cavalry, which levied contributions up to the very gates of Munich. Leopold, thus deprived of his magazines, retired with the Austrian contingent, and the Bavarians returned home.

The Duke of Bavaria, finding that his whole dominions would be captured unless he made terms, therefore opened negotiations, and on the 14th of March, 1646, peace was signed, the terms being that he should separate himself entirely from the empire and deliver five of his fortresses to the allies, who would thus, should he again break his word, have means of access into his dominions. The allied forces were now in a condition to march upon Vienna. They had during the winter plundered a large portion of Bavaria; they and their horses had recovered from their fatigue, and their force now amounted to fourteen thousand foot and twenty thousand horse. At this moment, when the Imperialists believed that all was lost, for without the assistance of Bavaria they could put no army in the field that could hope to make head against the allies, Mazarin interposed and saved Austria from destruction.

The Catholic powers had long been privately urging upon him the danger that would arise should Austria be crushed. The Swedes would acquire very large accessions of territory, the Protestant German princes, their allies, would similarly benefit, and Protestantism would become the dominant religion in Germany. Such would, indeed, have undoubtedly been the case had the allies marched to Vienna and dictated terms of peace there. An order was therefore sent to Turenne to march with his army to Flanders, where the Spaniards were gaining great advantages, as Enghien, now become Prince of Condé by the death of his father, had been sent into Catalonia with the greater portion of his army. Turenne, foreseeing that his German regiments would refuse to march to Flanders, leaving their own country open to invasion and plunder by the Imperialists, warmly opposed the plan, and sent messenger after messenger to the cardinal urging him to countermand the order. The friends of Bavaria and the Catholic princes urged strongly upon the queen that the continuance of the war would utterly destroy the Catholic religion in Germany, and that the Swedes alone would reap advantage from the fall of the house of Austria. Moved by their arguments and those of Mazarin to the same effect, she supported the latter, and peremptory orders were sent to Turenne to march to Flanders, where matters were going from bad to worse. Turenne obeyed them, captured on his march towards the Rhine several towns and fortresses, destroying their fortifications so that they would not be able to oppose him if he returned to Germany. But on arriving on the Rhine his anticipations of trouble were fulfilled. General Rosen, whose blunder had been the cause of the disaster at Marienthal, and who had since his return from captivity persistently worked in opposition to Turenne, fomented discontent among the troops of Weimar, and directly they crossed the Rhine they absolutely refused to advance. They had just cause for complaint; they had fought with distinguished valour, and they alone had saved the French army from suffering crushing defeat at Nördlingen; their pay was six months in arrear, and the proposal now that they should leave their own country and fight in Flanders was naturally most repugnant to them. They at once marched away towards Strasburg. Turenne followed them with three thousand infantry, four French regiments of horse, and the only one of the Weimar cavalry that had remained faithful to him, and came up just as they were about to recross the line.

Partly by entreaties, partly by showing his confidence in them, by putting himself wholly in their power, the marshal induced a portion of the Weimar cavalry to return to their duty. General Rosen, who was to a large extent responsible for the mutiny, was arrested and imprisoned at Philippsburg, the rest of the mutineers rode away with the loss of a portion of their number, and joined the Swedes. After this the order for Turenne to march to Flanders was countermanded.

The war languished for a few months, the Imperialists were defeated after a hard-fought cavalry battle by Turenne and the Swedes, and the country was overrun by the latter, whose horsemen raided almost up to Innsbruck. But all parties were growing weary of the conflict, which had now lasted thirty years. It had inflicted incredible suffering upon all who were concerned in it, and had produced no important results whatever, except that it had prevented the entire crushing out of Protestantism in Germany, and the peace conference for the first time began to work in earnest.

At last, after Bavaria had been wasted from end to end, and the duke driven into exile, peace was concluded, the emperor yielding every point demanded by France, as he saw plainly enough that unless he did so Turenne's army would be at the gates of Vienna at the commencement of the next campaign, and in October, 1648, hostilities ceased. Turenne went to Münster and acted as the French negotiator in arranging the peace, to which his genius, steadfast determination, and the expenditure of his own means, by which he had kept the army on foot, had so largely contributed.

CHAPTER XX
AN OLD SCORE

HECTOR was not present with the army during the last three campaigns of the war. He had joined Turenne in April, 1646, and shared in the general disappointment when the order was received that the army was not to cross the line, because Bavaria had promised to remain neutral if it did not do so.

"I cannot think," the marshal said to him a day or two after he received the order—for he had always maintained the same pleasant relations with Hector that had subsisted between them in Italy, and placed the most entire confidence in the discretion of the young colonel—"how Mazarin can allow Bavaria to hoodwink him. Indeed, I cannot believe that he is really deceived; he must know that that crafty old fox the duke is not to be relied upon in any way, and that he is merely trying to save time. 'Tis hard indeed to see us powerless to move, now that the season for campaigning is just opening, and when by advancing we could cut the Bavarians off from Austria. As to besieging Luxembourg, it would be but a waste of time, for before we could open a trench we should hear that the duke has again declared against us, and we should have to hurry back with all speed."

It was, indeed, but a fortnight later that the news came that the Bavarians were on the move to join the Imperialists, and a fortnight later it was known that the two armies had effected their junction. Turenne at once collected his troops from the towns and villages where they were placed, and marched to Mayence.

WON BY THE SWORD

"I am going to send you to Paris, Campbell," he said on the evening of their arrival there. "All is lost if the enemy, now united, throw themselves upon the Swedes, and I have resolved to take upon myself the responsibility of marching round through Holland and joining Wrangel. There is, of course, risk in such an expedition, and the cardinal may object very strongly to my undertaking such a movement, especially as it will leave the frontier of France virtually unguarded, but I have no fear that evil consequences will arise. The enemy will not hear of my march until ten days after I have started, and even then they will probably suppose that we have gone to Flanders. By the time they find out what my intentions are, it will be too late for them to take advantage of my absence.

"Even then they would have to storm Philippsburg or some other strong place before they could cross the Rhine, and before they could do that Wrangel and I would be at their heels. Moreover, as they would know that, instead of pursuing them, we might, after effecting a junction, make straight for Vienna, and that no army could be got together to oppose us, I consider that the movement is a perfectly safe one. Now, I am going to send you to Mazarin with my despatch telling him of my intention. I am choosing you for the purpose, because you will be able to explain and enforce the reasons that I have given him. He has a high opinion of you, and will listen to you when perhaps he would not pay any regard to Rosen or any other of these Weimar officers I might send. Remember that there is no occasion for extreme hurry," and he smiled. "Of course it is necessary that you should travel with a certain amount of speed, but do not founder your horse. Every day is of value to me, and if I am once well on my way north Mazarin could hardly recall me.

"Say that you take five days to get to Paris, by that time I should be north of Cologne, and a courier from Mazarin can hardly overtake me until I am in Holland, I should then feel justified in disregarding the order, seeing that I should by pushing on effect a junction with the Swedes quite as quickly as I could return here. Of course it would be too late for you to overtake me, and I shall give you a written order to remain in Paris until I am again so near the Rhine that you can join your regiment. I consider that it will be an advantage to have you near the cardinal, as, knowing my intentions and methods as you do, you would be able to so explain matters to him that he will understand the reasons for my various movements."

"Very well marshal, I am ready to start as soon as you hand me the despatch."

"I will do that to-morrow morning, and you will then be able to tell Mazarin that we were just setting out when you left us."

"As it will be some time before I shall rejoin my regiment, may I ask you to appoint Captain de Thiou as second colonel? He has now served as senior captain of the regiment for three years. He aided me heartily and cordially in organizing it. He has seconded me throughout in a manner of which I cannot speak too highly, and distinguished himself greatly at Freiburg, and on every occasion in which we have been in contact with the enemy. I think it very desirable that there should be an officer of rank superior to the others while I am away; and both for the sake of the regiment, and as a reward for the merit and conduct of Captain de Thiou himself, I should be very glad were he promoted and should feel that the regiment would in no way deteriorate during my absence."

"Certainly, Campbell, I will carry out your recommendation. He has fairly earned his promotion, and as you say, it is better in your absence that the regiment should be led by an officer of rank above the others, and not by a captain having but a very slight seniority to some of them. Doubtless you will be saying good-bye to the officers to-night. I authorize you to inform de Thiou that he will be placed in orders to-morrow morning as second colonel of the regiment."

WON BY THE SWORD

"I did not think that we were likely to be back in Paris before next winter, master," Paolo said rather discontentedly when Hector told him that they were to start early next morning.

"Nor did I, Paolo, and I should very much rather have remained with the regiment; but as the marshal is good enough to consider that my presence there may be of advantage to him, I have of course nothing to say against it."

There was great regret among the officers when they heard that their colonel was not going to lead them, but all were pleased that de Thiou, who was a general favourite, had obtained promotion. That officer was at once surprised and gratified at the news, for it was not often that men without strong family interest rose to the rank of colonel.

"I know that this is your doing," he said gratefully. "I never expected to get above my present rank, and I am sure that I should never have done so had it not been for you."

"You thoroughly deserve it, de Thiou, for it was by your support that I was enabled, when I first joined, to introduce reforms, and get the officers to take upon themselves more work and responsibilities, and thus make the regiment what it is. I hope I shall rejoin before the end of the campaign. This may be the last, for now that they have begun the peace conference at Münster, something must surely come of it sooner or later, for all parties must be thoroughly sick of this long and terrible war, which has ruined Germany and impoverished France, and from which neither party, after nigh thirty years of fighting, has gained any material advantage. At any rate it will be a great satisfaction to me to know that the regiment is in your hands. I know that during the time that I have been away this winter things have gone on satisfactorily; but it is clearly impossible for an officer to keep a regiment well in hand when, as in your case, your appointment was only a day or two earlier than that of some of the others. You are likely to have some stiff marching now, for only one other infantry regiment besides ours will accompany the cavalry, the rest will remain here until they get an opportunity of rejoining. Of course I shall take Paolo and my four mounted troopers back with me to Paris. I may probably send them on to la Villar, as it is not likely that I shall need them at court."

On the evening of the fifth day after leaving Mayence Hector arrived in Paris, and alighted at the cardinal's hotel.

"So you are again a bearer of despatches, Monsieur Campbell," the cardinal said, as Hector entered his apartment. "They need be important, or the marshal would hardly have sent you with them."

"They are, as you will see, important, your eminence, but I am sent rather to explain further than the marshal could do in a letter his reasons for the step that he has taken. As you have learned long before this, the Duke of Bavaria has proved false to his promises. He has effected a junction with the Imperialist army, and the marshal has news that both are marching against the Swedes, who are in no strength to show fight against so great a force."

The cardinal opened the despatch, and read it in silence.

" 'Tis a grave step for the marshal to have taken without orders," he said, frowning; "and do you mean to say that he has already started on this expedition?"

"The troops had fallen into their ranks when I started, and by this time they must be well on their way towards Holland. There was no time, sir, for the marshal to await a reply to the despatch. The matter was most urgent, every day was of importance, for if the Swedes fell back, as they might do, before the archduke, the latter would be able to overrun all northern Germany, to capture the towns of the Protestant princes, break up their confederation, and compel them to give in their submission; for Turenne with his small force would be powerless to interfere with their operations, even if by pressing after them with all speed he arrived within striking distance."

"And think you that he will reach Wrangel in time?"

"He hopes so, sir. He sent off a messenger before starting, with orders to buy fresh horses at all cost at each halting-place, to carry the news as quickly as possible to

Wrangel that he was on his way to join him, and imploring him to intrench himself in some strong position until he should come up."

"How long hence will that be?"

"The march will be pressed forward with all speed, your eminence, with such delays only as may be needed to keep the horses in such a state that they may be ready for fighting as soon as they join the Swedes. He hopes to be there in a month from the day of starting."

"And in the meantime," Mazarin said, "France is open to invasion. He says, indeed, that the Imperialists would hardly venture to march hitherward, as thereby they in turn would leave it open to him and the Swedes to march into the heart of Austria."

"Assuredly that is so, sir. The archduke will hardly get news that Marshal Turenne has moved until he has been some ten or twelve days on his march, and even when he hears it he will not know in what direction he has gone, but may think it likely that he either intends to seize Luxembourg or to reinforce your army in Flanders. By the time they discover his true object he will be within a week's march of the Swedes, possibly less than that. It will be too late for them then to think of marching to the Rhine. If they consider themselves strong enough to fight the marshal and the Swedes together, they will do so at once; if they fear to give battle, still more would they fear to be attacked by him when entering a country where they would have him in their rear, and be hemmed in between him and the Rhine, not to speak of the risk of leaving Austria open to invasion, should he, instead of pursuing them, direct his march thither. If I might presume to judge, I should say that the expedition that the marshal has undertaken is at once worthy of his military genius, and will at the same time do far more to ensure the safety of the Rhine provinces than he could do were he to remain there with his small army until the Imperialists, having chased the Swedes out of the country and reduced northern Germany, turned their whole forces against him."

"I see, Monsieur Campbell," the cardinal said, turning the subject, "that you have been five days coming here from Mayence. It is a very different rate of speed to that at which you travelled from Rocroi."

"It is so, your eminence; but on that occasion the Duc d'Enghien had placed relays of his best horses all along the road, so that we were enabled to travel without making a halt."

"And moreover, my dear colonel," Mazarin said, "Turenne, far from urging you to haste, was desirous of getting so far before he received my answer as to render it impossible for me to recall him."

"I cannot think that your eminence would do that. It is a grand enterprise, and almost without precedent in point both of daring and in the great advantages to be gained from it."

"And Turenne thought that by sending you, you would be able to assist him in persuading me to regard it favourably. Well, well, it is certainly too late to recall him now. He has taken the responsibility upon himself, and must stand or fall by the result. And now in the first place are you going to hurry back again or are you going to remain here?"

"My regiment is one of those that he has taken with him, sir, and as I could not hope to overtake him he has requested me to remain here until I receive orders from him."

"We shall be gainers so far," the cardinal said cordially, "and I am sure that from your knowledge of the country and of Turenne's methods your advice upon military matters will be of great service to us. I must now go and report to the queen this sudden change in the situation, and if she disapproves of it I shall tell her that if she will but listen to you, you will convert her to the view that this escapade of the marshal's is all for the best, and seems likely indeed to retrieve the position that has been caused by the treachery of Bavaria."

During his stay in Paris Hector soon found that intrigue was more rampant than ever. The Duke of Beaufort and others who had been implicated in the plot on Mazarin's life had been pardoned and had returned to Paris, and as the lesson that had been given them had taught them prudence, they were now openly on good terms with the court. They were secretly, however, intriguing with the parliament of Paris, which was now bitterly opposed to Mazarin, had refused to register some of his decrees, and had even forced him to dismiss his superintendent of finance, an Italian named Emeri. The latter had imposed taxes at his will to satisfy his extravagance and avarice, had raised the octroi duty, made the sale of firewood a monopoly, and in various ways had incurred the indignation and hatred of the Parisians.

Mazarin's own greed had been in no slight degree the cause of his unpopularity; he who had come to France a penniless priest was now the owner of great estates. It was even said that much of the money that should have been devoted to the needs of the army had been privately sent into Italy by him, and throughout the country it was felt to be scandalous that while the deepest distress was universal on account of the weight of taxation, these two Italians should be piling up wealth for themselves. But, avaricious as he was, the cardinal was lavish in his expenditure among his friends and adherents; honours, titles, dignities, and estates were freely bestowed upon them, and he did not hesitate to pay any sum that would gain him the support of those whose aid he deemed to be essential. Madame de Chevreuse was again at court, and was, as she had always been, the centre of the intrigues that were going on. One evening she made a sign for Hector to take a place by her side. She had taken a fancy to the young Scottish colonel on the evening when he had been first introduced to her, and was always gracious to him now.

"Monsieur le baron," she said in a low tone, "do you think that the air of Paris agrees with you as well as that of the army?"

He felt from the manner in which she spoke, that she meant more than she said.

"So far, madam, it has not disagreed with me," he said; "and even did it do so I should not be able to leave it, as I have orders to remain here."

"By the way, monsieur," she said, changing the subject of conversation, "it is whispered that that party of pleasure to which you took the officers of your regiment at St. Germain did not come off, at least none of the landlords of the hotels there can recall any such gathering, and it is even said that your falling in with the carriage of the Duke of Orleans was not altogether an accident. I only mention the reports; of course, it was a matter of no moment whether your party dined at St. Germain or at Sevres. But sometimes misapprehensions of this kind lead to trouble, especially when they happen a few days before serious events. I like you, Colonel Campbell, and that is why I have mentioned this; you understand me, I have no doubt;" and, turning to a gentleman who had at that moment approached her, she entered into a lively conversation with him, and Hector rose, and with the words, "Thank you, madam," bowed, and moved away.

It was easy to understand her meaning. Beaufort and the conspirators whose plan he had thwarted, and who had suffered imprisonment and exile thereby, had in some way discovered that it was to him that they owed their failure and disgrace. At the moment his explanation and that of his officers had deceived them, but doubtless someone whose connection with the plot was unsuspected had instituted inquiries, found that the party he had spoken of had not taken place, and had at once come to the conclusion that he had in some way discovered their intentions, had really ridden out with his officers to furnish a guard to Mazarin, and had afterwards acquainted the Duke of Beaufort with what he had discovered. Doubtless, as Madame de Chevreuse had warned him, the air of Paris was at present dangerously unwholesome for him. He had been the means of bringing disgrace and punishment upon the Duc de Vendôme and the Duke of Beaufort, two of the most powerful nobles in France, and a host of their friends.

WON BY THE SWORD

It was probable that they only recently assure themselves that it was he who had thwarted their plans; had it been otherwise he would scarcely have escaped their vengeance the last time that he was in Paris. Now, from what Madame de Chevreuse had said, he had no doubt whatever that some plot would be made against his life. He might thwart one such attempt, but others would follow. He resolved to lay the matter before the cardinal and take his advice. Accordingly he waited until he was leaving; several gentlemen of his suite accompanied him, and at the entrance to the Louvre the men of the cardinal's guard fell in on either side. When they reached Mazarin's hotel Hector moved up to him.

"Can I have a few words with you, your eminence?"

"Certainly, Colonel Campbell; I never retire to bed till long past midnight. It is something serious, I see," he said quickly as they entered his apartment, where a number of candles were burning, and he obtained a full view of Hector's face. "Another plot?"

"Not against your eminence; it is a matter which concerns myself only. I have been warned to-night that my share in the last affair has been discovered, that inquiries have been made at St. Germain, and that the various innkeepers have declared that no party of officers dined there that morning, and that it was therefore concluded that our presence behind your carriage was not accidental. They no doubt guessed that it was I who discovered the plot, in consequence of which so many were arrested and exiled. I have been distinctly warned that the air of Paris is unwholesome for me."

"Who warned you?" the cardinal said abruptly.

"It would not be fair of me to mention the name, but it is at any rate one who is of Beaufort's party."

"Ah!" the cardinal said sharply, "I noticed you sitting for a few minutes by Madame de Chevreuse. Never mind, I will respect your confidence. I can well understand, after what you have said, that there is great danger here, and it is a danger from which it is well-nigh impossible to protect you, unless you take up your residence here and never stir abroad. Nor do I know that you would be safer with the army; an assassin's knife can reach a man as easily in a camp as in a city, and with perhaps less risk of detection. Neither Beaufort nor Vendôme are men to forget or forgive an injury, and they have scores of fellows who would for a few crowns murder anyone they indicated, and if gentlemen of higher rank who, although not assassins, would willingly engage you in a duel, especially those who suffered in the plot that you discovered. Frankly, what do you think yourself?"

"I might retire to la Villar cardinal. I should be safe there in my own castle."

"So long as you did not leave it; but a man with a musket in ambush behind a hedge might cut your career short. It is probable enough that you are watched, and in that case I should doubt whether you would ever get to la Villar, nor do I think that if you left for the Rhine you would get halfway. Now you see, Monsieur Campbell, that your cause is mine, and that your safety touches me as if it were my own, for it was in my service that you incurred the danger. I must think the matter over. In the meantime I beg of you to sleep here to-night. I will send word to your servant that you will not return. I could of course send a guard with you to your hotel, but some of the servants there may have been bribed to murder you as you slept. I can look after myself; I seldom leave the house except to go to the Louvre, and I never go even that short distance without a guard, but it is much more difficult to protect you."

"I have my own body-guard, your excellency—four stout Scotch soldiers and my lackey, Paolo, who is a good swordsman also; and as it does not seem to me that I should be safer elsewhere than here, I shall at any rate stay for a time. I should imagine that the warning was a general one. They have just found out that I had a hand in thwarting their plot against you, and I dare say used threats; but the threats of angry men come very often to nothing; and at any rate, I do not choose that they should obtain the satisfaction of driving me from Paris against my will."

The cardinal shook his head. "You see, monsieur, that Beaufort is a man who hesitates at nothing. A scrupulous person would hardly endeavour to slay a cardinal, who is also the minister of France, in the streets of Paris in broad daylight. He is capable of burning down the Pomme d'Or, and all within it, in order to obtain revenge on you. I feel very uneasy about you. However, sleep may bring counsel, and we will talk it over again in the morning."

"Have you thought of anything, Monsieur Campbell?" Mazarin asked when they met in the morning.

"I have not, sir, save to go on trusting to my own sword and my followers."

"I can think of nothing," the cardinal said, "save to send an order to Turenne for two companies of your regiment to march hither, where, on their arrival, you will receive orders to proceed with them to your castle of la Villar, and to use them in the king's service in repressing all troubles that may occur in Poitou. What say you to that?"

"I would not deprive her majesty of two hundred of her best soldiers to guard me from what may not be after all a very real danger. My own conclusions, after thinking it over this morning, are that I will remain here for a time, trusting to my friends and my own sword. If a serious attempt is made on my life I could then consider whether it would be best to withdraw myself, and if so, whither to go; but I will not run away merely on a vague hint that my life is in danger. I have faced death in battle many times, and this danger can hardly be considered as more serious. I imagine that in the first case some of the duke's followers will force me into a duel, before proceeding to try assassination, and although doubtless he has some good blades among his friends, I do not think that I need to feel uneasy on that score. I was always practising with my sword as a boy. Since I have been in the army I have spent a good deal of my time when in winter quarters, in such practice with my own officers, and with any maitres d'armes in the towns where I have been, and while in Italy had the opportunity of learning much, for there are fine fencers there."

"So be it, then," Mazarin said. "But if matters go to extremes, remember that I consider myself responsible for you. I believe that you saved my life, and although there are many things that men say against me, none have ever charged me with ingratitude. If I can protect you in no other way I shall have you arrested, sent to the frontier, that is to say, to the sea frontier, and put on board ship and sent to England or Scotland, as you choose, with a chest containing a sum that will suffice to purchase any estate you may choose there.

"I am in earnest," he went on as Hector was about to answer. "It is for my own sake as much as yours; when my friends are attacked I am attacked, and I am doubly bound in your case. It needs but a stroke of my pen to make you a duke and lord of half a province; and if I cannot do that here, because you would still be within reach of your enemies, I can, as far as the estates go, do it for you abroad. Do not fail to let me know each day if anything new takes place."

Hector felt that there was no more to say, and bowing, left the cardinal's presence and went out.

Paolo and Macpherson were waiting outside.

"The cardinal's messenger, who brought the news last night that you would not return, master," the former said when he saw by Hector's look of surprise that he had not expected to see him there, "said also that I and one of your men had best be here at eight this morning and wait until you came out."

"I did not know that he had sent such a message, Paolo, but I will when we get to the hotel tell you why he sent it."

The street was somewhat crowded, and Hector had gone but a short distance when he saw three gentlemen, whom he knew to be intimates of the Duke of Beaufort, coming in the other direction. One of them was Monsieur de Beauvais, who said in a loud tone to his companions just as Hector was passing:

"That is the Scotchman whom the cardinal employs to do his dirty business."

Hector faced round at once.

"At any rate, Monsieur de Beauvais, the Scotchman in question is not employed by the cardinal as an assassin, which is an even more dishonourable post."

De Beauvais turned white with anger.

"Behind the Luxembourg in an hour's time, Monsieur de Villar."

"I shall be there," Hector said coldly.

He paused a minute, after the three gentlemen, with the customary salute, walked on. He did not like to go to the Hotel Mazarin lest the cardinal should obtain news of what was going to take place, so he waited in the neighbourbood, knowing that some of Mazarin's personal friends would be sure to arrive about this hour. Presently he saw a colonel who, like himself, was spending the winter in Paris, and who frequently attended the cardinal's levées.

"Colonel de Serres, as a fellow-soldier I have a service to ask of you."

"I am entirely at your disposal, Monsieur Campbell."

"I have just had a quarrel forced upon me by Monsieur de Beauvais, and I have to meet him in fifty minutes' time at the back of the Luxembourg. As he was in company with two gentlemen, the Comte de Marplat and Monsieur de Vipont, I shall be glad if you would kindly act as my second, and if you can find another officer who would do so, I shall be glad of his services also."

"I shall be glad to support you, Monsieur Campbell, and can lay my hand on another second at once, for here comes my friend and yours, Monsieur Emile de Chavigny, who will, like myself, be charmed to be concerned in any affair against the duke's friends."

De Chavigny, whom Hector had seen at the court on the previous day for the first time since they had parted in Italy, agreed at once to Hector's request.

"De Beauvais has the reputation of being a good swordsman, Campbell," he said as they walked together towards the Luxembourg, Paolo and his companion having now returned to the inn at his master's order; "but I should say that he will want all his skill now. You were by far the best swordsman among us when you left us suddenly in the south, and doubtless since then your skill will not have fallen off."

"No, I know a good deal more than I knew then, Chavigny. There were few days when we were in winter quarters that I had not an hour's work in the fencing school with the officers of my regiment, and whenever I heard that there was a professor of the art I have never failed to frequent his salon and to learn his favourite strokes."

"That is all right, then. We need have no fear whatever as to the result."

They reached the point fixed upon a minute or two before the clock struck, and just as it chimed de Beauvais and his friends made their appearance. The seconds exchanged a few words and selected a piece of ground for the encounter, the principals at once removed their doublets and faced each other.

"This is a duel à la mort," de Beauvais said in a loud voice.

"For that I am quite prepared," Hector said quietly; "but you are likely to find, Monsieur de Beauvais, that it is not so easy a thing to kill the colonel of one of her majesty's regiments as it is to stab a churchman in his carriage."

De Beauvais at once took up his position, and, without the parade of courtesy that usually preceded an encounter, fell furiously upon Hector. The latter did not give way a step. With a wrist of iron he put aside half a dozen thrusts, and then lunging, ran de Beauvais through the body, his sword-hilt striking against his adversary's chest.

De Beauvais' two seconds ran forward as their principal fell. "He is dead," one said as they knelt over him. Then rising he addressed Hector: "Monsieur le Colonel Campbell," he said, "I claim satisfaction at your hands, for I take it that your words applied to me as well as to de Beauvais, though addressed only to him."

"You may take it so," Hector replied coldly, "for you were also at that house in the Rue St. Honoré on that occasion you know of."

WON BY THE SWORD

Hector's two seconds endeavoured to interpose, but he said: "Gentlemen, I must ask you to let the matter go on. This is no ordinary duel. These gentlemen, with whom I have no personal animosity, have picked a quarrel with me at the request of one higher in rank than themselves, and are simply his agents. I had no hesitation in killing the first of them, but as Monsieur de Vipont wishes an encounter with me in spite of what he has seen I will give him one, but will content myself with a less severe lesson than that I have given Monsieur de Beauvais. Now, sir, I am at your service."

De Vipont, knowing now how dangerous an opponent he was meeting, fought cautiously. Hector, however, was anxious to finish the matter before they were interrupted, and therefore took the offensive, and after two passes ran his antagonist through the shoulder.

"Now, Monsieur le Comte, do you desire a turn?" he said carelessly.

The count was pale, but he answered steadily, "I claim it by the same right as Monsieur de Vipont."

"Agreed," Hector said; and as soon as the count had removed his upper garments they engaged.

The swords had scarcely clashed when the count's weapon was wrenched from his hand and sent flying for a distance of twenty paces.

"That is enough," Colonel de Serres said, stepping forward; "you have done what you thought to be your duty, Monsieur le Comte, but it needs very different blades from those of yourself and your companions to stand before Colonel Campbell. He had you at his mercy, and had a right to take your life if he chose; but as he refrained from doing that when you had your sword in your hand, he certainly will not do so now. Messieurs, we wish you good-morning."

"And you may mention," Hector added, "to this person of high rank, that I shall be happy to accommodate as many of the gentlemen of his following as choose to take the matter up."

"He will send no more to you, Campbell," Chavigny said as they moved off, leaving the count, whose valet now ran up, to obtain a vehicle and carry his dead and wounded comrades away.

"No, I fancy not; he will try other means now. The war has only begun. Men like Léi, Brillet, and the Campions are not the sort of men who would act as bravos, even for the Duke of Beaufort, and I do not think that he would even venture to propose it to them. It will be meaner instruments that he will employ next time. However, I shall of course go straight to the cardinal and acquaint him with what has happened. I doubt not but that he will lay the matter before the queen, and then that Beaufort will hear of it; but, passionate and revengeful as he is, I think that he will not be turned from his purpose, even if he knows that he may be forced to retire to his estates, or even leave the country till the matter blows over."

CHAPTER XXI
THE DUKE'S REVENGE

THE cardinal listened gravely to Hector's account of the duel, and of the circumstances that gave rise to it.

"I will go at once to the Louvre and appeal to her majesty," he said; "you know how warmly she spoke to you on the day when you saved my life. Still, I fear that the sternest reproof, or even an order to retire to his estates, would not turn him from his purpose."

"I am sure of it, your eminence; still, as I have proved victor in the first battle in the campaign I will bide a second."

"Mind that you do not get stabbed in the back, colonel."

"I will beware of that, sir; whenever I walk the streets in future Paolo shall keep a pace behind me, and I warrant that he will protect me from any attempt of that sort."

"At any rate remain here until I return from the Louvre."

In an hour Mazarin returned. "The duke has been beforehand with us," he said. "When I told the queen of what had happened, and why this quarrel had been fastened upon you, she sent at once for the duke, and drew out an order, which I signed, for him to retire at once to his estates; but the royal messenger returned with the news that he had half an hour before ridden away to visit his father at Vendôme. A courier will start at once with the order, but I doubt whether he will be found there. It is probable that he has gone to one of his own estates, and it may be some time before we find out where he is. However, it is something that he has gone."

On his return to the inn Hector told Paolo what had taken place.

THE DUKE'S REVENGE

"It is a pity that you did not kill them all, master."

"Not at all, Paolo; had I done so every one of their friends would have been set against me. Both these men are of good families, and will doubtless report that I had their lives at my mercy and spared them, and after that no gentleman of reputation would take the matter up. I shall have to be very careful in future, but now that the duke has gone there is not likely to be any further trouble just at present."

Paolo shook his head. "Nay, master, I think the danger all the greater. In the first place, we do not know that he has gone. I think it far more likely that he is hiding in the house of one of his friends. He has pretended to leave because he was sure the cardinal would take the matter up, and in order that, if he is absent from Paris when any harm befell you, it could not be brought home to him. I do not suppose that next time he will employ any of his own people. He is most popular among the mob of Paris, who call him the King of the Markets, and he will have no difficulty in getting as many daggers as he wishes from the scum of the faubourgs. It would be difficult in the extreme to prove that he had aught to do with it, for you may be sure that he would really go down into the country with all speed the moment the deed was done.

"In future, master, you must not go out without having me close behind you; as for the others, I would put them in ordinary citizen garb, and let them follow some twenty yards behind, so as to be in readiness to run up at once. They could carry swords openly, and have their pistols hidden under their doublets."

"It might be as well, at any rate for the present. If, as you think, Beaufort is hidden in Paris, it is certain he will lose no time."

Paolo nodded.

"I will get the men disguises at once. They had better be different; Macpherson can be dressed as a soldier, Nicholl as a burgher, and Sandy Grahame and Hunter as rough mechanics. They, of course, could not carry swords, but might take heavy cudgels. They would not walk together, or seem to have any knowledge of each other. Sandy might be ten paces behind you, Nicholl twenty, and the others thirty, or where the street is wide they could keep abreast of you on the other side. Are you going to the Louvre this evening?"

"Yes, the cardinal said that the queen wished that I should appear there. I would much rather have stayed away, as doubtless the affair behind the Luxembourg will be generally known by this evening, and I shall feel my position a very unpleasant one, though I imagine that the queen intends, by her countenance of me, to show that I have not fallen into disgrace for duelling."

Such was indeed the case. All eyes were turned upon Hector when he entered the royal saloon. Many of Mazarin's friends came up and shook hands with him warmly, while the adherents of Beaufort and Vendôme stood aloof from him with angry faces. Presently the door opened, and the queen, closely followed by Mazarin and a train of ladies and gentlemen, entered.

As she passed Hector she stopped. "Monsieur le Baron de la Villar," she said in clear tones, which were heard all over the apartment, "much as I object to duelling, and determined as I am to enforce the edicts against it, I feel that in the encounter this morning you were in no way to blame, and that it was forced upon you. It is scandalous that one who has so bravely shed his blood and risked his life in defence of France should be assailed in the capital, and for what reason? Because he proved faithful to the queen and her minister. You have punished the chief of the aggressors, and I shall know how to punish those who stood behind him;" and with a gracious bow in response to his deep reverence she moved on.

The little speech created a deep sensation among the courtiers. That the queen herself should so publicly give her countenance to this young Scottish gentleman, and should—for no one doubted to whom she alluded—even threaten one of the most powerful nobles in the land, showed how strongly she felt. No one, with the exception of half a dozen persons, understood her allusion to the service that he had rendered to her and the cardinal, but all felt that it must be something altogether exceptional. Many of the nobles who belonged neither to the party of Beaufort nor the cardinal came up and congratulated him.

He received these signs of the impression that the queens' words had conferred upon him quietly.

"I am very sorry for what has occurred," he said. "I have killed many in battle, but this is the first time that I have killed anyone in a private quarrel. It was not one of my seeking, but I am none the less sorry."

As he passed near Madame de Chevreuse, she made a gesture to him to come to her. "You did not accept my warning," she said sadly. "Remember, a storm is not past because the first flash of lightning does not strike."

"I am well aware of that, madam; I thank you for your warning, but I am bound here by my duties as a tree is bound to the earth by its roots, and neither can move at will to escape a storm passing overhead."

"Should I hear of any fresh danger, Monsieur Campbell," she said in a low voice, "I will have you informed of it, but it is more probable that I shall not know. Were it a state secret I should surely hear of it, but in a matter like this none save those concerned would be likely to know of it until it was over. Be always on your guard night and day, you cannot tell when the bolt may fall;" and she motioned to him to pass on again. As before, Hector accompanied the cardinal as far as his hotel, then he went towards his own lodgings, Paolo, with his hand on his dagger, keeping a pace behind him, while the four troopers followed one by one at a distance. The streets were almost deserted until, just as they approached the inn, a number of rough men rushed out from side alleys and doorways. Hector had just time to throw himself with his back to a house and draw his sword. Paolo's knife had levelled the first man who approached, and then drawing his sword he took his place by the side of his master. The ruffians stood round, each anxious to be the first to strike, and yet fearful of meeting the sword that had, as they had heard, mastered three gentlemen.

"Run in at him, fools!" a man in a cloak, with his hat pulled down over his eyes, and keeping in the rear of the others, shouted.

Before his orders could be carried out there was a sudden movement, and four men burst through them and joined Hector. The assailants hesitated.

But again the man behind shouted:

"Cowards, there are but six of them, and you are five-and-twenty, are you such curs that you are afraid to attack when you are nigh five to one?"

Then, with a hoarse yell the crowd rushed forward. One was struck down by a heavy cudgel, three fell on the pavement, and another one tottered back disabled, but others took their places, and for a time the little band were hardly pressed. The four Scotchmen fought stoutly, but although fair swordsmen they gained no great advantage over their opponents until they betook them to their pistols, when several of their assailants fell, but not without inflicting wounds. Paolo also fought well, and brought three to the ground. Hector, however, took the offensive, and before his swift blade, with its deadly thrust, those opposed to him fell back as one after another dropped dead.

"Down with him! down with him!" the voice shouted; "are ye men thus to give way before a single blade?"

"And are you a man," Hector shouted back, "to set on others to fight when you dare not fight yourself? Whoever you are, you are a coward!"

With a fierce oath the man pushed his way through those in front of him and drew his sword. He threw back his cloak to obtain the full use of his sword-arm, and the rich gold braiding of his doublet confirmed the opinion Hector had already formed as to his identity.

"That is better, my lord duke; it is at least more honourable to fight in your own quarrels than to employ a band of assassins to do your work."

360

"Hector ran his assailant through the shoulder."

WON BY THE SWORD

With a roar of fury Beaufort rushed upon him. He was a good swordsman, and personally brave, but his rage neutralized his skill, and after parrying two or three of his lunges Hector repeated the thrust with which he had that morning disabled de Vipont, and ran his assailant through the shoulder.

He fell back with a curse.

"Kill him! kill him!" he shouted.

But at that moment there was a cry, "The watch! the watch!" Four of the fellows caught up the wounded man and carried him off, some of the others skirmishing with the watch to hinder their advance.

"To the inn!" Hector cried to his men, "leave the matter to the watch."

And sheathing their weapons they ran on to the door of the hotel and obtained entry there before the watch came up. As soon as they had passed Hector said, "Come with me, Paolo, and see the cardinal; there is no fear of any renewal of the attack now. Do you know who it was I wounded, Paolo?" he asked as they hurried along.

"No, master, I was too busy myself to look round."

"It was Beaufort himself; I ran him through, low down in the shoulder."

Paolo uttered an exclamation of dismay.

"It cannot be helped now," Hector went on, "but there will be no living in Paris or even in France after this!"

Mazarin had not retired to bed when they reached his hotel.

"What now, monsieur?" he asked.

"We have had our second battle, your eminence, and it has been a serious one. We were attacked by five-and-twenty ruffians; we slew some ten of them. Then their leader, who had been keeping in the rear shouting to them, seeing that his men were not likely to get the best of us, pushed through them and himself attacked me. I wounded him somewhat seriously, at least the thrust was just below the shoulder; and when I tell you that it was Beaufort himself you will see that the matter is serious indeed."

THE DUKE'S REVENGE

"It could not be worse," the cardinal said gravely; "you will have the whole of the adherents of the house of Vendôme banded against you, and even your bravery could not long triumph over such odds. France is no longer a place for you. Neither the queen's protection nor mine would avail you aught."

He took two or three turns up the room.

"In the first place, Monsieur Campbell, I will buy your fief back from you; there are plenty who would gladly purchase it, or I can bestow it, as it was bestowed upon you, upon someone who has served the crown well. I will send the price to the banker who already holds money of yours in his keeping. I should advise you to mount to-night and ride for the sea-coast to-morrow would be too late."

He opened a cabinet.

"Here are a thousand crowns for your present expenses. Which road will you take? I should advise you not to go to Calais; that is the line on which, as soon as it is known that you have gone, they will pursue you, and even did they not overtake you on the way they might reach Calais before you could obtain a ship for England, for at present there is but little trade between the countries, and that not openly."

"I will make for Nantes, your eminence; there I can be joined by friends from my château."

A slight smile passed over the cardinal's face.

" 'Tis no time for jesting," he said; "but in truth I had intended to find a rich heiress for you. But when I heard that two ladies were staying at the castle I laid the project aside; and 'tis as well that I did so, for, were you married to a princess, your life would not be safe in France. Farewell, Monsieur Campbell, I have not so many friends that I can afford to lose so true and stout a one, especially one upon whom misfortunes have come through his good services to myself. I will send a messenger to the governor of Nantes with orders that he shall in every way forward your wishes as to your departure, as it is with my consent and approval that you are sailing for England. Your devotion has brought you into the gravest peril, and now it forces you to relinquish your profession, in which you have so greatly distinguished yourself. Truly, my friendship for you is genuine, and it cuts me to the heart that, although I could uphold you against the most powerful nobles in open enmity, I can do naught to save you from assassination. I trust some day that I may see you again, but, should it not be so, remember that I shall always feel myself your debtor; and should you have friends for whom you may ask my protection be sure that I will for your sake do all in my power for them."

There was no doubting the real emotion with which Mazarin spoke.

"There is one thing that I forgot," the latter said; "here is a pass for you to leave the gates at once. You had better go out by the north, so that they may think that you have ridden to Calais, and then take a wide detour and ride for Nantes."

Hector returned to the hotel.

"We must mount at once," he said to the troopers; "my enemies have failed twice, but they might not fail the third time, and by to-morrow morning it is certain that the hotel will be watched. I have a pass to issue out through the gate at once."

While he had been away the troopers had bandaged each other's wounds, and had packed their valises, for they thought it probable after what had happened that their master would be obliged to fly.

As the horses were being saddled and brought out Hector saw the innkeeper and paid him his bill.

"Monsieur," he said, "I am going away on business of the cardinal's, and he desires that none shall know that I have left; therefore I pray you keep the matter secret as long as you can. It may be reasonably supposed that after the fray in which we have just been engaged, we might well keep our beds for a day or two."

Going out in the court-yard, he gave a couple of crowns to the hostler.

"You are like to be asked to-morrow if we are still here," he said. "Give such answers as to lead them to believe that our horses are still in the stalls."

They mounted and rode rapidly through the streets to the northern gate, which was immediately, upon Hector's handing the guard the cardinal's pass, opened to them. To the surprise of the men, he turned off after riding a few miles.

"Are you not going to make for Calais, master?"

"No, I am bound for Poitou. We will cross the Seine by the bridge of boats at Nantes, ride down through Dreux and Le Mans. There we will separate. I shall follow the Sarthe, strike the Loire at Angers, and then go on to Nantes. You will cross the Loire at Tours, and then make for la Villar. I shall take you, Macpherson and Hunter, with me. Paolo will ride with the other two, and will be the bearer of letters from me."

Daylight was breaking when they crossed the bridge of boats. Hector halted a mile from the river, keeping Paolo with him, and telling the others to pass at intervals of a quarter of an hour apart.

"You will go first, Macpherson. You will ride south for an hour, and then wait till the rest of us join you. It is like enough that as soon as they find out that we have left they will send men off in all directions to find out which way we followed, though doubtless the chief pursuit will be directed towards Calais. I am afraid that it will not be very long before they find we have left the hotel, for the landlord, however well he may wish us, will not dare mislead any person of consequence that Beaufort may send."

They had, however, a much longer start than Hector expected, for early the next morning ten of the cardinal's guards appeared at the hotel. The officer in command of them told the innkeeper that, in consequence of the tumult before his doors, in which, as he heard, some of those lodging there had been concerned, he had orders to post his men round the house, and to allow no one to enter or leave under any pretence whatever until the cardinal himself had examined into the affair. These orders were delivered in a loud voice before the servants of the inn, but the officer privately assured the innkeeper afterwards that he would be well paid for his loss of custom, and that it was probable that the guard would be removed in a day or two. Thus Beaufort's emissaries were not able to obtain news of what was passing within, and did nothing until past noon, when it occurred to them that the cardinal had taken this strange step of closing the inn in order to prevent its being known that Hector and his followers had left Paris.

Men were at once sent off to the different gates of the city, and one of these returning with the news that the north gate had been opened at one o'clock in the morning and that six men bearing a pass from the cardinal had ridden out, a party of twenty horsemen started out in pursuit, while others were ordered to ride by all the different routes to Poitou, in case, as was likely enough, Hector had ridden to his castle. The fugitive, however, and his followers were all well mounted, and had fourteen hours' start. They separated at Le Mans. Hector here wrote a long letter to the Baronne de Blenfoix, and a shorter one to MacIntosh. The latter he told only that his fief had again reverted to the crown, and gave instructions that the steward should be ordered to return, from the moneys he had in hand, three months' rent to every tenant, to hand the balance to MacIntosh himself, and to hold possession of the château and estate until he received orders from the cardinal himself.

MacIntosh was then, with Paolo, two troopers, and his own two sergeants, to escort the baroness and her daughter to Nantes, if she decided to go there. All arrangements were to be completed within twelve hours of Paolo's arrival there.

To the baroness he related briefly what had passed.

"Therefore, as you see," he said, "there is no course open for me but to fly for England or Ireland, where I intend to settle. I trust, madam, that you and your daughter will accompany me. Putting aside my respect and, I may say, my affection for yourself, you will have understood from what I said to you when last at la Villar, that I hope some day to make your daughter Norah my wife, if I should be so fortunate as to obtain her affections. How this may be I cannot say, but at any rate I trust that you will return to England, and as I have ample funds you may be assured that my first care will be to provide for your future."

On arriving at Nantes Hector at once rode to the governor, and presented the cardinal's letter to him.

"You may be assured, Colonel Campbell, that I shall carry out his eminence's instructions," he said, after perusing the cardinal's letter. "I will send an officer down to the port with you to aid you in obtaining passage, should there be a ship leaving for England, or to take up a ship for your service."

"I would rather the latter," Hector said. "I may have ladies with me, and so should wish to have plenty of accommodation."

"I am also instructed," the governor said, "to close the gate, in case any party, followers of the Dukes of Vendôme or Beaufort, or of any families connected with them, arrive before you leave, and to grant them no admittance until a messenger from the mouth of the river informs me that you are fairly out at sea."

"I am indeed obliged to his eminence for that order, sir; he did not mention to me that he was giving it, but it will certainly save me from much anxiety."

As Hector was not disposed to haggle about terms, he had no difficulty in hiring a vessel to carry them across the Channel. Twenty-four hours after his arrival the party from the château rode in, and but half an hour later fifty horsemen wearing the cognizance of Vendôme galloped up to the gate. They were headed by four or five gentlemen, one of whom demanded angrily why the gates were shut.

"They are closed by order of the governor," the officer in charge replied.

"Tell the governor that the Count d'Erlon, with a party of gentlemen, retainers of the Duke of Vendôme, are here, and demand instant admittance."

Twenty minutes later the governor himself arrived at the gate. "I am sorry, gentlemen," he said, "that I am compelled to keep the gates closed. I have an order from Cardinal Mazarin to that effect, and that, coming from the first minister of France, I dare not disregard even if the duke himself were with you. It would cost me my place, and possibly gain me a cell in the Bastille; and, grieved as I am to refuse admittance to such honourable gentlemen, still I must do so."

"And for how long is this monstrous edict to remain in force?" the leader of the party asked.

"That I am unable to say precisely, but I believe that I can open them to-morrow morning."

"You see, we were right, count," another of the horsemen said. "The description of the man who rode along here with two attendants tallies with that of this Scot, and doubtless this order was brought by him from Mazarin to enable him to get either by water away abroad or to his château of la Villar."

"Well, gentlemen, at any rate we have done our best, and though we must have slain the fellow if we had overtaken him, I cannot say that I am altogether grieved that he has escaped. His name is well known to everyone. He did brave service to France under Turenne and Condé. We learned from the messenger who brought the letter from Beaufort that he killed de Beauvais in fair fight, wounded de Vipont, and disarmed the Comte de Marplat, that at night he and five of his followers, though attacked by some thirty ruffians from the faubourgs under Beaufort himself, killed twelve of them outright, and that he himself seriously wounded the duke. Well, there is nothing for us but to ride back to the village we last passed through and wait there until to-morrow."

So saying, he mounted his horse and galloped off with his party.

THE DUKE'S REVENGE

"Who could have thought when we parted last, Colonel Campbell, that we should meet again under such greatly changed circumstances!" Madame de Blenfoix exclaimed as Hector met the party as they alighted before the principal inn of Nantes.

"It is a change indeed," he replied; "so great that I myself can hardly realize it, and not sure whether I am sorry or the reverse at what has taken place."

"I am very glad to hear you say so, as I feared that it would be a terrible blow to you to give up the army."

"I have hardly had time to think of it," he said, "I have had so much else to occupy my thoughts. Now, I pray you, enter the inn for a few minutes; I have warned them to get a meal ready to be served at the shortest notice, for I am anxious that no time shall be lost; everything is ready for our embarkation."

"Had we not best go aboard at once?" she said. "Your enemies might arrive at any moment by what Paolo tells us."

"The matter is not so pressing as I thought, madam, for the cardinal sent orders to the governor that he is not to open the gates to any armed party of friends of Beaufort or Vendôme until I am fairly at sea."

He went with the ladies to a private room he had secured.

"I must leave you for a few minutes," he said, "while I have a talk with MacIntosh and the others."

"Well, old friend," he said as he went out to where the little party of Scotchmen were standing in a group, "what are your plans and wishes? 'Tis a pity now that I persuaded you to leave Paris and go down to la Villar, but I did it for the best. I thought of you much as I rode hither."

"Do not trouble about me, colonel, I am by no means sorry at the change. I was getting tired of the cabaret, and should soon have given it up even had you not come to offer me the wardenship of your château. I have chatted matters over with my two friends, and we have not yet agreed whether to return to Scotland or to remain in France. At any rate we shall go to Paris first; my money is there all in good keeping, together with the two years' payment for the cabaret. Are you thinking of going to Scotland yourself, colonel?"

"Certainly not to Scotland, I have no friends there, and from all that I have heard the people are so hard and bigoted, so full of their religious differences, that I should feel sorely out of place with them.

"Well, MacIntosh, as soon as I am settled in England I will have a letter conveyed to you in some way at the address of The Scottish Soldier. Wherever I am, there will be a home always open to you, and glad indeed I shall be to have you near me. My four troopers are going to accompany me. I have talked the matter over with them, and have promised that I will find a house with a small farm for them on any estate I may purchase, where they can do such an amount of work as pleases them, or that they can remain in my service on the present conditions. You can make the same offer in my name to your two comrades. After all, things are not so settled across the water that I can dispense with old friends on whom I can rely. Paolo, of course, goes with me, and will be my right hand."

"I will think it all over, Hector, and maybe one of these days I and the other two may knock at your door. It is hard if seven old fellow-soldiers could not end their days happily and quietly together."

As soon as the meal had been eaten Hector went to say good-bye to the governor, and heard how Vendôme's men had been refused entrance. After thanking him for the courtesy that he had shown him, he returned to the inn. As the party would require horses on landing, and there was plenty of room on board the vessel that he had engaged, Hector shipped the three horses that Condé had given him, and four others for the use of his men, and after a hearty farewell to MacIntosh on his part and that of the ladies, they went on board, and a few minutes later the sails were set and the vessel started down the river. The wind was favourable, and they made a fast voyage down to the sea. Before they reached the mouth of the river, however, Hector had ascertained to his satisfaction that Norah O'More returned the feeling that he felt for her.

"I have loved you," she said, "from the moment when you came to us as our saviour from death on the summit of the turret; and though as time went on I did not venture to think that you, who had so fair a future before you, would ever think of the girl whom with her mother you had so nobly entertained and treated, I should never have loved any other man to the end of my life."

The voyage was without incident, and five days after leaving Nantes they arrived at Plymouth. Here Hector hired a house, and when the ladies were comfortably settled he left them in charge of Paolo and two of the men, and rode to London accompanied by the others. Here he called upon the banker whose address Mazarin had given him, and on sending in his name was shown into the room in which private business was transacted.

"You have certain moneys of mine in your hands, Mr. Wilson?"

"I have had fifty thousand crowns for the past three years and have put them out on good security, so that the sum stands at present in my books at sixty-four thousand crowns. Three days ago I received from Cardinal Mazarin bills to the amount of one hundred and fifty thousand crowns, being, he said, due to you for the surrender of the fief of la Villar, and for other services rendered to him. The cardinal is a good paymaster," he added with a slight smile at seeing Hector's surprise at the news, "but it was plain from his letter to me that he considered that the value of your services was greatly in excess of the sum, large as it is, that he sent, especially as they had brought great misfortunes upon you, and had forced you to abandon France, and give up your profession, in which, he said, your prospects of gaining the highest rank were of the brightest. Now, sir, if there are any services that I can render you I am at your disposal. You will naturally wish to invest your money in some way, and, though I say it myself, I know of no one who could lay it out to better advantage."

"You may help me assuredly," Hector said, "for I am an entire stranger in England. I wish to purchase an estate, but have no idea how to set about it, while, doubtless, you are acquainted with many such domains at present for sale. I may say that I will on no account purchase an estate which has been confiscated by parliament on account of its owner being loyal to the crown. Charles II. may, and I believe will, return and mount the throne, and these estates will then beyond doubt be restored to their former owners, therefore I will have nought to do with such property."

"You could not choose a better time for laying out your money in land," the banker said. "Great numbers of the nobles and gentlemen of England have been killed or are in exile; many, again, who still hold their land are well-nigh ruined by the moneys they spent in the king's service, and would gladly sell now could they obtain anything like a fair value for their estates. I know of a score at least of such properties which are so deeply mortgaged that the owners can scarce afford to live in their own homes, and would gladly take a sum that would suffice to pay off the mortgage and give them the wherewithal to live upon, either abroad or in Virginia, to which colony many loyal gentlemen have already gone to settle. If you will call to-morrow I will give you a list of such estates, with their size, the amount of their revenues, and the price at which their owners would, I know, be glad to sell, for I and some of my friends have been approached by them with that view."

Hector spent the next three weeks in visiting eight of the estates that seemed suitable and were all situated in counties near London. Finally he settled upon one in Berkshire, which was of considerable size and with a stately house in a fair position. This he purchased, and then, returning to Plymouth, his marriage with Norah was celebrated there, and he, with his wife and Madame de Blenfoix and his five followers, rode down into Berkshire and took possession of the estate, with which all were delighted. The troopers, instead of accepting the house he offered them, preferred to remain in his service, and Paolo was installed as major-domo of the household. Six months later MacIntosh and his two comrades came over.

The former declined Hector's offer to take up his abode at the house.

"No, colonel, I have an abundance for myself and my two comrades, and would rather be near you, where we can live in our own fashion, and give trouble to no one."

"Well, if you will not come here, MacIntosh, there is a house a quarter of a mile away which will, I think, suit you well. It is not a large place, but is a comfortable one, and has been used as the house of the steward of the estate. As I shall be my own steward it is vacant, and will, I think, suit you well. It is furnished, so that you and your comrades can move in when you like, though the longer you stay with us the better we shall be pleased."

A fortnight later MacIntosh and his comrades moved in, and there, when not occupied with their duties, one or other of the troopers was generally to be found. Hector often dropped in, and one day laughingly said that the house ought to be renamed The Scottish Soldier.

Until the Restoration Hector kept aloof from London, but when Charles II. mounted the throne of his fathers he went up, and was presented at court by one of the many English gentlemen whom he had known in France, where they had sought refuge with the queen when the royal cause was lost in England. He did not, however, repeat the visit very often. He was perfectly happy in his country life, and never once regretted the chain of events that had forced him to give up his life of adventure and excitement and to settle down peacefully in England.

THE END

PrestonSpeed Publications 51 Ridge Road Mill Hall, PA 17751
(570) 726-7844
www.prestonspeed.com

Historiae Dona Repertum

Other titles available from PrestonSpeed Publications

Books by G. A. Henty

For The Temple

The Dragon & The Raven

In Freedom's Cause

By Pike & Dyke

Beric The Briton

St. Barthlomew's Eve

With Lee in Virginia

By Right of Conquest

The Young Cartheginian

Winning His Spurs

Under Drake's Flag

The Cat of Bubastes

Wulf The Saxon

A Knight of the White Cross

St. George for England

With Wolfe in Canada

By England's Aid

The Dash for Khartoum

The Lion of the North

Won by the Sword

Other Publications

By Right of Conquest (unit study guide)

A Journey of Souls

The Henty Companion

English Bible Translations

Ethics & God's Law

Preston/Speed Publications takes great pride in re-printing the complete works of G. A. Henty. New titles are regularly being released. Our editions contain the complete text along with all maps and/or illustrations. In order to ensure the most complete Henty editions, we review all previous releases for the most comprehensive version.